STRUCTURED ACTIVITIES FOR PRIMARY MATHEMATICS

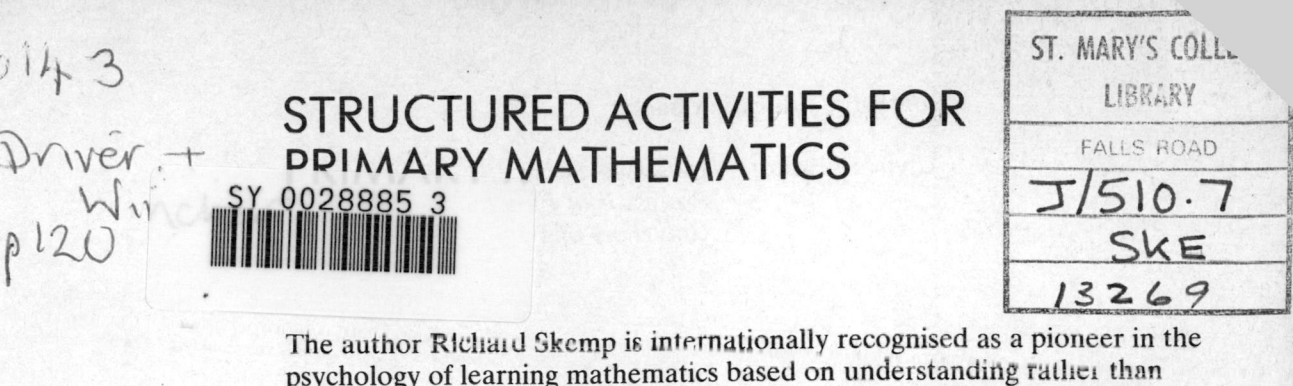

The author Richard Skemp is internationally recognised as a pioneer in the psychology of learning mathematics based on understanding rather than memorising rules. A former mathematics teacher, he has lectured in seventeen countries, is a former Professor of Educational Theory and Director of the Mathematics Education Research Centre at Warwick University, and a Past President of the International Group for the Psychology of Mathematics Education.

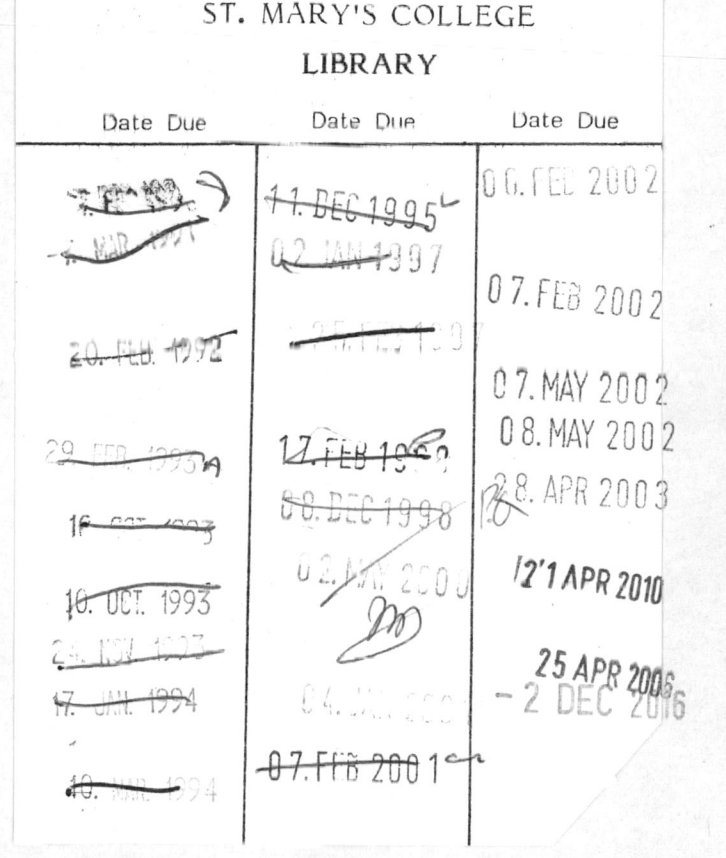

Routledge Education Books

Advisory Editor: John Eggleston
Professor of Education
University of Warwick

STRUCTURED ACTIVITIES FOR PRIMARY MATHEMATICS

How to enjoy real mathematics

Richard R. Skemp

Emeritus Professor
University of Warwick

Volume 1

R

Routledge
London

First published in 1989 by
Routledge
11 New Fetter Lane, London EC4P 4EE

© Richard R. Skemp 1989

Typeset by Columns of Reading
Printed in Great Britain by T.J. Press (Padstow) Ltd.,
Padstow, Cornwall

British Library Cataloguing in Publication Data

Skemp, Richard R. (Richard Rowland), 1919–
    Structural activities for primary
    mathematics : how to enjoy real maths.—
    (Routledge education books).
    Vol. 1
    1. Primary schools. Curriculum subjects :
    Mathematics
    I. Title
    372.7'3

0-415-02817-5

CONTENTS

Acknowledgements   vi
Notes   vii

Introduction   1

1   Why this book was needed and what it provides   1
2   The invisible components and how to perceive them   2
3   How this book is organised and how to use it   5
4   Getting started as a school   6
5   Organisation within the school   7
6   Getting started as an individual teacher   8
7   Making and storing the materials   10
8   Parents   11
9   Some questions and answers   12

Concept Maps and Lists of Activities   17

The Networks and Activities   39

                                          reference codes
Set based organisation   Org 1   41
Numbers and their properties   Num 1   66
The naming of numbers   Num 2   84
Addition   Num 3   102
Subtraction   Num 4   131
Multiplication   Num 5   163
Division   Num 6   181
Shape   Space 1   199
The number track and the number line   NuSp 1   211

Glossary   232

Alphabetical List of Activities   234

ACKNOWLEDGEMENTS

I am very grateful to all the following for their help.

The Nuffield Foundation and the Leverhulme Trust, for their financial support of the Primary Mathematics Project during a total period of eight years.

Ms Janet Ainley and Mr David Pimm, Research Associates during phases one and two, and my wife Valerie, Project Assistant during phase three, for their contributions to so many aspects of this project. (Janet Ainley is now Lecturer in Primary Mathematics at Warwick University, and David Pimm is Lecturer in Mathematical Education at the Open University.)

In the Solihull Local Education Authority: Mr Colin Humphrey, Director of Education, the late Mr Paul Turner and his successor Mrs Marion Idle, Mathematics Advisers, Mr Alan Stocks, Assistant Director of Education, Mrs Barbara Furniss, Head Teacher, and the staff and children of Bentley Heath Primary School; Mrs Rita Chapman, Head Teacher, and the staff and children of Lady Katherine Leveson's Primary School. In the Dyfed Local Education Authority, Dr David Finney, former Mathematics Adviser, Mrs A. Cole, Head Teacher, and the staff and children of Loveston County Primary School. In the Shropshire Local Education Authority: Dr David Finney, Science Adviser; Mrs Susan Boughey, Head Teacher, and the staff and children of Leegomery County Infant School; Mrs Ishbel Gamble, Head Teacher, and the staff and children of Holmer Lake County First School; Mr David Tyrrell, Head Teacher, and the staff and children of Leegomery County Junior School; Mrs Pamela Haile, Head Teacher, and the staff and children of St Lawrence Primary School. I am grateful to all who allowed me to work in their schools during the pilot testing of the project materials, and also for their advice, suggestions, and helpful discussions; and to the children for the many hours of enjoyment which I have had while working with them.

My colleague Professor John Eggleston, Professor of Education at Warwick University, and Advisory Editor for Routledge Education Books, for his encouragement and editorial advice.

And finally, but by no means least, yourselves, for allowing our efforts to find their hoped-for destination in your own classrooms.

NOTES

Volume 1 is intended for use in infant and first schools, and Volume 2 for junior schools and the lower forms in middle schools. Because of the wide range of children's abilities, this division can only be very approximate. In particular, some of the later activities in Volume 1 will be found useful for children in their first year at a junior school, especially if they come from infant schools where this approach has not been used.

Since the English language lacks a pronoun which means either he or she, I have used these alternately by topics.

INTRODUCTION

1 Why this book was needed and what it provides

There is now a wide consensus, which was well expressed in the Cockroft report,[1] that practical work is essential throughout the primary years, and not just for younger children. There are now a number of these activities available, and individually many of them are attractive and worthwhile. But collectively, they lack two essential requirements for long-term learning: structure, and clear stages of progression. The present volume provides a fully structured collection of more than 300 activities, covering a core curriculum for children aged from five to eleven years old, which uses practical work extensively at all stages.

This collection is not, however, confined to practical work. Mathematics is an abstract subject, and children will need in the future to be competent at written mathematics. Putting one's thoughts on paper can be a help in organising them, as well as recording them for oneself and communicating them to others. What is important is that this should not come prematurely. It is their having had to memorise a collection of rules without understanding which has put so many generations of learners off mathematics for life, and destroyed their confidence in their ability to learn it. Practical, oral, and mental work can provide the foundation of understanding without which written work makes no sense. Starting with these, the present collection provides a careful transition from practical work to abstract thinking, and from oral to written work.

Activities for introducing new concepts often take the form of a teacher-led discussion. Many of the other activities take the form of games which children can play together without direct supervision, once they know how to play. These games give rise to discussion; and since the rules and strategies of the games are largely mathematical, this is a mathematical discussion. Children question each other's moves, and justify their own, thereby articulating and consolidating their own understanding. Often they explain things to each other, and when teaching I emphasise that 'When we are learning it is good to help each other.' Most of us have found that trying to explain something to someone else is one of the best ways to improve one's own understanding, and this works equally well for children.

This volume also provides the following:

(a) A set of diagrams (concept maps) showing the overall mathematical structure, and how each topic and activity fits into this.
(b) Clear statements of what is to be learnt from each group of activities.
(c) For each activity, a list of materials and step by step instructions. (A volume of photomasters is also provided to simplify the preparation of materials.)

(d) For each topic, discussion of the mathematical concept(s) involved, and of the learning processes used.

The last of these will, it is hoped, be useful not only for classroom teachers, but also for advisory teachers, support teams, mathematics advisers, those involved in the pre-service and in-service education of teachers, and possibly also those whose main interests are at the research level.

2 The invisible components and how to perceive them

The activities in this collection contain a number of important components which are invisible, and can only be perceived by those who know what to look for. These include (i) real mathematics (ii) structure (iii) a powerful theory.

(i) *Real mathematics.* Here I can begin to answer questions which may have arisen in your mind when you read the sub-title of this book. 'What do you mean by this? Is it just a puff?' I say 'begin', because a fuller answer depends on personal experience. If someone asks 'What is a kumquat?' I can tell them that it is a small citrus fruit, but two of the most important things for them to know are what it tastes like, and whether they like it or not. This knowledge they can only acquire by personally tasting a kumquat.

Real mathematics is a kind of knowledge. I can describe it, and I hope you will find this a useful start. But some of the most important things about mathematics people cannot know until they have some of this kind of knowledge in their own minds; and those who acquired real mathematics when they were at school are, regrettably, in a minority. A simple preliminary test is whether you enjoy mathematics, and feel that you understand it. If the answers are 'No', then I have good news for you: what you learnt was probably not real mathematics. More good news: you can acquire real mathematics yourself while using these activities with your children. You will then begin to perceive it in the activities themselves: more accurately, in your own thinking, and that of your children, while doing these activities. And you will begin to discover whether or not what you yourself learnt as a child was real mathematics.

Mathematics (hereafter I will use 'mathematics' by itself to mean real mathematics) is a kind of knowledge which is highly adaptable. In the adult world, this adaptability can be seen in the great variety of uses to which it is put. Mathematics is used to make predictions about physical events, and greatly increases our ability to achieve our goals. Our daily comfort and convenience, sometimes our lives, depend on the predictive use of mathematics by engineers, scientists, technicians, doctors and nurses. At an everyday level, we use mathematics for purposes such as predicting approximately how long we should allow for a journey. Highly sophisticated mathematics is required to project communication satellites into orbits whereby they hang stationary relative to the earth; and also in the design of the satellites themselves, whose electronic equipment allows us to watch on our television screens events many thousands of miles away.

Mathematics has also an important social function, since many of the complex ways in which we co-operate in modern society would not be possible without mathematics. Nuts could not be made to fit bolts, clothes to fit persons, without the measurement function of mathematics. Businesses could not function without the mathematics of accountancy. If the person in charge of this gets his calculations wrong, his firm may go out of business: that is to say, others will no longer co-operate by trading with them.

Another feature of mathematics is creativity – the use of one's existing knowledge to create new knowledge. Can you say what are ninety-nine sevens? Probably not, but if you think 'A hundred sevens make seven hundred, so ninety-nine sevens will be one seven less: six hundred and ninety three', then you are using your own mental creativity. Creating new mathematics which nobody ever knew before is creativity at the level of the professional mathematician; but anyone who has some real mathematics is capable of creating knowledge which is new to them, and this way of using one's mind can give a kind of pleasure which those who have not experienced it may find hard to understand.

These are some of the adult uses of mathematics, which make it so important in today's world of advanced science, technology, and international commerce. At school, most children still learn a look-alike which is called by the same name, but whose uses have little in common with the uses of real mathematics. School mathematics as it is experienced by children is mostly for getting ticks, pleasing teachers, avoiding reproofs and sometimes also the humiliation of being made to feel stupid. It is also used for passing exams, and thereafter quickly forgotten. Yet real mathematics can be taught and learnt at school. For an example of mathematics used predictively, try 'Missing stairs' (Org 1.5/1). Success in most of the games also depends largely on making good predictions. Mathematics is used socially in all children's work together in groups; and in some, e.g. 'Renovating a house' (Num 3.8/3), a social use is embodied in the activity itself. Examples of creativity I hope you will find in the thinking of your own children, when they are learning real mathematics.

(ii) *Structure.* This is an essential feature of real mathematics. It is this which makes possible all the features described in (i), so for emphasis I am giving it a section to itself.

By structure we mean the way in which parts fit together to make a whole. Often this whole has qualities which go far beyond the sum of the separate properties of the parts. Connect together a collection of transistors, condensers, resistances, and the like, most of which will do very little on their own, and you have a radio by which you can hear sounds broadcast from hundreds of miles away. That is, if the connections are right: and this is what we mean by structure in the present example.

In the case of mathematics, the components are mathematical concepts, and the structure is a mental structure. This makes it much harder to know whether it is there or not in a learner's mind. But the difference between a mathematical structure and a collection of isolated facts is as great as the difference between a radio and a box of bits. There is the same difference between a radio set and a wrongly connected assortment of components, but this is harder to tell by looking. The important test of the presence or absence of structure, i.e. of the right set of connections, may best be inferred from performance. This is also true for mathematics, and for its look-alike which goes by the same name. Of these two, only real mathematics performs powerfully, enjoyably, and in a wide variety of ways.

Each individual learner has to put together these structures in his own mind. No one can do it for him. But this mental activity can be greatly helped by good teaching, an important part of which is providing good learning situations.

The requirements of a good learning situation include full use of all the three modes of building conceptual structures. Mode 1 is learning by the use of practical materials; mode 2 is learning from exposition, and by discussion; and mode 3 is expanding one's knowledge by creative thinking. These categories are expanded and discussed more fully in *Mathematics in the Primary School*.[2]

The activities in this book are intended to help teachers provide learning situations of the kind described. They are also fully structured, meaning that the concepts embodied in each fit together in ways which help learners to build good mathematical structures in their own minds. This also includes consolidation, and developing mathematical skills.

(iii) *A powerful theory*. In 1929, Dewey wrote 'Theory is in the end . . . the most powerful of all things';[3] and I have been saying the same for many years, even before I knew that Dewey had said it first. The activities in this book embody a new theory of intelligent learning. This had its origins in the present author's researches into the psychology of learning of mathematics,[4] and was subsequently expanded and generalised into a theory of intelligent learning which can be applied to the learning of all subjects.[5] It is not essential to know the theory in order to use the activities. But readers who are professional teachers will want to know not only what to do, but why. Mathematics advisers, or lecturers in mathematical education, will wish to satisfy themselves of the soundness of the underlying theory before recommending the activities.

This theoretical understanding is best acquired by a combination of first-hand experience, reading, and discussion. Each of the activities embodies some aspects of the general theory, so by doing the activities with children we can observe the theory in action. For school teachers, this is a very good way to begin, since the theoretical knowledge acquired in this way begins with classroom experience, and as it develops further will continue to relate to it. This also has the advantage that we get 'two for the price of one', time-wise: what might be called a 'happy hour' in the classroom! These observations can then form the first part of the trio

OBSERVE AND LISTEN   REFLECT   DISCUSS

whose value for school-based in-service education will be mentioned again in Section 5.

Reading helps to organise our personal experience, and to extend our knowledge beyond what can be gathered first-hand. A companion book to the present volume is *Mathematics in the Primary School*,[6] and this also offers suggestions for further reading.

3   How this book is organised and how to use it

These two volumes contain teaching materials for seven school years, together with explanations and discussions. This is a lot of information. Careful thought has therefore been given to its organisation, to make it easy to find as much as is required at a given stage, and to avoid feeling overloaded with information. Mathematics is a highly concentrated kind of information, so it is wise to take one's time, and to go at a pace which allows comfortable time for assimilation. The amount eventually to be acquired in detail by a class teacher would be no more than one-seventh of the total, if all children in the class were of the same ability. In practice it will, of course, be more because of children's spread of ability: but let us take this figure as a starting point. There are 326 activities in all, so if we spread these over a 30-week school year, allowing for times when the school is concentrating on other matters such as concerts, plays, seasonal festivities, sports, etc, this averages to about three new activities every two weeks. This should allow a fairly comfortable pace for the parts which need to be acquired in detail. It is also useful to have an overview of what went before, what comes after, and how it all fits together.

The aim has been to provide first an overview; then a little more detail; and then a lot of detail, of which many readers will not need all, nor all at the same time. This has been done by organising the subject matter at four levels, into THEMES, NETWORKS, TOPICS, and ACTIVITIES. The themes and networks are tabulated below.

THEMES	NETWORKS	CODES
Organising	Set based organisation	Org 1
Number	Numbers and their properties	Num 1
	The naming and recording of numbers	Num 2
	Addition	Num 3
	Subtraction	Num 4
	Multiplication	Num 5
	Division	Num 6
Space	Shape	Space 1
Synthesis of Number and Space	The number track and the number line	NuSp 1

The four main themes run in parallel, not sequentially, though some will be started later than others. Within the theme of Number, there are seven networks. For the other themes, there is at present just one network each; but I have kept to the same arrangement for consistency, and to allow for possible future expansion. By 'network', I mean a structure of inter-related mathematical ideas. It can well be argued that all mathematical ideas are inter-related in some way or other, but the networks help to prevent information overload by letting us concentrate on one area at a time.

Greater detail for each network is provided by a concept map and a list of activities. These begin at page 18, and it will be useful to look at a pair of these as illustrations for what follows. Each concept map shows how the ideas of that network relate to each other, and in particular, which ones need to be understood before later ones can be acquired with understanding. These interdependencies are shown by arrows. A suggested sequence through the network is shown by the numbers against each topic. Use of the concept map will help you to decide whether other sequences may successfully be followed, e.g. to take advantage of children's current interests. The concept map is also useful diagnostically. Often a difficulty at a particular stage may be traced to a child's not having properly understood one or more earlier concepts, in which case the concept map will help you to find out which these are. Another function of the concept maps is to help individual teachers to see where their own teaching fits into a long-term plan for children's learning, throughout the primary years: what they are building on, and where it is leading.

Below each concept map is shown a list of the activities for each topic. (I call them 'topics' rather than 'concepts' because some topics do not introduce new concepts, but extend existing ones to larger areas of application.) Usually these activities should be used in the order shown. An alphabetical list of the activities is also given, at the end of the book.

To find activities for a particular topic, the best way is via the concept maps and the lists of activities opposite them. Suppose, for example, that you want activities for adding past ten. For this you naturally look at the concept map for addition, and find adding past ten here as topic 6. On the adjacent page, for this topic, you will find seven activities. Not all topics have so many activities, but this indicates the importance of this stage in children's learning of addition. If on the other hand you want to find a particular activity by name, then the alphabetical index at the end of the book will enable you to do so.

The codes for each topic and activity are for convenience of reference. They show where each fits into the whole. Thus Num 3.8/2 refers to network Num 3, topic 8, activity 2. If the packet for each activity has its code written on it, this will help to keep them all in the right order, and to replace each in the right place after use.

4   Getting started as a school

Since schools vary greatly, what follows in this section and the rest of this introduction is offered as no more than suggestions, based on the experience of a number of the schools where the materials have already been introduced.

It has been found useful to proceed in two main stages: getting acquainted, and full implementation. Since the latter will be spread over one or two years at least, the first stage is important for getting the feel of the new approach, and to help in deciding that it will be worth the effort.

For getting acquainted, a good way is for each teacher to choose an activity, make it up, and learn it by doing it with one or more other teachers. (Different activities are for different numbers of persons.) Teachers then use these activities with their own children, and afterwards they discuss together what they have learnt from observation of their own children doing the activities. It is well worth while trying to see some of the activities in use, if this can be arranged. Initially, this will convey the new approach more easily than the printed page.

When you are ready to move towards a full implementation, it will be necessary to decide the overall approach. One way is to introduce the activities fully into the first and second years, while other teachers gradually introduce them into later years as support for the work they are already doing. This has the advantage that the full implementation gradually moves up the school, children being used to this way of learning from the beginning. Alternatively, activities may be introduced gradually throughout the school, individual teachers choosing which activities they use alongside existing text-based materials while they gain confidence in the new approach.

Arrangements for preparation of the materials need to be planned well in advance. This is discussed in greater detail in Section 5. A detail which needs to be checked in good time, because of the slowness of most educational suppliers, is whether the commercial materials needed, such as Multilink or Unifix and base ten materials, are already in the school in the quantities needed.

In considering the approach to be used, it is important to realise that while benefit is likely to be gained from even a limited use of the activities, a major part of their value is in the underlying structure. The full benefit, which is considerable, will therefore only be gained from a full implementation, with text-based materials moving into a subsidiary function.

5   Organisation within the school

Overall, the organisation of the new approach is very much a matter for the head teacher and staff of each individual school to work out for themselves; so as has already been emphasised, what follows is offered as no more than suggestions, based on what has been found successful in schools where this approach has been introduced.

Whatever organisation is adopted, it is desirable to designate an organiser who will co-ordinate individual efforts, and keep things going. It is a great help if this teacher can have some free time for planning, organising, advising, and supporting teachers as need arises.

One approach which has been found successful is as follows. The maths organiser holds regular meetings with the staff in each one- or two-year group, according to their number. Each teacher chooses an activity, makes it up if necessary, and teaches it to the other teachers in the group. They discuss the mathematics involved, and any difficulties. Subsequently they discuss their observations of their own children doing these activities, and what they have learnt by reflecting on these. This combination may be summarised as

OBSERVE AND LISTEN   REFLECT   DISCUSS

and is an important contribution to school-based in-service education. (So much so, that several leading maths educators have said that it should be printed on every page. As a compromise, I have printed it at the end of every topic.)

It is good if the maths organiser is also in a position to help individual teachers, since it is only to be expected if they sometimes feel insecure when teaching in a style which may be very different from that to which they are accustomed. Two useful ways to help are by looking after the rest of a teacher's class for a while, so that this teacher is free to concentrate entirely on working with a small group; and by demonstrating an activity with a small group while the class teacher observes, the rest of the class being otherwise occupied.

6   Getting started as an individual teacher

The most important thing is actually to do one or more activities with one's own children, as early on as possible. This is the best way to get the feel of what the new approach is about. After that, one has a much better idea of where one is going. If there are particular topics where the children need help, suitable activities may be found via the concept maps and their corresponding lists of activities. Alternatively, here is a list of activities which have been found useful as 'starters'.

The stages correspond roughly to years at school.

			vol	page
Stage 1	Lucky dip	Org 1.3/1	1	46
	'Can I fool you?'	Org 1.3/2	1	46
	Missing stairs	Org 1.5/1	1	49
Stage 2	Stepping stones	Num 3.2/3	1	105
	Crossing	Num 3.2/4	1	106
	Sequences on the number track	NuSp 1.2/1	1	214
Stage 3	The handkerchief game	Num 4.6/1	1	148
	'Please may I have. . .?' (complements)	Num 4.6/2	1	148
	Number targets	Num 2.8/1	1	97
Stage 4	Slippery slope	Num 3.6/3	1	120
	Slow bicycle race	NuSp 1.5/1	1	223
	Doubles and halves rummy	Num 1.9/3	1	80
Stage 5	Place-value bingo	Num 2.10/3	2	57
	Renovating a house	Num 3.8/3	2	76
	Constructing rectangular numbers	Num 6.4/1	2	151
	The rectangular numbers game	Num 6.4/2	2	152
Stage 6	Cycle camping	Num 3.9/2	2	79
	One tonne van drivers	Num 3.9/3	2	80
	Multiples rummy	Num 5.6/6	2	127
Stage 7	Cargo boats	Num 5.7/3	2	132
	Classifying polygons	Space 1.8/1	2	232
	Match and mix: polygons	Space 1.8/3	2	233

When the children are doing an activity, I recommend that you think about the amount of maths which they are doing, including the mental and oral activity as well as the written work, and compare it with the amount of maths they would do in the same time if they were doing written work out of a textbook.

Consideration also needs to be given to classroom management. I am assuming that your children are already sitting in small groups, and not in rows of desks facing the front. Even so, they may be more used to working individually than co-operatively, and if this is the case then their social learning will also need to be considered. Such things as listening to each other, taking turns, discussing sensibly and giving reasons rather than just arguing, which we may take for granted, may need to be learnt. The ways of learning mathematics which are embodied in this scheme both depend on, and also contribute to, social learning and clear speech. If some of the foregoing are already well established, then you are off to a flying start.

You will find that the activities fall into two main groups: those which introduce new concepts, and those which consolidate these and provide variety of applications. Activities in the first group always need to be introduced by a teacher, to ensure that the right concepts are learnt. Once they have understood the concepts, children can go on to do the second kind together with relatively little supervision. These activities could be introduced by another adult helper; and in some cases, children themselves can teach it to others with the help of the printed rules in each packet. The policy in one school I know, where these activities are being used with great success, is for a teacher to give (in the headteacher's words) 'high quality input' to each group once a week. For the rest of the time, the children learn mainly on their own. It is in fact one of the advantages of this way of organising your classroom that a teacher can only be with one group at a time. While with a group, it is very difficult, if one is a teacher, not to keep on actively teaching when it might be better to wait for children to do their own thinking. The kind of teaching involved here includes ways of managing children's learning experiences which are less direct, and more sophisticated, than more traditional approaches. They are also more powerful.

Management of the materials also need thought and organisation. Ways of storing these are discussed in Section 7. The children's contribution will include checking that all the materials for an activity are there at the beginning of an activity, and that they all go back in their right places at the end. I have been pleased to find how well most children respond when I point out the importance of putting everything back carefully, so that it is all there for the next people who do this activity.

So far, I have interpreted the heading of this section as meaning that the reader is an individual teacher within a school where most, or at least some, colleagues are also introducing the new approach. But what if this is not the case? When talking with teachers at conferences, I have met some who are the only ones in their school who are using this kind of approach to the teaching of mathematics.

This is a much more difficult situation to be in. We all need support and encouragement, especially when we are leaving behind methods with which we are familiar – even though they have not worked well for many children. We need to discuss difficulties, and to share ways we have found for overcoming them. So my suggestion here is that you try to find some colleague with whom you can do this. At the very least, you need someone with whom to do the activities before introducing them to the children; and further discussions may arise from this.

7 Making and storing the materials

Practical work and activity methods necessarily involve the preparation of physical materials. For the school as a whole, there will be quite a lot of these. Ideally, we would have liked to provide a complete set in ready-to-use form. Unfortunately, to do this for over 300 activities would have made the cost prohibitive. On the other hand, to prepare all the materials starting from nothing would be excessive in its demands on your time. So to give as much help as we can at reasonable cost, we provide with each volume a set of photomasters which will save you many hours of drawing. The other materials needed are of two kinds. The first is commercial materials such as Multilink, Unifix, number tracks to go with these, base ten materials. You are likely to have some of these already. The second is everyday materials such as thin cord for set loops, and little objects for sorting, such as acorn cups, shells, pebbles – we do not want children to think that mathematics only involves plastic cubes and other objects not found outside schools, useful as these materials are. You will also need plenty of plastic self-seal bags, usually one for each activity. The size is not critical, but they must take an A4 card with room to spare. To keep the photocopied material under control until it is all safely in its right bags, I suggest that you work on one network at a time. Initially, most schools make a complete set as a central resource; after which teachers have a model for making up additional sets according to their individual needs.

How the preparation of materials is organised is a matter for you to agree among yourselves. Some schools have had very useful help from parents: see Section 8. Here are some suggestions on matters of detail.

Our own materials are on cards of a number of different colours. This greatly helps to organise them, e.g. by having different packs of cards used for the same activity in different colours. You can do this by copying the photo-masters onto different coloured cards, if your copier will take card. If it will not, you can copy on white paper and stick this on coloured card. Though one side will be white, the back will be coloured and this will suffice for the organising function. We have not specified the colours to be used, since what you can obtain may be different from what was available to us. Instead, we have simply labelled the masters 'colour 1', 'colour 2', etc. You can then make your own list: 'colour 1 = blue, colour 2 = light yellow. . .'. Game boards will need to be protected by covering them with plastic film. Before doing this, it gives an attractive appearance to trim the white sheet a little, so that when stuck on card there is a coloured border.

For card games we find it best to cover the whole sheet, on one side only, with transparent plastic film before cutting out. As well as protecting the surface, it makes for easier handling, giving just the right amount of slipperiness. Covering both sides with plastic film is not as good. Anyone who is not familiar with plastic film is advised to experiment first.

To get different colours within the same activity, it has been necessary to spread some of the activities over more than one card. This also means that one card may have materials for more than one activity on it. It is therefore important to make sure that when cutting out, each set of cards stays with its own reference code. One good way is to put them straight into a small self-seal plastic bag with the code cut out and included, or attached to the bag with a small piece of the sticky film. Some teachers use cardboard box tops as trays to keep materials sorted. Rubber bands for the cards are also a help.

We have found that the best way to keep together all the materials for each activity is to have them in a labelled plastic bag. Usually a separate bag is used for each activity, but sometimes it is convenient to put two together. These can then be stored upright in a suitably sized open cardboard box. Alternatively, they can be suspended from a rail by a string attached to a clothes peg or bulldog clip.

In each bag, we find it useful to have the concept, ability, materials, and details of the activity (these may be rules for a game) written on coloured A4 cards which stay in the appropriate bags. This information can be read through the bags. The discussions of concepts and activities may be written on the back if desired. The card can be used for quick reference, and also serves as a reminder what has to go back in the bag afterwards. Underlining in red the materials (such as base 10 materials) which are not kept in these individual bags will indicate what else has to be collected at the start of an activity. These cards also give rigidity to the bags, which makes them easier to store upright. The colour of the instructions card may also be used as a colour code as to which network it belongs to.

It is worth remembering that the work of preparing the materials will not have to be repeated, except for occasional replacements. The time spent is a capital investment, which will pay dividends in years to come.

8 Parents

Parents are naturally interested in their children's progress at school. Written work is something they can see – what they cannot see is the lack of understanding which so often underlies children's performance of these 'rules without reasons'. Sometimes also they try to help children at home with their mathematics. Unfortunately, this often takes the form of drill-and-practice at multiplication tables, and pages of mechanical arithmetic. This is the way they were taught themselves, and some parents have been known to respond unfavourably when their children come home and say that they have spent their maths lessons playing games. As one teacher reported: 'Games are for wet Friday afternoons. Maths is hard work. They aren't meant to enjoy it.'

How you deal with problems of this kind will, of course, depend partly on the nature of existing parent-teacher relationships in your own school. When explaining to parents who may be critical of what you are doing, it also helps if you are confident in your own professional understanding, and if there is a good consensus within the school. These are areas in which Sections 2 and 5 offer suggestions. Some approaches which have been used with success are described here. They may be used separately or together.

A parents' evening may be arranged, in which parents play some of the games together. Teachers help to bring out the amount of mathematics which children are using in order to decide what move they will make, or what card to play. To do this well, teachers need to be confident in their own knowledge of the underlying mathematics, and this can be built up by doing the activities together, and discussing with each other the mathematics involved.

A small group of parents may be invited to come regularly and help to make up activities. This needs careful organising initially, but over a period it can be a great saving in teacher's time. When they have made up some activities, parents naturally want to do them in order to find out what they are for; so this combines well with the first approach described.

Some parents may also be invited to come into classrooms and supervise consolidation activities. (It has already been mentioned in Section 6 that activities which introduce new concepts should be supervised by a teacher.)

For parents who wish to help children at home with their mathematics, the games provide an ideal way to do this. Many of these can be played at varying levels of sophistication, which makes them suitable as family games; and there is usually also an element of chance, which means that it is not always the cleverest player who wins. None of the games depends entirely on chance, however. Good play consists in making the best of one's opportunities. Parents who help their children in this way will also have the benefit of knowing that what they are doing fits in with the ways in which their children are learning at school.

9   Some questions and answers

Q.   How long will it take to introduce these materials?
A.   The materials embody many ideas which are likely to be new to many teachers, in two areas: mathematics, and children's conceptual learning. So it is important to go at a pace with which one feels comfortable, and which gives time to assimilate these ideas to one's personal thinking and teaching. It took me twenty-five years to develop the underlying theory, three to find out how to embody it in ways of teaching primary mathematics, and another five to devise and test the integrated set of curriculum materials in this volume. If a school can have the scheme fully implemented and running well in about two years, I would regard this as good going. But of course, you don't have to wait that long to enjoy some of the rewards.

Q.   Isn't it a lot of work?
A.   Changing over to this new approach does require quite a lot of work, especially in the preparation of the materials. The initial and on-going planning and organisation are important, so that this work can go forward smoothly. As I see it, nearly all worthwhile enterprises, including teaching well, involve a lot of work. If you are making progress, this work is experienced as satisfying and worth the effort. As one teacher said, 'Once you get started, it creates its own momentum.' And once it is established, the fact that children are learning more efficiently makes teaching easier.

Q.   How were the concept maps constructed?
A.   First, by a careful analysis of the concepts themselves, and how they relate to each other in the accepted body of mathematical knowledge.[7] This was then tested by using it as a basis for teaching. If an activity was unsuccessful in helping children to develop their understanding, this was discussed in detail at the next meeting with teachers. Sometimes we decided that the activity needed modification; but sometimes we decided that

the children did not have certain other concepts which they needed for understanding the one we had been introducing – that is, the concept map itself needed revision. So the process of construction was a combination of mathematics, applied learning theory, and teaching experiment.

Q.　Is it all right to use the activities in a different order?
A.　Within a topic, the first activity is usually for introducing a new concept, and clearly this should stay first. Those which follow are sometimes for consolidation, in which case the order may not matter too much. Sometimes, however, they are for developing thinking at a more abstract level, in which case the order does matter. However, once the activities have been used in the order suggested, it is often good to return to earlier ones, for further consolidation and to develop connections in both directions: from concrete to abstract, and from abstract to concrete.

Whether it is wise to teach topics in a different order you can decide by looking at the concepts map itself. These, and the teaching experiments described, show that the order of topics is very important. They also show that for building up a given knowledge structure, there are several orders which are likely to be successful – and many which are likely to be unsuccessful.

Q.　Is it all right to modify the activities?
A.　Yes, when you are confident that you understand the purpose of the activity and where it fits into the long-term learning plan. The details of every activity have been tested and often re-written several times, both from the point of view of the mathematics and to help them to go smoothly in the classroom; so I recommend that you begin by using them as written. When you have a good understanding of the mathematics underlying an activity, you will be in a position to use your own creativity to develop it further.

Sometimes children suggest their own variation of a game. My usual answer is that they should discuss this among themselves, and if they agree, try it together next time: but that rules should not be changed in the middle of a game. They may then discuss the advantages and disadvantages of the variation.

Q.　Can I use the materials alongside an existing scheme? And what about written work, in general?
A.　Especially with the older children, I would expect you to begin by introducing these activities alongside the scheme you are already using and familiar with. With younger children, the activities introduce as much written work as I think is necessary, and for the first three years I envisage them as replacing written work from textbooks. Thereafter, existing textbook schemes can be put to good use for gradually introducing more written work of the conventional kind. But these should come after the activities, rather than before. Children will then get much more benefit from the written work because they come to it with greater understanding. (See again the second italicised passage quoted from the Cockcroft report, in note 1.)

Q.　When children are working through a text book, it is easy to keep track of their progress. Have you any suggestions for progress records when using these activities?

A.   With the volume of photomasters there is one which I hope you will find helpful for this. With regard to textbooks, the page children have reached is not always a reliable indicator of their progress in understanding. Many teachers have found that observation of children while doing activities of this kind, with judicious questioning, is much more diagnostic of their thinking. Piaget was the pioneer of this approach.

Q.   What about measurement?

A.   My present thinking is that measurement is best used in the context of project work. It is one of the less abstract parts of mathematics, so I have concentrated initially on those areas where there are the greatest problems, and where primary school maths is particularly important as a foundation for understanding of later work.

Q.   Doesn't all this sound too good to be true?

A.   Frankly, yes. Only personal experience will enable you to decide whether it can become true for you yourself, and in your school. Each school has its own microclimate, within which some kinds of learning can thrive and others not. Where the microclimate is favourable to this kind of learning, what I have been describing can become true, and I think you will find it professionally very rewarding. Where this is not at present the case, the problems lie beyond what can be discussed here. I have discussed them at length elsewhere.[8]

Q.   What do you see as the most important points when implementing this approach?

A.   Good organisation; personal experience of using the activities; observation, reflection and discussion.

Notes

1. In the following extract from the Cockcroft report, the bold type is in the original; the italics are my own.

   289   Practical work is essential throughout the primary years if the mathematics curriculum is to be developed in the way which we have advocated in paragraph 287. It is, though, necessary to realise at the outset that such work requires a considerable amount of time. However, *provided that the practical work is properly structured with a wide variety of experience and clear stages of progression*, and is followed up by the teacher by means of questions and discussion, this time is well spent. *For most children practical work provides the most effective means by which understanding of mathematics can develop.*

   290 . . . It is therefore a mistake to suppose that there is any particular age at which children no longer need to use practical materials or that such materials are needed only by those whose attainment is low. It is not 'babyish' to work with practical materials while the need exists and *we believe that many children would derive benefit from a much greater use of these materials in the later primary years that occurs in many classrooms.*

3.5 . . . *a premature start on formal written arithmetic is likely to delay progress rather than hasten it.*
W.H. Cockcroft (Chairman of Committee of Inquiry), *Mathematics Counts*, London, HMSO, 1982, pp. 84, 85, 89.

2. R.R. Skemp, *Mathematics in the Primary School*, London, Routledge, 1989.
3. J. Dewey, *Sources of a Science of Education*, New York, Liveright, 1929.
4. R.R. Skemp, *The Psychology of Learning Mathematics*, Harmondsworth, Penguin, 1971, 2nd edn 1986.
5. R.R. Skemp, *Intelligence, Learning, and Action*, Chichester, Wiley, 1978.
6. Skemp, 1988, op. cit.
7. Skemp, 1971 and 1978, op cit. See chapter 2 of the first edition, or chapter 1 of the second edition.
8. Skemp, 1978, op cit., chapter 15.

CONCEPT MAPS AND
LISTS OF ACTIVITIES

Activities in **bold** are those found in this volume.

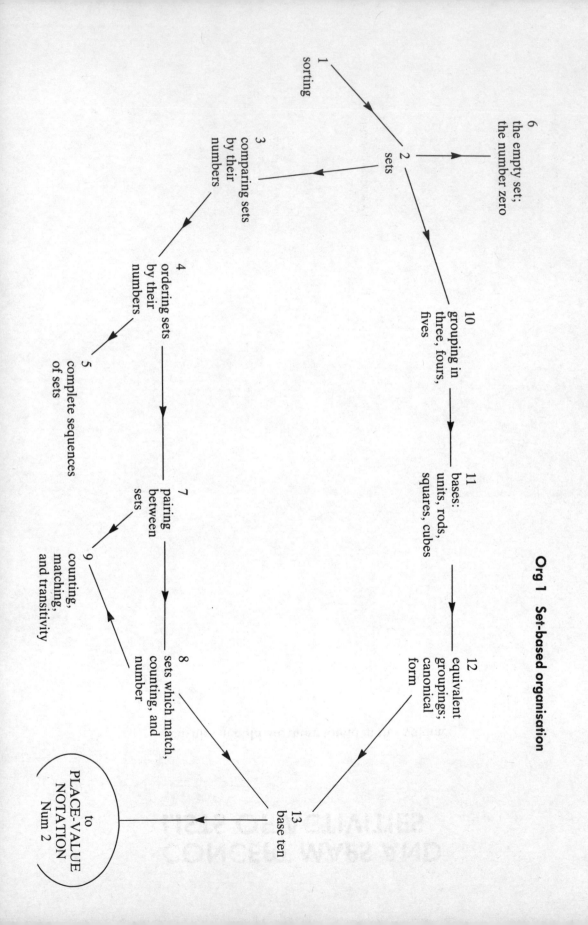

Org 1 Set-based organisation

1
sorting

2
sets

6
the empty set;
the number zero

3
comparing sets
by their
numbers

4
ordering sets
by their
numbers

5
complete sequences
of sets

10
grouping in
three, fours,
fives

11
bases:
units, rods,
squares, cubes

12
equivalent
groupings;
canonical
form

7
pairing
between
sets

8
sets which match,
counting, and
number

9
counting,
matching,
and transitivity

13
base ten

to
PLACE-VALUE
NOTATION
Num 2

Org 1 Set-based organisation

1 *Sorting*
1/1 Perceptual matching of objects
1/2 Matching pictures
1/3 A picture matching game
1/4 Dominoes
1/5 Conceptual matching
1/6 Conceptual matching
1/7 Attribute cards

2 *Sets*
2/1 Introduction to Multilink or Unifix
2/2 Making picture sets
2/3 'Which set am I making?'
2/4 'Which two sets am I making?'

3 *Comparing sets by their numbers*
3/1 Lucky dip
3/2 'Can I fool you?'

4 *Ordering sets by their numbers*
4/1 Ordering several rods by their lengths
4/2 Combining order of number, length, and position

5 *Complete sequences of sets*
5/1 Missing stairs

6 *The empty set; the number zero*
6/1 The empty set

7 *Pairing between sets*   52
7/1 Physical pairing   52
7/2 Mentally pairing   53

8 *Sets which match, counting, and number*   53
8/1 Sets which match   54

9 *Counting, matching, and transitivity*   55
No activity: but a note for teachers

10 *Grouping in threes, fours, fives*   57
10/1 Making sets in groups and units   58
10/2 Comparing larger sets   59
10/3 Conservation of number   59

11 *Bases: units, rods, squares and cubes*   60
11/1 Units, rods and squares   61
11/2 On to cubes   62

12 *Equivalent groupings: canonical form*   63
12/1 'Can I fool you?' (Canonical form)   64
12/2 Exchanging small coins for larger   64

13 *Base ten*
13/1 Tens and hundreds of cubes
13/2 Tens and hundreds of milk straws
13/3 Thousands

Num 1 Numbers and their properties

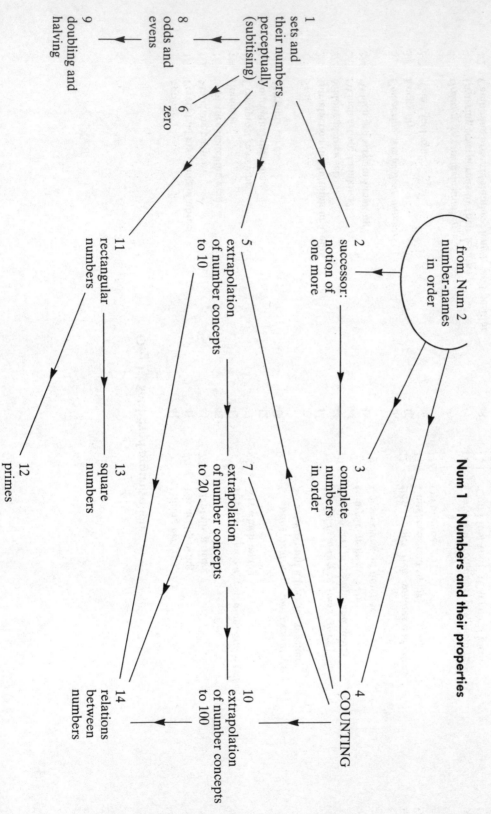

1
sets and
their numbers
perceptually
(subitising)

8
odds and
evens

6
zero

9
doubling and
halving

11
rectangular
numbers

5
extrapolation
of number concepts
to 10

2
successor:
notion of
one more

from Num 2
number-names
in order

12
primes

13
square
numbers

7
extrapolation
of number concepts
to 20

3
complete
numbers
in order

10
extrapolation
of number concepts
to 100

14
relations
between
numbers

4
COUNTING

Num 1 Numbers and their properties

1	*Sets and their numbers perceptually (subitising)*	66
1/1	Sorting dot sets and picture sets	66
1/2	Picture matching game using dot sets and picture sets	67
2	*Successor: notion of one more*	67
2/1	Making successive sets	68
2/2	Putting one more	68
3	*Complete numbers in order*	69
3/1	'Which card is missing?'	69
4	*Counting*	70
4/1	Finger counting to 5	70
4/2	Planting potatoes	71
5	*Extrapolation of number concepts to 10*	71
5/1	Finger counting to 10	72
5/2	Missing stairs, 1 to 10	72
6	*Zero*	73
6/1	'Which card is missing?' (Including zero)	73
6/2	Finger counting from 5 to zero	74
7	*Extrapolation of number concepts to 20*	74
7/1	Finger counting to 20: 'Ten in my head'	75
8	*Odds and evens*	76
8/1	'Yes or no?'	76
8/2	'Can they all find partners?'	76
8/3	'Odd or even?'	77
9	*Doubling and halving*	78
9/1	'Double this and what will we get?'	78
9/2	'Break into halves, and what will we get?'	79
9/3	Doubles and halves rummy	80
10	*Extrapolation of number concepts to 100*	81
10/1	Throwing for a target	81
10/2	Putting and taking	82
11	*Rectangular numbers*	
11/1	Constructing rectangular numbers	
11/2	The rectangular numbers game	
12	*Primes*	
12/1	Alias prime	
12/2	The sieve of Eratosthenes	
12/3	Sum of two primes	
13	*Square numbers*	
13/1	Square numbers	
13/2	An odd property of square numbers	
14	*Relations between numbers*	
4/1	'Tell us something new'	
4/2	'How are these related?'	

These activities will also be found in Num 6 (Division) in topics 6.4 and 6.5

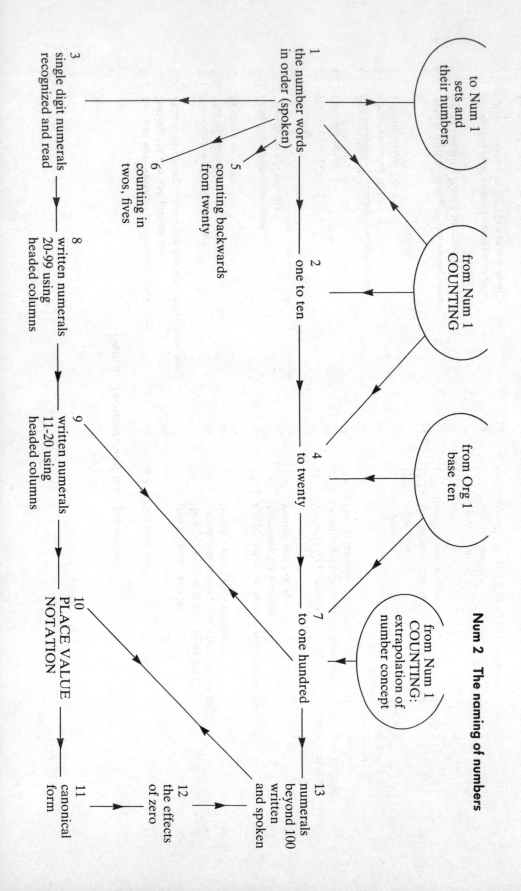

Num 2   The naming of numbers

to Num 1
sets and
their numbers

from Num 1
COUNTING

from Org 1
base ten

from Num 1
COUNTING:
extrapolation of
number concept

1
the number words
in order (spoken)

2
one to ten

4
to twenty

7
to one hundred

3
single digit numerals
recognized and read

5
counting backwards
from twenty

6
counting in
twos, fives

8
written numerals
20-99 using
headed columns

9
written numerals
11-20 using
headed columns

10
PLACE VALUE
NOTATION

13
numerals
beyond 100
written
and spoken

12
the effects
of zero

11
canonical
form

		Page
1	*The number words in order (spoken)*	84
1/1	Number rhymes	84
2	*Number words from one to ten*	85
2/1	Number rhymes to ten	85
3	*Single-digit numerals recognised and read*	86
3/1	Saying and pointing	87
3/2	'Please may I have . . .?'	87
3/3	Joining dots in order, to make pictures	87
3/4	Sets with their numbers	88
3/5	Sequencing numerals 1 to 10	89
4	*Continuation of counting: one to twenty*	89
4/1	Number rhymes to twenty	90
5	*Counting backwards from twenty*	90
5/1	Backward number rhymes	91
5/2	Numbers backwards	92
6	*Counting in twos, fives*	92
6/1	Counting with hand clapping	93
6/2	Counting 2-rods and 5-rods	93
6/3	Counting money: 2p and 5p coins	93
6/4	Counting sets in twos and fives	94
7	*Extrapolation of counting pattern to one hundred*	94
7/1	Counting in tens	

Num 2 The naming of numbers

		Page
7/2	Tens and units tray	95
7/3	Counting two ways on a number square	95
8	*Written numerals from 20 to 99, using headed columns*	96
8/1	Number targets	97
8/2	Number targets beyond 100	99
9	*Written numerals from 11 to 20*	99
9/1	Seeing, speaking, writing 11–19	100
9/2	Number targets in the teens	101
10	*Place-value notation*	
10/1	'We don't need headings any more'	
10/2	Number targets using place-value notation	
10/3	Place-value bingo	
11	*Canonical form*	
11/1	Cashier giving fewest coins	
11/2	'How would you like it?'	
12	*The effects of zero*	
12/1	'Same number, or different?'	
12/2	'Less than, greater than'	
13	*Numerals beyond 100, written and spoken*	
13/1	Big numbers	
13/2	Naming big numbers	

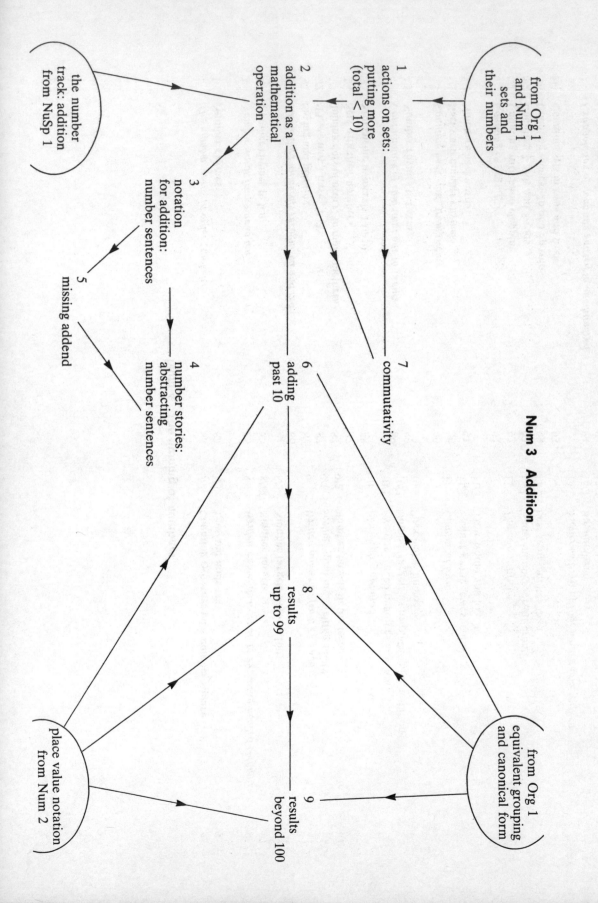

Num 3 Addition

from Org 1 and Num 1
sets and their numbers

the number track: addition from NuSp 1

1 actions on sets: putting more (total < 10)

2 addition as a mathematical operation

7 commutativity

3 notation for addition: number sentences

4 number stories: abstracting number sentences

5 missing addend

6 adding past 10

8 results up to 99

9 results beyond 100

place value notation from Num 2

from Org 1 equivalent grouping and canonical form

Num 3 Addition

1	*Actions on sets: putting more (Total < 10)*	102
1/1	**Start, Action, Result (do and say)**	102
1/2	**Putting more on the number track (verbal)**	104
2	*Addition as a mathematical operation*	104
2/1	**Predicting the result (addition)**	104
2/2	**'Where will it come?' (Same as NuSp 1.3/3)**	105
2/3	**Stepping stones**	105
2/4	**Crossing (Same as NuSp 1.3/2)**	106
3	*Notation for addition: number sentences*	107
3/1	**Writing number sentences for addition**	108
3/2	**Write your prediction**	108
4	*Number stories: abstracting number sentences*	110
4/1	**Personalised number stories**	110
4/2	**Abstracting number sentences**	111
4/3	**Personalised number stories – predictive**	112
5	*Missing addend*	114
5/1	**'How many more must you put?'**	114
5/2	**Secret adder**	115
5/3	**Personalised number stories: what happened?**	116
6	*Adding past 10*	117
6/1	**Start, Action, Result over ten**	117
6/2	**Adding past 10 on the number track**	119
6/3	**Slippery slope**	120
6/4	**Artefacts practice**	121
6/5	**Artefacts at speed**	121
6/6	**Predictive number sentences past 10**	123
6/7	**Explorers**	123
7	*Commutativity*	125
7/1	**Introducing commutativity**	125
7/2	**Introducing non-commutativity**	126
7/3	**Using commutativity for counting on**	127
7/4	**Commutativity means less to remember**	128
8	*Adding, results up to 99*	
8/1	**Start, Action, Result up to 99**	
8/2	**Odd sums for odd jobs**	
8/3	**Renovating a house**	
8/4	**Planning our purchases**	
8/5	**Air freight**	
9	*Adding, results beyond 100*	
9/1	**Start, Action, Result beyond 100**	
9/2	**Cycle camping**	
9/3	**One tonne van drivers**	
9/4	**Catalogue shopping**	

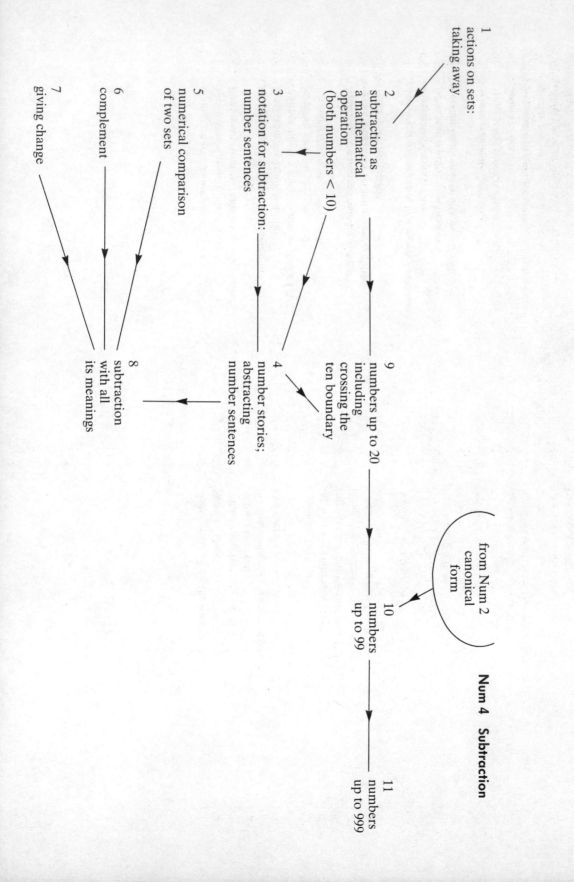

1
actions on sets:
taking away

2
subtraction as
a mathematical
operation
(both numbers < 10)

3
notation for subtraction:
number sentences

5
numerical comparison
of two sets

6
complement

7
giving change

4
number stories;
abstracting
number sentences

8
subtraction
with all
its meanings

9
numbers up to 20
including
crossing the
ten boundary

10
numbers
up to 99

from Num 2
canonical
form

11
numbers
up to 999

Num 4 Subtraction

Num 4 Subtraction

1 *Actions on sets: taking away* — 131
1/1 **Start, Action, Result (do and say)** — 131
1/2 **Taking away on the number track (do and say) (NuSp 1.4/1)** — 132

2 *Subtraction as a mathematical operation* — 132
2/1 **Predicting the result** — 133
2/2 **What will be left? (NuSp 1.4/2)** — 133
2/3 **Returning over the stepping stones** — 134
2/4 **Crossing back** — 134

3 *Notation for subtraction: number sentences* — 135
3/1 **Number sentences for subtraction** — 135
3/2 **Predicting from number sentences** — 137

4 *Number stories; abstracting number sentences* — 138
4/1 **Personalised number stories** — 138
4/2 **Abstracting number sentences** — 139
4/3 **Personalised number stories – predictive** — 140

5 *Numerical comparison of two sets* — 142
5/1 **Capture (NuSp 1.4/4)** — 143
5/2 **Laying the table** — 143
5/3 **Diver and wincher** — 143
5/4 **Number comparison sentences** — 145
5/5 **Subtraction sentences for comparisons** — 146

6 *Complementary numbers* — 147
6/1 **The handkerchief game** — 148
6/2 **'Please may I have . . .?' (complements)** — 148

7 *Giving change* — 150
7/1 **Change by exchange** — 150
7/2 **Change by counting on** — 150
7/3 **Till receipts** — 151

8 *Subtraction with all its meanings* — 153
8/1 **Using set diagrams for taking away** — 153
8/2 **Using set diagrams for comparison** — 153
8/3 **Using set diagrams for finding complements** — 154
8/4 **Using set diagrams for giving change** — 155
8/5 **Unpacking the parcel** — 156

9 *Subtraction up to 20, including crossing the 10 boundary* — 158
9/1 **Subtraction from teens: choose your method** — 158
9/2 **Subtracting from teens: 'Check!'** — 160
9/3 **Till receipts up to 20p** — 160
9/4 **Gift shop** — 161

10 *Subtraction up to 99*
10/1 **'Can we subtract?'**
10/2 **Subtracting two-digit numbers**
10/3 **Front window, rear window**
10/4 **Front window, rear window – make your own**

11 *Subtraction up to 999*
11/1 **Race from 500 to 0**
11/2 **Subtracting three-digit numbers**
11/3 **Airliner**
11/4 **Sweet shop: selling and stocktaking**

Num 5 Multiplication

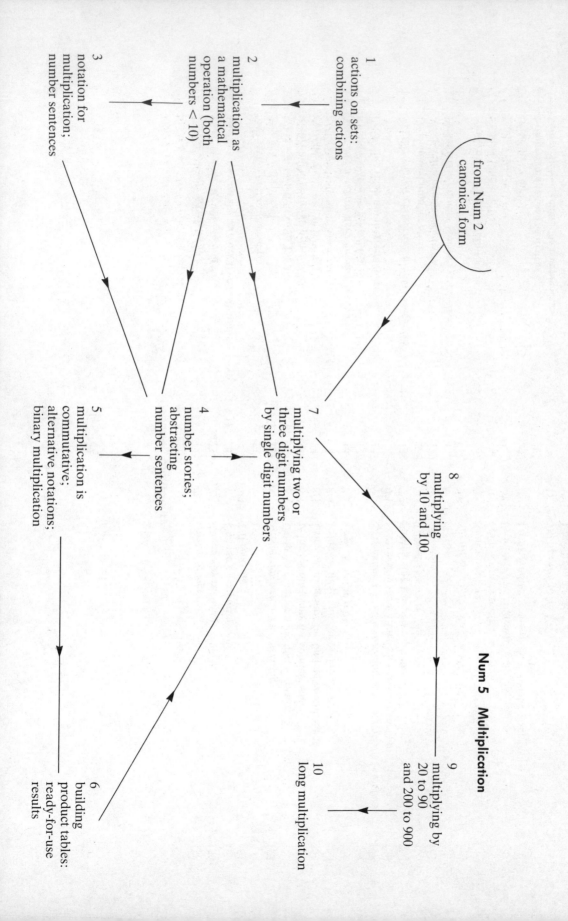

from Num 2
canonical form

1
actions on sets:
combining actions

2
multiplication as
a mathematical
operation (both
numbers < 10)

3
notation for
multiplication;
number sentences

4
number stories;
abstracting
number sentences

5
multiplication is
commutative;
alternative notations;
binary multiplication

6
building
product tables:
ready-for-use
results

7
multiplying two or
three digit numbers
by single digit numbers

8
multiplying
by 10 and 100

9
multiplying by
20 to 90
and 200 to 900

10
long multiplication

Num 5 Multiplication

1   *Actions on sets; combining actions*   163
1/1 **Make a set. Make others which match**   164
1/2 **Multiplying on a number track**   165
1/3 **Giant strides on a number track**   165

2   *Multiplication as a mathematical operation*   169
2/1 **'I predict – here' using rods**   169
2/2 **Sets under our hands**   170

3   *Notation for multiplication: number sentences*   171
3/1 **Number sentences for multiplication**   172
3/2 **Predicting from number sentences**   174

4   *Number stories: abstracting number sentences*   175
4/1 **Number stories**   176
4/2 **Abstracting number sentences**   177
4/3 **Number stories, and predicting from number sentences**   177

5   *Multiplication is commutative; alternative notations: binary
     multiplication*   175
5/1 Big Giant and Little Giant   9/2
5/2 Little Giant explains why
5/3 Binary multiplication
5/4 Unpacking the parcel (binary multiplication)
     Alternative notations

6   *Building product tables: ready-for-use results*
6/1 Building sets of products
6/2 'I know another way'
6/3 Completing the products table
6/4 Cards on the table
6/5 Products practice
6/6 Multiples rummy

7   *Multiplying 2- or 3-digit numbers by single-digit numbers*
7/1 Using multiplication facts for larger numbers
7/2 Multiplying 3-digit numbers
7/3 Cargo boats

8   *Multiplying by 10 and 100*
8/1 Multiplying by 10 or 100
8/2 Explaining the shorthand
8/3 Multiplying by hundreds and thousands

9   *Multiplying by 20 to 90 and by 200 to 900*
9/1 'How many cubes in this brick?' (Alternative path)
9/2 Multiplying by n-ty and any hundred

10   *Long multiplication*
10/1 Long multiplication
10/2 Treasure chest

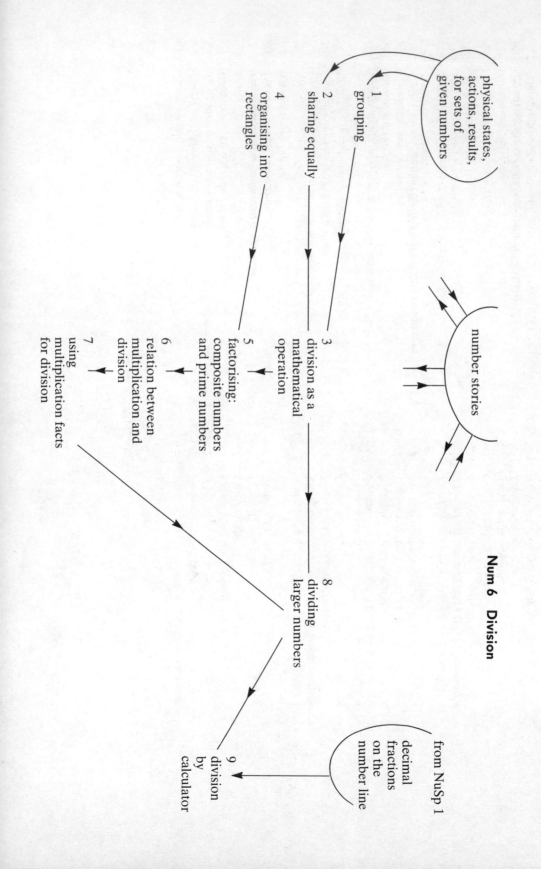

physical states,
actions, results,
for sets of
given numbers

1
grouping

2
sharing equally

4
organising into
rectangles

3
division as a
mathematical
operation

5
factorising:
composite numbers
and prime numbers

6
relation between
multiplication and
division

7
using
multiplication facts
for division

number stories

Num 6   Division

8
dividing
larger numbers

9
division
by
calculator

from NuSp 1

decimal
fractions
on the
number line

Num 6 Division

1   *Grouping*
1/1   **Start, Action, Result: grouping**
1/2   **Predictive number sentences (grouping)**
1/3   **Word problems (grouping)**

2   *Sharing equally*
2/1   **Sharing equally**
2/2   **'My share is . . .',**
2/3   **'My share is . . . and I also know the remainder, which is . . .'**
2/4   **Word problems (sharing)**

3   *Division as a mathematical operation*
3/1   **Different questions, same answer. Why?**
3/2   **Combining the number sentences**
3/3   **Unpacking the parcel (division)**
3/4   **Mr Taylor's game**

4   *Organising into rectangles*
4/1   Constructing rectangular numbers   } Also in
4/2   The rectangular numbers game   } Num 1.11

5   *Factorising: composite numbers and prime numbers*   181
5/1   Factors bingo   181
5/2   Factors rummy   183
5/3   Alias prime   183
5/4   The sieve of Eratosthenes (Also in Num 1.12)   187

6   *Relation between multiplication and division*   187
6/1   Parcels within parcels   189

7   *Using multiplication results for division*   189
7/1   A new use for the multiplication square   189
7/2   Quotients and remainders   192
7/3   Village Post Office   192

8   *Dividing larger numbers*   194
8/1   'I'm thinking in hundreds . . . .'   195
8/2   'I'll take over your remainder'   195
8/3   Q and R ladders   196
8/4   Cargo Airships   196

9   *Division by calculator*
9/1   Number targets: division by calculator

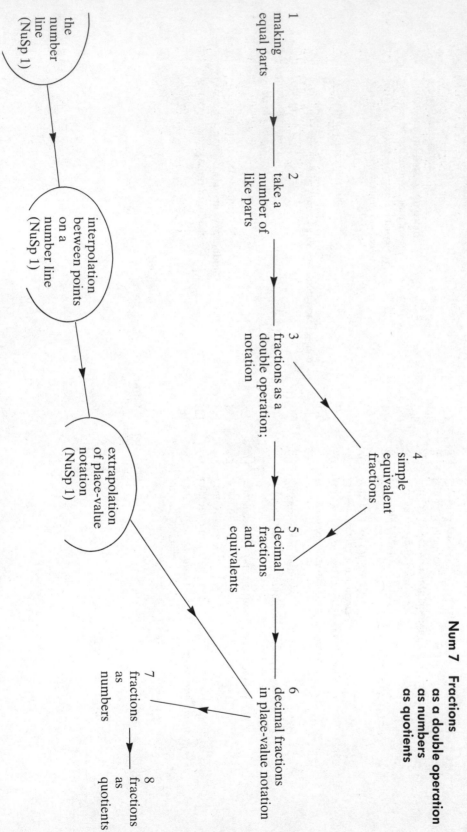

**Num 7 Fractions
as a double operation
as numbers
as quotients**

1
making
equal parts

2
take a
number of
like parts

3
fractions as a
double operation;
notation

4
simple
equivalent
fractions

5
decimal
fractions
and
equivalents

6
decimal fractions
in place-value notation

7
fractions
as
numbers

8
fractions
as
quotients

the
number
line
(NuSp 1)

interpolation
between points
on a
number line
(NuSp 1)

extrapolation
of place-value
notation
(NuSp 1)

33

1   *Making equal parts*
1/1 Making equal parts
1/2 Same kind, different shapes
1/3 Parts and bits
1/4 Sorting parts
1/5 Match and mix: parts

2   *Take a number of like parts*
2/1 Feeding the animals
2/2 Trainee keepers, qualified keepers
2/3 Head keepers

3   *Fractions as a double operation: notation*
3/1 Expanding the diagram
3/2 'Please may I have?' (Diagrams and notation)

4   *Simple equivalent fractions*
4/1 'Will this do instead?'
4/2 Sorting equivalent fractions
4/3 Match and mix: equivalent fractions

Num 7   Fractions

5   *Decimal fractions and equivalents*
5/1 Making jewellery to order
5/2 Equivalent fraction diagrams (decimal)
5/3 Pair, and explain
5/4 Match and mix: equivalent decimal fractions

6   *Decimal fractions in place-value notation*
6/1 Reading headed columns in two ways
6/2 Same number, or different?
63/ Claiming and naming

7   *Fractions as numbers. Addition of decimal fractions in place-value notation*
7/1 Target, 1
7/2 'How do we know that our method is still correct?'

8   *Fractions as quotients*
8/1 Fractions for sharing
8/2 Predict, then press
8/3 'Are calculators clever?'
8/4 Number targets by calculator

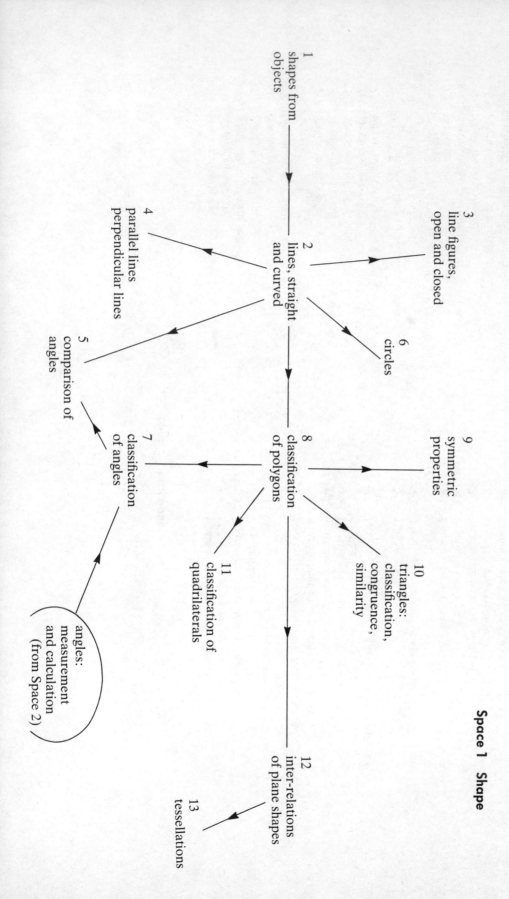

Space 1 Shape

1
shapes from
objects

3
line figures,
open and closed

2
lines, straight
and curved

4
parallel lines
perpendicular lines

6
circles

9
symmetric
properties

5
comparison of
angles

7
classification
of angles

8
classification
of polygons

10
triangles:
classification,
congruence,
similarity

11
classification of
quadrilaterals

angles:
measurement
and calculation
(from Space 2)

12
inter-relations
of plane shapes

13
tessellations

1 Shapes from objects
1/1 Matching objects to outlines
1/2 'I spy . . .' (shapes)

2 Lines, straight and curved
2/1 Drawing pictures with straight and curved lines
2/2 'I have a straight/curved line, like . . .'
2/3 'Please may I have . . .?' (Straight and curved lines)

3 Line figures, open and closed
3/1 'Can they meet?'
3/2 Escaping pig
3/3 Pig puzzle
3/4 Inside and outside

4 Parallel lines, perpendicular lines
4/1 'My rods are parallel/perpendicular'
4/2 'All put your rods parallel/perpendicular to the big rod'
4/3 Colouring pictures

5 Comparison of angles
5/1 'All make an angle like mine'
5/2 'Which angle is bigger?'
5/3 Largest angle takes all
5/4 Angles in the environment

6 Circles
6/1 Circles in the environment
6/2 Parts of a circle
6/3 Circles and their parts in the environment
6/4 Patterns with circles

7 Classification of angles
7/1 Right angles, acute angles, obtuse angles
7/2 Angle dominoes

Space 1 Shape

Page		
199	7/3	'Mine is the different kind'
199	7/4	'Can't cross, will fit, must cross'
200	**8**	**Classification of polygons**
201	8/1	Classifying polygons
201	8/2	Polygon dominoes
201	8/3	Match and mix: polygons
202	**9**	**Symmetric properties**
203	9/1	Testing for line symmetry
203	9/2	Collecting symmetries
203	**10**	**Triangles: classification, congruence, similarity**
205	10/1	Classifying triangles
205	10/2	Triangles dominoes
206	10/3	Match and mix: triangles
206	10/4	Congruent and similar triangles
207	**11**	**Classification of quadrilaterals**
	11/1	Classifying quadrilaterals
	11/2	Relations between quadrilaterals
	11/3	'And what else is this?'
209	11/4	'I think you mean . . .'
	12	**Inter-relations of plane shapes**
	12/1	Triangles and polygons
	12/2	Circles and polygons
	12/3	'I can see . . .'
	12/4	Triangles and larger shapes
	13	**Tessellations**
	13/1	Tessellating regular polygons
	13/2	Tessellating other shapes
	13/3	Inventing tessellations
	13/4	Tessellating any quadrilateral

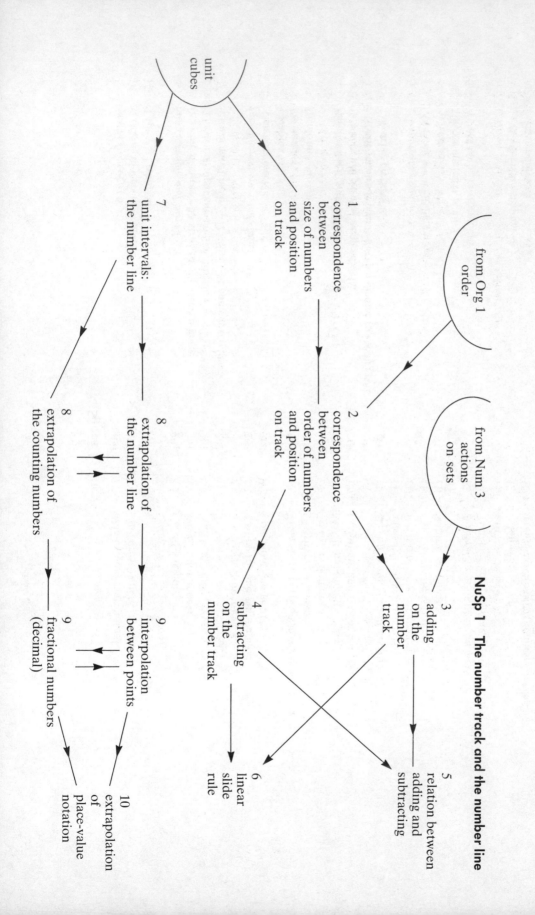

NuSp 1 The number track and the number line

unit
cubes

from Org 1
order

from Num 3
actions
on sets

1
correspondence
between
size of numbers
and position
on track

2
correspondence
between
order of numbers
and position
on track

7
unit intervals:
the number line

3
adding
on the
number
track

4
subtracting
on the
number track

5
relation between
adding and
subtracting

6
linear
slide
rule

8
extrapolation of
the number line

8
extrapolation of
the counting numbers

9
interpolation
between points

9
fractional numbers
(decimal)

10
extrapolation
of
place-value
notation

NuSp 1 The number track and the number line

1   *Correspondence between size of number and position on*
     track
1/1 'I predict – here' on the number track   211

2   *Correspondence between order of numbers and position on*
     track
2/1 Sequences on the number track   211

3   *Adding on the number track*
3/1 Putting more on the number track (verbal)   215
3/2 Where will it come?   215
3/3 Crossing (also as Num 3.2/4)   217
3/4 Where will it come? (Through 10)   217

4   *Subtracting on the number track*   219
4/1 Taking away on the number track (verbal)   220
4/2 What will be left?   220
4/3 Crossing back   221
4/4 Capture   221

5   *Relation between adding and subtracting*   221
5/1 Slow bicycle race   222
5/2 Ups and downs   223
                                                                   223

6   *Linear slide rule*   223
6/1 Add and check   225
6/2 Adding past 20   226
                                                                   226
                                                                   226

7   *Unit intervals: the number line*   227
7/1 Drawing the number line   228
7/2 Sequences on the number line   228
7/3 Where must the frog land?   228
7/4 Lopping backwards   229
7/5 Taking   229
7/6 A race through a maze   229

8   *Extrapolation of the number line*
8/1 What number is this? (Single starter)
8/2 What number is this? (Double starter)
8/3 Is there a limit?
8/4 Can you think of . . .?

9   *Interpolation between points*
9/1 *Fractional numbers (decimal)*
9/2 What number is this? (Decimal fractions)
9/3 Snail race
     Snails and frogs

10   *Extrapolation of place-value notation*
10/1 *Extrapolation of the counting numbers*
10/2 'How can we write this number?' (Headed columns)
10/3 Introducing the decimal point
10/4 Pointing and writing
     Shrinking and growing

THE NETWORKS AND ACTIVITIES

[Org 1] SET BASED ORGANISATION
Organising in ways which lay foundations for concepts relating to number

Org 1.1   SORTING

Concept   Likeness between objects.

Ability   Sorting a mixture of objects into sets whose members are alike in some way. This common property may be perceptual or conceptual.

Discussion of concept   Children will do this with little prompting, given suitable materials: sometimes spontaneously. This is because sorting is closely linked with intelligence. Until we have classified an object, i.e. until we know what it is, we do not know in what ways we can use it to help us achieve our goals.

Activity 1   **Perceptual matching of objects**

A teacher-led activity for a small group of children. Its purpose is to help them to become aware of the likenesses and differences in the objects.

Materials
- Boxes of different kinds of assorted small objects, several of each kind. E.g. sea shells, crayons, empty matchboxes, screws.
- Shallow trays for sorting into. E.g. box lids.
- Large box into which the sorted trays can be put.
- For later stages, with older children: objects of the same kind, but not identical. E.g. all screws, or all sea shells, etc.

What they do
1. Tip the assorted objects onto the table and say, 'These are all mixed up. Can you sort them?' If necessary demonstrate: 'Like this,' placing the objects into the trays.
2. When the objects have been sorted, place all the separate trays in the box. We don't want to undo the children's sorting before their eyes, as soon as they have finished.

Activity 2   **Matching pictures**

An activity for a small group. The purpose is to progress from sorting the actual objects to sorting pictures which represent them.

Materials
- A pack of picture cards, which can be sorted into sets.*
  * The pictures should not be identical, but different objects of the same

41

kind. Pictures cut from mail order catalogues, stuck on plain cards, are a useful source for these.

What they do   The cards are sorted into sets as before.

Activity 3   A picture matching game

For a small group. This is to give more practice in sorting.

Materials   •   As in Activity 2.

What they do   1.   The cards are shuffled and dealt face down.
2.   The player on the left of the dealer turns over his top card and puts it face upwards on the table.
3.   Each player in turn does likewise. If his card is like a card or pile already there, it is added to that pile and the player has a second turn. (But not more, or the game ends too quickly.)
4.   If it does not match one of the existing piles, a new pile is started.
5.   The winner is the first to have put down all his cards, after which the others may play out their hands until all the cards are down.
6.   Encourage naming the sets which result from the sorting.

Activity 4   Dominoes

This is a very useful game for two players, since once the rules have been learnt (and they are not difficult), the game can be played with the same rules but using increasingly advanced concepts of matching.

Materials   •   3 sets matching by
a) colour
b) shape
c) number of dots*
* These should be positioned irregularly, so that children match by number and not by patterns. The set may go up to 5 dots, but for beginners only up to 3, then 4. These are numbers which can be recognised perceptually, without counting.

What they do   1.   The rules are as in conventional dominoes.
2.   Children will match by colour, shape, number of dots.

Activities 5 and 6   Conceptual matching

As for activities 2 and 3. Its aim is to begin sorting by properties which are conceptual, not perceptual. This means that the likenesses are not visible but in our thinking.

Materials   •   A pack of picture cards which can be sorted into sets. E.g. vehicles, tools, garments, dwellings.
Functional concepts (what we use things for) are a fruitful source of ideas here.

Activity 7   Attribute cards

An activity for a small group. Its purpose is to extend what has gone before to matching by two attributes simultaneously.

Materials
- A pack of attribute cards.*
- 3 reminder cards on which are written respectively 'Number', 'Colour', 'Shape'.**

* Each card has one, two, three, or four shapes, all alike. These shapes may be squares, circles, triangles, oblongs, all of the same colour. The colours may be red, blue, yellow, green. This gives 64 cards, leading to 16 piles.

** The word on each card should be written 4 times so that every player can see it the right way up.

What they do
1. Two of the reminder cards are placed on the table to show which two attributes are currently to be used for sorting: e.g. colour and shape.
2. The game is then played as for activities 3 and 6, except that matching is by two attributes simultaneously. E.g. if matching by colour and shape, a card with 2 red triangles would be matched with cards having any number of red triangles.
3. The game may be introduced using only one attribute, and a small number of cards.

Discussion of activities

In activities 1, 2, 3, 5, 6, children learn to sort by qualities which are increasingly abstract. This progression may need plenty of time and repetition, and should not be hurried. Activity 4 provides variety, and this may also be given by different boxes of objects to be sorted, different packs of cards. Activity 7 introduces greater complexity. The later stage of activity 1 (e.g. all shells, all buttons) requires careful observation and thought in order to decide on qualities by which they can be sorted. This heightens consciousness of what they are doing, and is valuable for older children.

In all cases, discussion should be encouraged for reaching agreement, or explaining, which objects or cards are put together. This, together with naming the sets, encourages mode 2 schema construction.

These activities can only be done by the use of conceptual learning – they would be impossible by rote learning. So sorting is of even greater importance as a foundation for mathematical learning than is generally realised, since it 'switches in' the right kind of learning from the beginning.

OBSERVE AND LISTEN   **REFLECT**   **DISCUSS**

Org 1.2   SETS

Concept   A set, as the result of the process of sorting.

Abilities   (i)   To be able to make the mental decision as to what goes into a set and what does not, with physical objects.

(ii) Also with mental objects.

(iii) To be able to sort the same mental or physical objects differently according to choice.

Discussion of concept

The result of sorting is a collection of objects (physical or mental) called a *set*. So we can think of sorting as a process, and a set as the result. What goes into a set, or does not, is the result of a mental decision, so the same objects may be sorted differently according to choice, and the resulting sets will be different.

Activity 1   Introduction to Multilink or Unifix

Its purpose is to introduce the cubes to the children, and give them experience in manipulating them. Also, to give further experience of making sets.

Materials
- Multilink or Unifix cubes in a variety of colours for each child.

What they do

1. Sort these by colour.
2. Join into rods, to form 'the blue set', 'the red set', etc.

Activity 2   Making picture sets

An activity for any number of children. The purpose is to give practice in naming sets.

Materials
- Envelopes containing pictures cut from mail order catalogues.
- Sheets of paper.
- Glue.

What they do
1. The children sort the pictures into sets.
2. They stick each of these onto a separate sheet of paper.
3. Name these sets, e.g. 'a set of flowers', 'a set of milk bottles'.
4. These can then form permanent sets for display.

Activity 3   'Which set am I making?'

An activity for a small group. Its purpose is to give the children experience of sorting the same objects by different attributes.

Materials
- A set of attribute blocks, which can be sorted by colour, shape, size, or thickness.
- A set loop.

What they do   *Stage (a)*
1. The children familiarise themselves with the attribute blocks. Let them take one each, and ask in turn 'What can you say about your block?' E.g. 'It's red. It's a circle.' And, comparing it with others, 'It's small and thick.' (Or, smaller and thicker).

2. Tip all the blocks onto the table.
3. Put out the set loop and discuss how we could make a set by choosing, e.g. all the blue blocks, or all the squares, or all the thin ones.
4. Let the children together pick out the blocks which belong to the chosen set and put them into the loop.
5. Ask them to describe this set, e.g. 'The set of oblongs'.
6. Repeat until the children are confident, using different kinds of attribute, e.g. colour, or shape, or size, or thickness.

Stage (b)
1. As before, the blocks are spread out on the table and a set loop is put down.
2. One player decides on an attribute.
3. She begins to sort by this attribute, putting inside the loop all blocks which belong to the set she is thinking of.
4. She should also put some non-examples outside the loop.
5. The others watch and try to discover which set she is making.
6. If one of the players thinks that she knows, she demonstrates this by sorting the next two or three blocks. In this way the others are not told prematurely.
7. Finally the set is named, e.g. 'The set of red blocks.'
8. Repeat, using different kinds of attribute.

Activity 4   **'Which *two* sets am I making?'**

An activity for a small group. This activity extends the concept of a set to two attributes.

Materials   ● A set of attribute blocks.
● 2 set loops.

What they do   1. This is played as in activity 3, except that two loops are put down, not overlapping.
2. Initially, the player doing the sorting is likely to choose two attributes of the same kind, e.g. red, green.
3. With experience, attributes of different kinds may be used, e.g. red, circle.
4. So all the red blocks will be put in one set loop, and all the circular blocks in the other loop. But what about the red circles?
5. Given time, children will usually arrive at the idea of overlapping the two set loops. It is good to allow them time to think of this themselves.

Discussion of activities   The purpose of all these activities is to separate out the idea of a set from the sorting activity which leads to it. In activity 4, both these ideas are used in a more sophisticated way.

As in topic 1, conceptual learning is the only way in which these activities can be done successfully.

OBSERVE AND LISTEN   **REFLECT**   **DISCUSS**

Org 1.3   COMPARING SETS BY THEIR NUMBERS

Concepts   (i)   A set as being composed of units.
(ii)   Larger or smaller sets as referring to the number of units, not the size or location of the objects.

Ability   To say which of two sets has more units, or whether they both have the same number.

Discussion of concepts	By 'Comparing sets by numbers' I only mean 'Which set has the larger number? Or have they both the same number?' This is the preliminary stage only for Num 4.5, in the subtraction network, where the further question is asked 'How many more, or less?'
	A set of three large objects, widely spaced, *looks* much larger than one of five small objects close together. To realise that the latter has the larger number of objects therefore requires the ability to think of the elements just as units, regardless of size, location, or anything else except the fact that they are separate objects. This isn't easy, and we must give children time to form this concept starting with unit objects which are all the same size.

Activity 1   Lucky dip

An activity for a small group. Its purpose is to introduce the comparisons 'larger' and 'smaller' in relation to sets.

Materials   • Cubes: equal numbers of each colour.*
• An opaque bag.
• A box or container for discarded cubes.
* Hereafter used to mean Multilink or Unifix.

What they do   1.   The cubes are mixed up in the bag.
2.   Each player chooses a colour.
3.   In turn they reach in and take out a cube. The first cube each takes out determines what colour he collects thereafter.
4.   If a player gets a cube of the colour he is collecting he joins it to those he already has to form a rod.
5.   If the wrong colour, he discards it.
6.   The winner is the one who finishes with the longest rod.
7.   Discarded cubes should be put into the container, not returned to the bag.
Variation
If a player gets a cube of the wrong colour for himself, he may either discard it, or give it to another player who is collecting that colour and take out two more cubes for himself. These he uses or discards.

Activity 2   'Can I fool you?'

A group game, for a teacher and children together. Its purpose is to emphasise that the number of units in a set does not depend on their positions.

Materials
- Cubes of different colours for each child.
- Some counters.

What they do
1. Each child in turn puts down some cubes. The cubes must be separate, not joined.
2. The teacher also puts down some cubes for the child to compare with his own set, and predict which will make the longer rod.
3. If his prediction is correct, the child receives a counter.
4. The teacher tries to 'fool' the children by the way he arranges his cubes. E.g. he might put a smaller number of cubes, more widely spaced; or a larger number, closer together.
5. The winner is the child who has the most counters.

Discussion of activities

In these activities, the alternation between a set of scattered cubes and the set joined into a rod is of great value in developing the two aspects of the set concept: a single entity, made up of a number of units.

OBSERVE AND LISTEN   **REFLECT**   **DISCUSS**

Org 1.4   ORDERING SETS BY THEIR NUMBERS

Concepts
(i)   Order in space (left to right). ⎫ These three
(ii) Order of length.   ⎬ concepts are
(iii) Order of number of units.   ⎭ closely connected.

Abilities
(i)   To put several sets in order of number, ascending from left to right.
(ii) The same descending.

Discussion of concepts

The difficulty of doing this should not be under-estimated, since it involves not just a single comparison as in Org 1.3, but combining the result of several comparisons. We therefore take it quite slowly.

Activity 1   **Ordering several rods by their lengths**

An activity for a small group of children with their teacher. Its purpose is to teach them to combine ordering by length with ordering in space.

Materials   For each pair:
- cubes of different colours
- a shallow tray or box lid.

What they do
1. Each child makes three rods, all of different lengths and colours.

2. They put these on the tray in order of length, shortest on the left, tallest on the right.
3. They then mix up the rods, while leaving them on the tray; and exchange with another child, who puts them back in order again.
4. Steps 1, 2, 3 are repeated with different lengths and colours. This may conveniently be done by exchange between different children.
5. When they can do this easily, repeat with four rods, then five.

Activity 2   Combining order of number, length, and position

A harder version of activity 1. This makes a start with ordering by number, independently of length. This is then tested as in activity 1.

Materials   • As for activity 1.

What they do   Steps 1 and 2 are the same as in activity 1, starting with three rods.
3. They then break the rods into single cubes. These are left in groups of the same colour, not in a row.
4. They exchange with another child. This child first says which group she thinks will make the longest rod. A spare cube of the same colour is put down to record her prediction.
5. The cubes are then re-formed into rods, and put in order of length. The prediction made in step 4 is tested.
6. Steps 3, 4, and 5 are repeated. This time, the other child has to predict which group will make the shortest rod.
7. When they can do this easily, repeat with four rods, then five.
Variation
After 2, a colour record is made of the order by forming cubes of appropriate colours into a rod. After 5, this colour record is compared with the re-constituted collection.

Discussion of activities   We are asking the children to combine three orderings: by length, position, and number. Moreover, each of these orderings involves a number of comparisons. E.g. when ordering by length, a given rod has to come after every shorter rod, and before every longer rod. So we should allow them as much time as they need to work through the stages described. This greatly varies between children.

OBSERVE AND LISTEN   **REFLECT**   **DISCUSS**

Org 1.5   COMPLETE SEQUENCES OF SETS

Concept   An ordered sequence of sets with 'no gaps', i.e. in which each set is of number one more than the one before, and one less than the one after (except for the first and last sets).

Abilities   (i)   To construct a sequence of this kind.

(ii)   To extrapolate such a sequence.

(iii)   To tell whether a sequence is complete or not; and if it is not, to locate and fill the gaps.

Discussion of concept

When we have ordered a given tray-full of rods, we have a sequence of a kind. But there is no regularity about it. If we take a rod away, there is nothing to show which one is missing. And between any two rods, as likely as not we can insert another which will conform to the same ordering.

A sequence of counting numbers, however, has a special property. Provided we know where it starts and finishes, we can tell whether or not it is complete: and if not, which ones are missing and where they should go in order.

A staircase of rods shows this property very clearly.

Activity 1   **Missing stairs**

An activity for children to play in pairs. Its purpose is to introduce them to the concepts described, in a way which allows testable predictions.

Materials   ●   Cubes. A different colour for each of the pair.

What they do   *Stage (a)*

1.   Child A makes a staircase from rods made up of one to five cubes, all the same colour, as illustrated.

2.   B removes one rod, hiding the missing rod from sight.

3.   A then makes from loose cubes of a different colour a rod which he predicts will fit the gap.

4.   This prediction is tested in 2 ways: by insertion into the gap in the staircase, and by comparison with the rod which was removed.

Stage (a) Step 1   Step 2

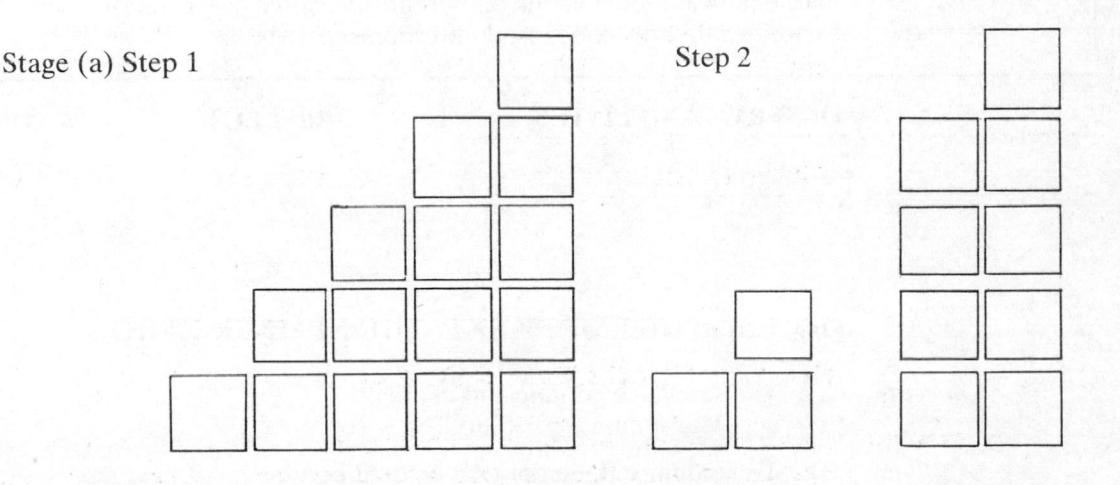

Stage (b)

Step 2

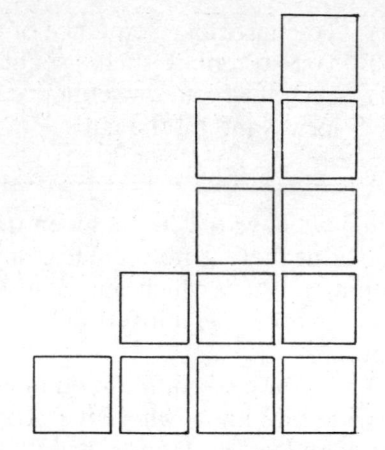

Stage (b)
As above, except that in step 2, child B closes the gap.
Stage (c)
As in stage (b), except that now child A closes his eyes during step 2. So he now has to decide where there is a missing rod, as well as make a matching replacement.
Stage (d)
The number of rods may gradually be increased to ten. Children will often make this extrapolation spontaneously.
The first 3 stages may usually be taken in fairly rapid succession.

Discussion of activity	This was one of the earliest activities I devised, and it was an important learning experience for me. I realised that even such a simple mathematical model as the first 5 counting numbers, in order, could be used to make testable predictions; and I observed the pleasure of 5-year-old children when their predictions were correct.
	With further reflection, I came to realise that the simplicity of this mathematical model is only apparent. On closer examination, one begins to appreciate how condensed and sophisticated it is.

OBSERVE AND LISTEN   **REFLECT**   **DISCUSS**

Org 1.6   THE EMPTY SET; THE NUMBER ZERO

Concepts   (i)   The set which contains no element,
(ii)   and whose number is therefore zero.

Abilities   (i)   To recognise the empty set when it occurs.
(ii)   To state its number, zero.

Discussion of concepts

The mathematical name for this is 'the null set', but I think that 'the empty set' is a better name for beginners. It is the set which has no member, like an empty box. Why 'the'? Because mathematicians argue that there is only one null set: but we do not need to stress this point.

The number of this set is zero. 'Nothing', or 'None', are reasonable answers to the questions 'What is in the loop?', or 'How many objects in the loop?' But a number is a property of a set, and the question we are asking is 'What is the number of this (the empty) set?'

From the foregoing, we see that the concept of zero is more subtle than usually realised. It is the only number in all these networks which has a topic all to itself.

Activity 1

The empty set

A teacher-led discussion for a small group. Its purpose is to introduce the concept of the empty set, together with that of its number zero.

Materials
- Cubes in 3 different colours.
- 4 set loops.

What they do
1. Set the children to sorting the mixture of colours (say) red, blue, yellow, using the 4 set loops (see Org 1.2/3).
2. One of the loops will remain empty.
3. Point to one of the loops with cubes in it and ask 'What do we call this set?' 'And what is its number?'
4. Answers, e.g. 'The blue set'; 'Three'. Likewise for the red and yellow sets.
5. Then point to the empty set loop and ask 'What can we call this set?'
6. Accept any reasonable suggestions, and explain that many people call it 'The empty set' because the loop is empty.
7. 'Does anyone know what we call the number of this set?' 'Nothing', or 'None', are perfectly sensible replies, but these are not names of any number. 'Oh' is incorrect, since this is the name of a letter. Explain that the correct word for the number of this set is 'zero'. ('Nought' is also correct, but 'zero' is used internationally to avoid possible confusion between 'nought' and 'eight' when spoken over radio or telephone, e.g. ground to air.)

Variations
Other mixtures to be sorted; other containers (e.g. lids, shallow boxes.) We shall return to the empty set in Num 1.6.

Discussion of activity

We are here extrapolating the idea of a number, which until now has applied only to sets of objects which we can see. So the concept of zero is more abstract than the number concepts which children have encouraged so far.

The children are thus dependent on their imaginations to form this new number concept. It is mode 3 reality building, with help from mode 2 (communication and discussion). Vocabulary is important here, since it helps to give precision to the new idea.

OBSERVE AND LISTEN   **REFLECT**   **DISCUSS**

Org 1.7   PAIRING BETWEEN SETS

Concept   That of pairing between objects in different sets.

Abilities   (i)   To be able to make mental and physical pairs of single objects in one set with single objects in another set.

(ii)   To understand and use the associated vocabulary.

Discussion of concepts

When we collect objects into sets, physically or mentally, we are putting together objects which in some way 'go together'. If we reflect on this further, we find that the important connection is the mental one. Putting things within set loops, or into the same box, are helpful ways of representing this; but a set is a mental entity, not a physical one. (Don't bother if this is not clear right away.)

Another important kind of connection is pairing: putting together, physically or mentally, single objects in one set with single objects in another set. Everyday examples abound. Given a set of children and a set of milk bottles, we (physically) pair one child with one milk bottle. Cups and saucers, socks and feet, car wheels and tyres, are other examples of 'natural' pairings.

At this stage we are not concerned about whether all the objects in both sets can be paired, or whether there are some left over. This comes in the next topic. The present topic is about the pairing activity itself.

Activity 1   Physical pairing

An activity for a small group of children. Its purpose is to introduce the concept and vocabulary of pairing.

Materials
- A box of physical objects, not necessarily equal numbers of each kind, e.g. model dogs, men, sheep, lambs.
- Likewise, in pictures: one picture to a card.
- Cubes in different colours.

What they do
1. Take from the box 2 sets of objects which it makes sense to pair, e.g. men and dogs.
2. Put together a man and a dog, explaining 'I'm *pairing* this man and this dog. The two together make a pair.'
3. Let the children continue until no more pairs can be made. If there are objects of one set left over, point this out. E.g. 'We can't pair these because there aren't any more dogs to pair the men with'.
4. Repeat with other objects. In some cases there should be the same number of articles of each kind (we feel that each lamb should have a ewe, and vice versa); and in other cases, there should be unequal numbers.
5. Repeat with materials (b) and (c).
6. Also use naturally arising situations, e.g. coats and pegs, children and chairs, foot and shoe.

Note that we are not 'putting the men with the dogs', which would mean doing this:

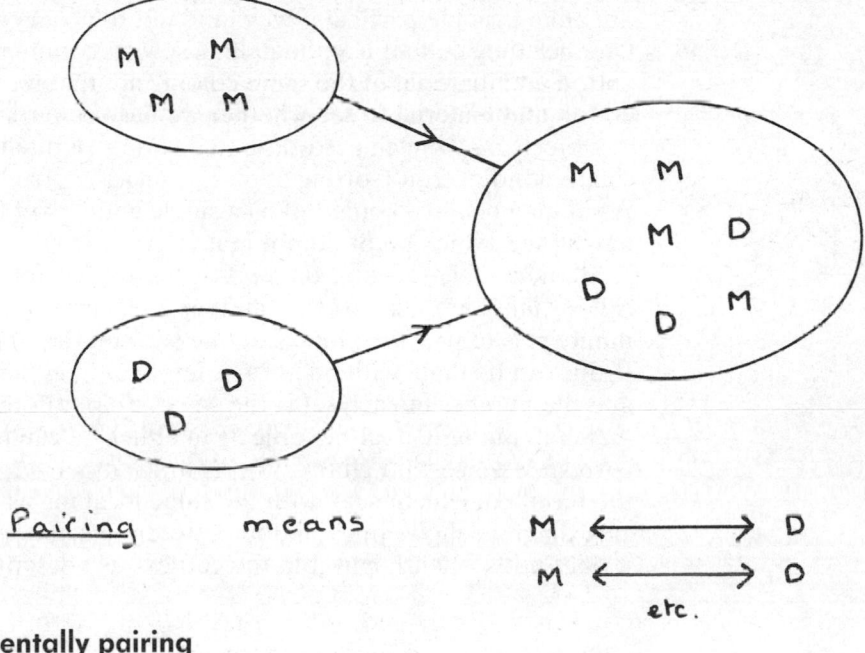

Pairing means
M ⟵⟶ D
M ⟵⟶ D
etc.

Activity 2 **Mentally pairing**

A continuation of activity 1. Its purpose is to move them on to pairing mentally.

Materials The same as for activity 1.

What they do Get children to discuss. Move on to other natural pairings which are not perceptually present, e.g. cup and saucer, car and driver.

Discussion of activities	In activity 1, the children build the concept of pairing (verb) and that of a pair (noun) from physical examples. In activity 2 they use these at an abstract level of thinking, seeking in their memories for other examples of these concepts. They are thus moving around ideas, in their minds, instead of physical objects, on a table. In ways such as these we help them to progress in the abstract way of thinking which is characteristic of mathematics.

OBSERVE AND LISTEN   **REFLECT**   **DISCUSS**

Org 1.8   SETS WHICH MATCH, COUNTING, AND NUMBER

Concepts (i)   One-to-one correspondence. (The concept, not the vocabulary yet.)
(ii) Sets which match, as described overleaf.

Ability To state correctly whether two sets match.

Discussion of concepts

'Match' is used with more than one meaning, as an adjective and a verb. To avoid confusion, I shall use it to describe objects which do match, i.e. are alike in some particular way; and not to mean comparing them to see whether they match. E.g. 'matching sewing cotton and material' means cotton and material of the same colour, not that we are comparing cotton and material to see whether we have colours which match.

Objects may match according to a variety of qualities, such as colour, shape, kind of fruit (sorting apples, oranges. . .), what they are used for. A set may be also thought of as a single entity, so the possibility arises of having sets which do or do not match.

Mathematicians centre on a particular quality for matching sets, which is their number. The test for whether 2 sets match, i.e. have the same number, is to pair the objects in one set with the objects in the other set. If this can be done with no objects left over in either set, the sets match, and the number of each set is the same. To put it in other words, 2 sets match if and only if all the objects in either set can be put in one-to-one correspondence with all the objects in the other set. Mathematicians use the term 'equivalent sets' with the same meaning as 'sets which match'.

A diagram shows this relation between sets better than words, though it does not so clearly put it in the context just described.

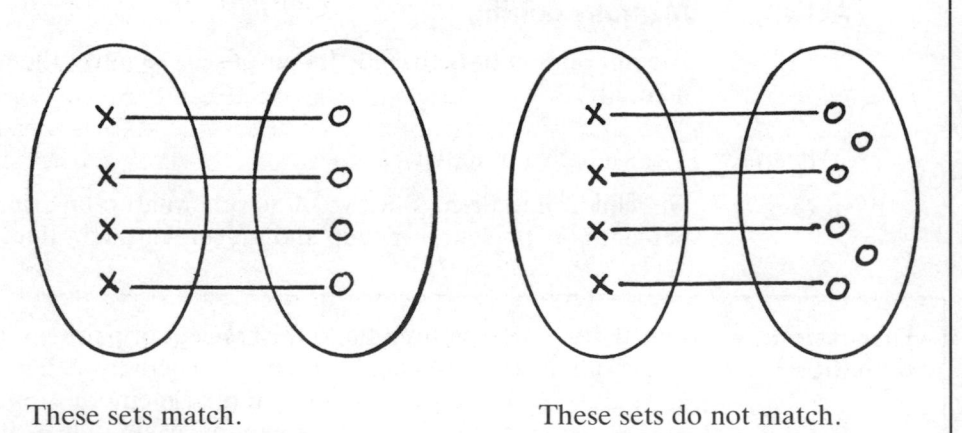

These sets match.
They have the same number.

These sets do not match.
They have different numbers.

Activity 1   Sets which match

An activity for two children, or a small group. Its purpose is (i) to develop the idea of pairing objects into that of making sets which match, i.e. are in one-to-one correspondence. (ii) To relate the concept of matching sets with the process of counting.

Materials   For each child:
- A set loop.
- A container with 10 objects of the same kind, e.g. bottle tops, conkers, sea shells, cubes (not more than one per child).

What they do   *Stage (a)*
1.   One child lays out some of her objects, roughly in a line.
2.   Another child pairs one of her own objects with each of the objects on the table.
3.   The pairs are then separated, and put into different set loops.
4.   Explain that these sets *match*, because every object makes a pair with an object in the other set.
5.   Each of the two sets is then counted.
6.   Steps 1 to 4 are repeated with other objects and children.

Stage (b) (Predictive)
1.   One child puts some of her objects into her set loop.
2.   One (or more) of the others tries to make a matching set, of her own objects in her own set loop.
3.   For small numbers this can be done visually, but for large numbers counting is the only reliable way. I suggest that children be left to use this of their own initiative. (See discussion of activities.)

Discussion of activities

Piaget has demonstrated that children can count a set of objects correctly while failing to realise its full significance – that all sets which have the same count must match each other in the manner described. Without this realisation, counting remains just a verbal activity, not truly related to number. (For a fuller discussion, see *The Psychology of Learning Mathematics*, Chapter 8.)

Stage (a) is for building the concept of matching sets, and relating it to counting and number. Stage (b) uses this relationship to make sets which, it is predicted, will match. This prediction is then tested. If children do not spontaneously use counting, I think it is better to go back to stage (a) than to tell them. The latter will give them the method, but with the risk that it is no more than a method, without the underlying conceptual understanding.

OBSERVE AND LISTEN   **REFLECT**   **DISCUSS**

Org 1.9   COUNTING, MATCHING, AND TRANSITIVITY

Concept   The relationships between these concepts.

Ability   To use these relationships: for children, only at the intuitive level.

Discussion of concept

When we use counting to find the number of a set, we are pairing the objects in the set with the words in a set of number-names.

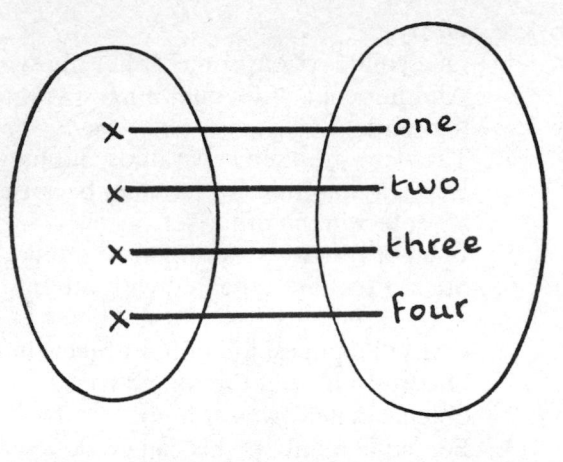

The last word, in this case 'four', is the number of words and also the number of the other set.

All sets of objects which match this set of number-names will have the same number as each other.

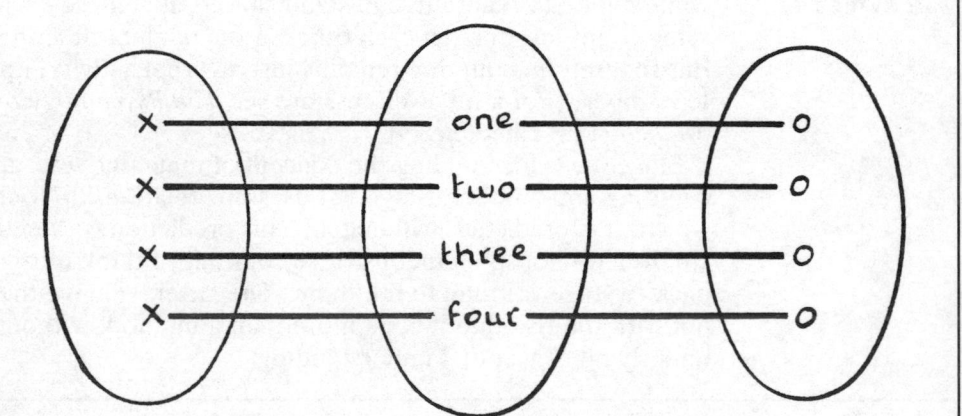

(Imagine joining these lines, through the words in the middle set.)

This is an example of *transitivity*. Transitivity is a property of a relationship, in this case of matching between sets. Some relationships have this property, some do not. E.g. if a person A has the same name as B, and B has the same name as C, then A has the same name as C. So the relationship 'has the same name as' is transitive. But the relationship 'is the parent of' is not transitive.

The following three mathematical relationships, which we have already been working with, are all transitive.

'Matches'
'Has smaller number than' } relations between two sets.
'Has larger number than'

'Is equal to', written   =
'Is less than', written   < } corresponding relations between their numbers.
'Is greater than', written >

In the case of counting, we use a set of number words as a 'portable' set to see whether two sets have the same number, without physically pairing. This is valid only because the relationship 'matches' is transitive.

Children use this concept intuitively in the present context, and also in that of ordering. For them, I think this is sufficient, so I have not provided activities to make it explicit. In view of how much depends on this property, however, I suggest that we ourselves need to use it more consciously, and to know its name. Hence the foregoing discussion.

OBSERVE AND LISTEN   **REFLECT**   **DISCUSS**

Org 1.10   GROUPING IN THREES, FOURS, FIVES

Concepts   (i)   Threes, fours, fives (meaning groups of these numbers).
           (ii)   A group regarded as a single object.

Abilities   (i)   To group (physically re-arrange) a set of physical objects into threes, fours, fives.
           (ii)   To count how many groups there are in a set, and how many single objects (units).

Discussion of concepts

We are now beginning on the path towards decimal notation. ('Decimal' simply means 'relating to ten': its meaning is not confined to decimal fractions.) We start by grouping objects in tens and then treating these groups-of-ten as single objects with which we repeat the process to get new groups, each of ten groups-of-ten. And so on. In combination with place-value notation, it is a powerful and sophisticated technique for dealing with large numbers: representing them, thinking about them, and calculating with them.

Place-value notation is a critical stage in children's mathematical development. It can be either a major stride forward in their powers of mental organisation, using clever arrangements of symbols which carry rich meaning; or downwards on the road towards (mathematical) ruin, the rote manipulation of near-meaningless symbols. So it is very important to build up this conceptual structure gradually and methodically, and this we do over topics 10 to 15 in Org 1 and the whole of Num 2.

We start with the concept of grouping, using groups small enough to be subitised. (This means that we can perceive their numbers without counting.)

Regarding these groups as single entities in themselves is the next step. It is quite a large step. We are now going to describe (e.g.)

this

as 'three fours and two units'.
This implies that we are counting
each of the groups as if
it were a single object

> For those who are familiar with the term 'group' as used in higher mathematics, I should explain that I am using it here with a different meaning. This is closer to the everyday meaning, with the addition that all the groups have the same number.

Activity 1 **Making sets in groups and units**

An activity for a small group of children. Its purpose is to introduce them to the concepts of groups and units.

Materials For each player:
- A set loop.
- Not fewer than 36 cubes.
- A container to keep separate those not in use.

For each group:
- 2 dice of different colours.
- A shaker.
- 3 cards as in the diagram below. One card is marked THREES, one FOURS, and one FIVES.

threes	units
red	green

What they do
1. One of the cards is chosen and put on the table.
2. The first player throws the dice, and puts them on the card according to colour.
3. All the players then construct sets as determined by the fall of the dice, making all their groups of the number shown on the card.
4. Explain that UNITS means single objects which have not been grouped. These must be spaced apart from each other to show this.
5. All spares must be kept in the containers.
6. Children check each other's sets for match with their own, and discuss if there is disagreement. The ultimate test is physical pairing, and it is good revision to use this occasionally. Groups should be paired with groups, units with units.
7. When agreement has been reached, the thrower says 'Clear set loops', and every one returns their cubes to their stores.
8. The dice and shaker are passed to the next player, and steps 1 to 7 are repeated, using the same card or a different one as desired.

Notes
(i)   There is nothing against forming the groups of cubes into rods, but this takes quite a time, and is not necessary conceptually at this stage.

(ii)   If the number of units is larger than the number of a group, children may spontaneously make another group. This is a sensible thing to do. It anticipates topic 12, canonical form.

Activity 2   Comparing larger sets

An activity for a small group of children. Its purpose is to show the usefulness of grouping for dealing with larger numbers of objects than they are yet able to count. (We assume that they can count up to about 10.)

Materials   For each player:
- A set loop.
- About 30 cubes.
- A container.

What they do
1. One of the players puts a largish number (over 20) of cubes into her loop.
2. Ask the others if they can make sets which match this one. Since the number is too large for them to count, they'll have to use a different way.
3. Matching them singly (as in Org 1.7) would work, but this would be rather slow. Can we think of a better way?
4. Let's ask the first player to group her set in threes, making as many of these groups as she can.
5. She does this. Result (e.g.) 7 threes and 2 units.
6. Now we are back to something which we can all count. We can count the groups, and we can count the units.
7. The children are now able to make matching sets. They check each other's. If there is disagreement which cannot be resolved by discussion, the ultimate test is physical pairing: group with group, unit with unit.
8. If they like, they can break up the groups and check that the sets do match unit-to-unit.
9. Steps 1 to 7 (or 8) are repeated, starting with a different player and using a different group number.

Activity 3   Conservation of number

An activity for a small group of children. This follows on from activity 2. Its purpose is to help children to realise that the number of a set is not changed by the way in which it is grouped.

Materials   As for activity 2.

What they do
1. One of the players makes a set in groups and units, choosing 3, 4, or 5 as group number: whichever she likes. (Suppose she chooses 4.)
2. The others make matching sets.
3. Ask: 'If everyone broke up their groups, and made groups of 3 (or 5) instead, would all the sets still match?'
4. The children check their predictions by re-grouping.
5. Repeat steps 1, 2, 3, 4 until the children decide if the sets will match in

any particular grouping (or singly), they will still match in any other grouping.

Discussion of activities

Physically grouping the objects together makes it easier to think of the result as a single entity. So also does naming these groups, e.g. 'a THREE'. Choosing small group numbers takes away the need for counting to get the correct numbers in each group.

In activity 2, grouping is used to change a set which was (for them) too large to count into one which is countable. The simplicity of this technique makes it easy to overlook how powerful it is in extending the organising ability of our thinking.

In activity 3, the assumption which has been implicit in activity 2 is made conscious. This is, that the number of objects in a set is not changed by changes in position of the objects, such as grouping. If this were not true, place-value notation (and much else in mathematics) would be invalid.

OBSERVE AND LISTEN   **REFLECT**   **DISCUSS**

Org 1.11   BASES: UNITS, RODS, SQUARES, AND CUBES

Concepts   (i)   Groups of groups which make larger groups.
            (ii)   A base: i.e. a number used for each repeated grouping.

Ability   To make these, using suitable objects.

Discussion of concepts

The key step in place-value notation is to repeat this grouping process, treating as units the groups already formed. We have been preparing the children for this step in two ways: (i) by the use of cubes such that a group of these can be joined into a single rod; (ii) by activities such as Org 1.10/1 in which groups are treated as single entities which can be counted and matched.

The same number is used each time the grouping process is repeated. This number is called the *base*. For example:

Base 3

units   threes   these grouped in threes   if we have three of these we can make this new group.

rods   squares   cubes

60

Base 4

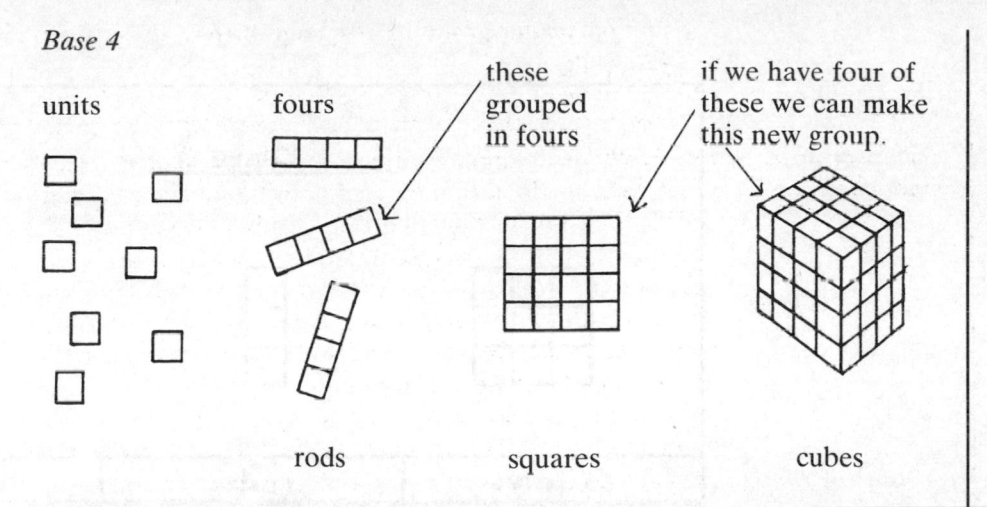

units   fours   these grouped in fours   if we have four of these we can make this new group.

rods   squares   cubes

In this topic we use bases 3, 4, 5. These numbers are small enough to be subitised (perceived without counting), and allow attention to be focused on the process and products of grouping. The reason for using several bases is to provide several examples from which to form the concept. I see no point at all in teaching children to *calculate* in these bases. The only bases in which they need to calculate are base 10, and possibly in the future (for working with computers) bases 2 and 16.

Activity 1   Units, rods, and squares

An activity for a small group of children. Its purpose is to introduce the two concepts described above. This follows on from Org 1.10/1. (Making sets in groups and units.)

Materials
- Base card for base 3, 4, or 5 (see figure below showing base card 3).
- 2 dice of different colours, as on the base card.
- A shaker.
- A set loop.
- Multilink cubes.*
- A container for the cubes.

* Although ready-made squares and cubes for various bases are available, and useful perhaps for later work, there is nothing so good as having the children themselves physically put together single cubes into rods, rods into squares, squares into cubes. Ten cubed would need a lot of cubes, but we are at present using much smaller bases. It is worth going to some trouble to make sure that enough cubes are available for the activities in this section to be done properly.

What they do
1. The dice are thrown and put on the base board according to colour.
2. A set is made in the set loop, according to the numbers shown by the dice.
3. Some situations will occur which result in a number of units equal to or greater than the base.

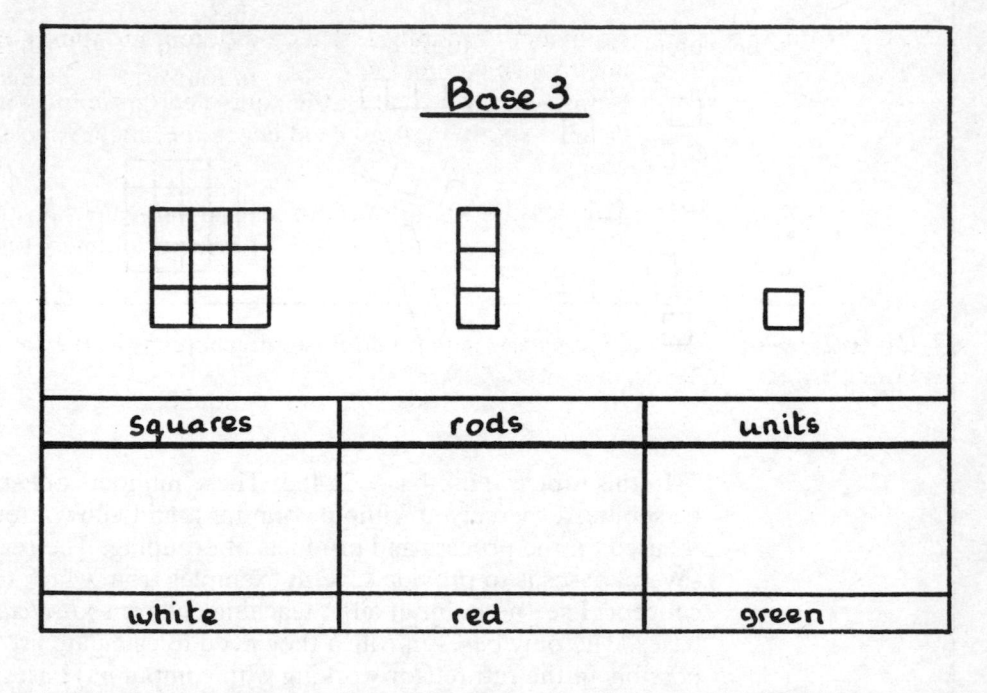

4. Suppose that we are using base 3 and there are 5 units. Ask 'Could we do something with these?'
5. The card suggests the answer: make three-rods.
6. If there are now 3 or more three-rods, the same question arises. This time the answer is, make three-squares.
7. Repeat steps 1 to 6. Emphasise that if we are working in base 3, only groupings based on 3 are allowed. We may have units, three-rods, three-squares and later three-cubes; but *not* two-rods, or three-by-two rectangles.
8. Repeat with other bases.

Activity 2 On to cubes

Also for a small group of children. It follows on from activity 1, and is played in the same way but using 3 dice. There will now be occasions when there are enough squares to be grouped according to the base currently in use, resulting in a cube. In this case the card does not cue the children. When they have decided to group squares to make a cube, they also have to decide where to put it.

Discussion of activities	In this topic, we concentrate on physical activities for building a good understanding of the concepts underlying place-value notation. These provide foundations which are essential if later work using this notation is to be meaningful.

OBSERVE AND LISTEN   **REFLECT**   **DISCUSS**

Org 1.12   EQUIVALENT GROUPINGS: CANONICAL FORM

Concepts   (i)   Equivalent groupings: that is, different groupings of a set which do not change its number.

(ii)   Canonical form: that is, the equivalent grouping which uses only the largest possible groups (and hence the smallest possible number of groups).

Abilities   (i)   To re-arrange a given set in several equivalent groupings.

(ii)   To recognise whether or not a set is in canonical form.

Discussion of concepts

Below are shown several equivalent groupings of the same set. Only the last is in canonical form.

Base 3

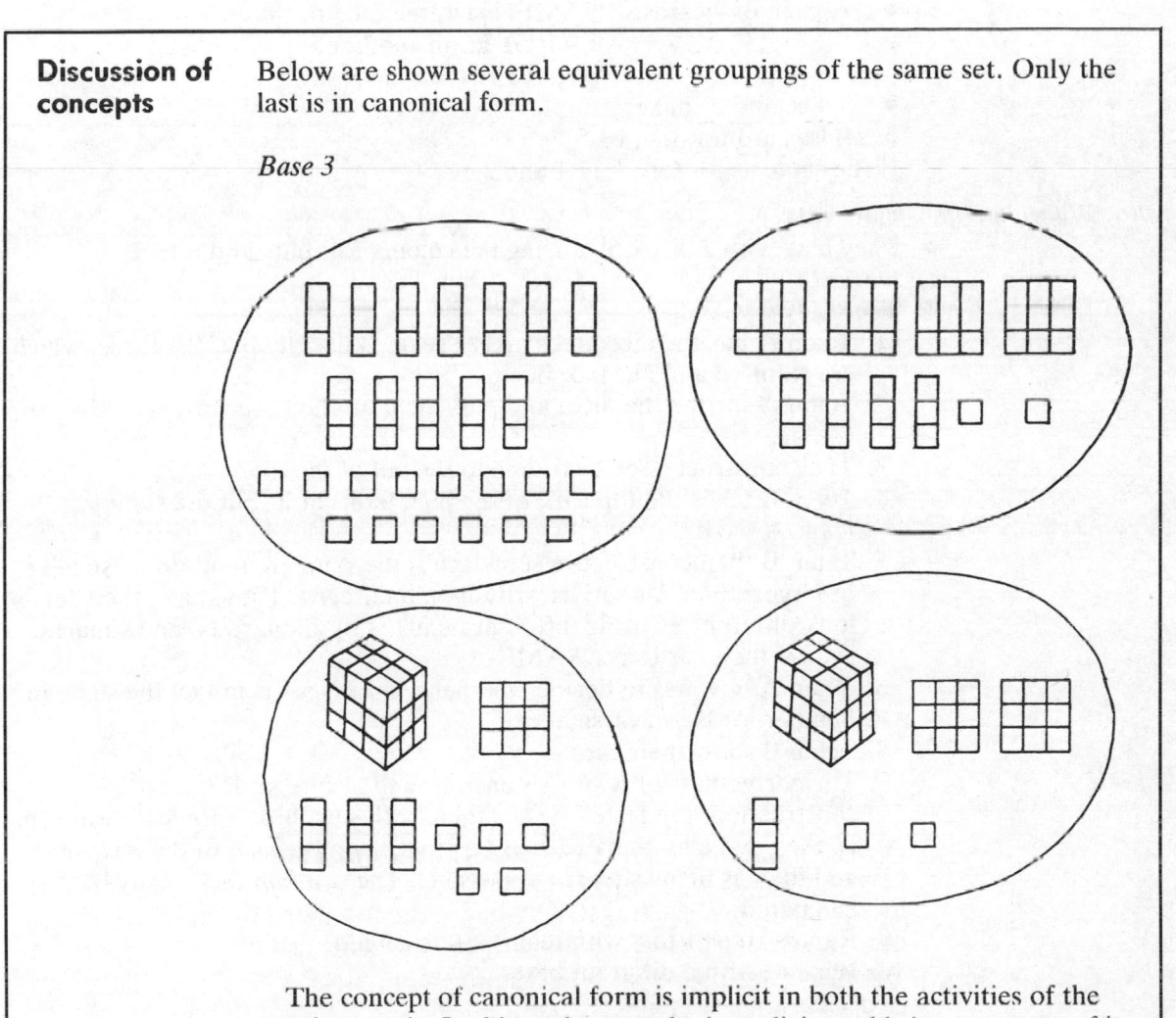

The concept of canonical form is implicit in both the activities of the previous topic. In this topic we make it explicit, and bring out some of its usefulness for showing the number of a set unambiguously.

Changes to and from canonical form are an important part of the techniques used for adding and subtracting, multiplying and dividing. These would not be valid if the number of a set was changed by grouping it differently. Activities 2 and 3 of Org 1.10 have taken care of this requirement in advance.

Activity 1   **'Can I fool you?' (Canonical form)**

An activity for a small group, in two teams. Its purpose is to teach children the name for canonical form, and introduce them to its use.

Materials   For each team:
- Plenty of cubes.
- A set loop.
- A container for the cubes.

For the group:
- A pack of 9 cards.   'SAME' is written on 3 of these,
                        'LARGER' on another 3,
                        'SMALLER' on the rest.
- 3 dice and a shaker.*
- Base card for 3, 4, or 5.*

* The same as for Org 1.11/1 and 2.

What they do   *Stage (a)*

They play with 2 dice only, using the colours for units and tens.

Stage (b)

They play with 3 dice.

1. Team A has the dice and shaker. Team B has the pack of cards, which are shuffled and put face down.
2. Team A throws the dice, and puts them on the base card according to colour.
3. They construct a set according to the fall of the die.
4. Team B takes the top card of the pile, looks at it, but does not let team A see it.
5. Team B then constructs a set which is the same in number, or smaller, or larger, than A's set, as written on their card. They make their set look different by using different numbers of units, rods, and squares, even if their card says 'SAME'.
6. Team A now has to decide whether team B's set is in fact the same in number, or larger or smaller.
7. Team B show their card.
8. The correctness of team A's answer, and also team B's set construction, are tested by changing both sets into canonical form. That is, they make as many rods as possible having regard to the base in use; and then as many squares as possible. The sets can then easily be compared.
9. Repeat steps 1 to 8 with teams interchanged.
10. Repeat, with a different base.

Activity 2   **Exchanging small coins for larger**

A game for a small group, of not more than 4 players. Its purpose is to practise canonical form in a different embodiment, and to introduce the concept of exchanging instead of grouping.

Materials
- Single die marked 1 to 6.
- Shaker.

● Box of 1p coins.
● Box of 5p coins.

What they do

1. The players in turn throw the die, and take that amount of money in pence. E.g. a player who threw 2 would take two 1p coins; one who threw 6 would take a 5p and a 1p coin.
2. Whenever possible, they exchange five 1p coins for one 5p coin.
3. They agree in advance how many rounds are to be played. (Say, 3 to begin with.)
4. The winner is the player who has the smallest total number of coins.
5. If at the end there is a tie, those concerned may agree to play a given number of extra rounds.

Discussion of activities

In activity 1, both teams have to think equally hard. If team B's card reads 'LARGER' they have to put out a set which is larger in number, but looks smaller; and vice versa. Team A has to try not to be 'fooled' by appearance. But of course the purpose of this activity does not depend on whether or not children are fooled, since the purpose is to practise converting to canonical form and see how much easier this makes comparison. Nor is the purpose defeated even if they use counting in base 10 (though for 3 dice this might involve counting up to 186, if 3 sixes are thrown in base 5). In that case they are converting mentally to canonical form in base 10.

Activity 2 is somewhat easier than stage (b) of activity 1, so it might be used after stage (a). This uses base 5, with exchange instead of physical grouping. They may well have encountered this in everyday experience. In this case, the present activity will relate that experience to the present context.

OBSERVE AND LISTEN   **REFLECT**   **DISCUSS**

[Num 1] NUMBERS AND THEIR PROPERTIES

Numbers as mental objects which, like physical objects, have particular properties

Num 1.1   SETS AND THEIR NUMBERS PERCEPTUALLY (SUBITISING)

Concept   Number as a way in which different sets may be alike.

Ability   To sort sets by number, ignoring all else. At this stage this ability is only involved at the perceptual level, using only numbers from 1 to 5. These numbers can be subitised – perceived without counting.

Discussion of concept	In everyday life, we often treat collections of objects or persons as single entities: e.g. a football team, a form at school. Here we do the same for the mathematical concept of a set, and begin sorting and matching sets in the same way as in Org 1.1 we sorted single objects. For example, in Org 1.1/5 and 6 (conceptual matching), we put together hammer, saw, screwdriver . . . because although they are different objects we can think of them as alike in a particular way – they are all tools. The most important likeness between different sets is that of having the same number.

Activity 1   **Sorting dot sets and picture sets**

An activity for a small group. Its purpose is to start children thinking about the number of a set as something independent of what are the objects in the set, their nature or position. This activity should come after Org 1.2, so that the children are already used to sorting cards and looking for likenesses between them by which to sort.

Materials
- A pack of cards having on them various numbers of dots from 1 to 5, all of the same size and colour. There should be several cards of each number, with the dots differently positioned.
- A harder pack in which the dots are of different sizes and colours.
- A pack in which the dots are replaced by 'blobs' or 'patches' of irregular shape.
- A pack of cards on which are 1 to 5 little pictures of the same or similar objects. (Many schools have rubber stamps which are useful for this.)

What they do
1. Start with the easiest pack, using only cards with numbers 1 to 3 to begin with. Mix the cards, and let the children sort them.
2. When the children can sort these cards, introduce 4, then 5.
3. When they are ready, introduce the harder packs.
4. If the children start to attach numbers to sets, good. If they count

spontaneously, of course do not discourage this. But do not deliberately introduce counting at this stage. It is a more sophisticated concept than is usually realised, and we want to give children the means for constructing it correctly. This involves several earlier stages.

Activity 2 **Picture matching game using dot sets and picture sets**

A game for up to six children. Its purpose is to consolidate the concept and ability learnt in activity 1.

Materials As in activity 1.

What they do The game described in Org 1.1/3 may now be played in a harder version, using the dot sets and picture sets from activity 1.

Discussion of activities A considerable feat of abstraction is required here, since (e.g.) a set of two red dots and a set of three red dots *look* more alike than a set of three red dots and a set of three pictures of cows. Attaching the same number-word helps, and this is a good way of relating the informal knowledge which most children acquired before they come to school to the more organised learning which they are now beginning. In this topic, we are helping children to expand their concepts of likeness and matching from single objects to sets, and to think of a set as a single entity.

OBSERVE AND LISTEN **REFLECT** **DISCUSS**

Num 1.2 SUCCESSOR: NOTION OF ONE MORE

Concepts (i) The successor of a number, i.e. the number which is one more.
(ii) The predecessor of a number, i.e. the number which is one less.

Abilities (i) To construct and recognise the successor of a number.
(ii) To construct and recognise the predecessor of a number.

Discussion of concepts Easier words for the children to use are 'next number' and 'number before'. These concepts only apply to whole numbers, but for the present these are the only numbers children know.

In this context, the next number, the number which is one more, and the next number-name in the counting sequence all belong together. The close connection between these ideas is an important part of the foundations we are building for counting with understanding, as against counting mechanically.

Activity 1   Making successive sets

An activity for a small group. Its purpose is to start children forming the concepts and connections described above.

Materials
- A sorting tray, with compartments.
- Some objects for sorting.

What they do
1. Starting with the tray empty, the first child puts (e.g.) one button into a compartment.
2. He says 'We have one button on the tray', and passes it on.
3. The next child puts 2 objects into the next compartment, says 'We have one button and 2 sea shells on the tray,' and passes it on.
4. The next child puts 3 objects into the next compartment, says 'We have one button, 2 sea shells, and 3 conkers on the tray'.
5. And so on, as far as they know the number names.

Activity 2   Putting one more

An activity for a small group.

Materials
- A single container.
- A set of small objects such as buttons or beans.

What they do
1. The first child puts in one button (or whatever it is) and says 'One button in the cup'.
2. He then passes the container to the next child.
3. The next child puts in another button, saying as he does so: 'One in the cup, put one more, two in the cup.'
4. It is then passed to the next child, who puts in another button and describes what happens as before.
5. Continue as long as they know the number-names.
6. They can then pass round in the reverse direction, taking one at a time out and making the appropriate statements.
7. What the children say may be varied according to their language ability. The important ideas to be put into words are the actions, putting in one more or taking out one object, and the results, different numbers of objects.

Discussion of activities

In these activities, children are both learning new mathematical ideas from physical activities, and linking these activities and ideas with spoken language. This will help them, in the future, to use language to manipulate mathematical ideas mentally, without the need for physical activities. Here we are particularly concerned with the ideas which connect counting and number; but the principle is one which is widely used in our present approach.

OBSERVE AND LISTEN   **REFLECT**   **DISCUSS**

Num 1.3 COMPLETE NUMBERS IN ORDER

Concept A complete sequence of numbers in order, i.e., in which every number has a successor and every number except the first has a predecessor.

Abilities (i) To put numbers in order.
(ii) To recognise whether the sequence is complete.
(iii) If it is not, to provide the missing one(s).

Discussion of concept In 'Missing stairs' (Org 1.5/1) we were working with successive sets. Now we move on to successive numbers. The connection is a close one, but the thinking involved is one level more abstract, since numbers (unlike 'stairs') cannot be seen.

Activity 1 **'Which card is missing'?**

A game for children to play in pairs. Its purpose is to develop children's thinking to the more abstract level described above.

Materials ● Dot-set cards 1 to 5, later 1 to 10 and then 0 to 10.*
* These are like the cards used in sorting dot sets (Num 1.1/1), but there is only one of each. Zero is represented by a blank card. Note that the dots are random, not in patterns, and the cards do not have numerals.

Rules of the game 1. Before beginning, the children lay these out in order, and observe the sequence.
2. Player A shuffles the cards and holds them out face downwards to player B.
3. Player B takes a card without letting A see which card it is.
4. Player A then has to say which card is missing.
5. Player B shows the missing card, thereby checking A's prediction.
6. They then interchange as A and B.

Stages (a) With cards 1 to 5.
(b) After Num 1.5, with cards 1 to 10.
(c) After Num 1.6, with cards 0 to 10.

Discussion of activity This activity cannot be done by rote, and ensures the use of an abstract sequence of numbers. It thus continues the emphasis on conceptual learning which has been present from the beginning.

OBSERVE AND LISTEN   **REFLECT**   **DISCUSS**

Num 1.4 COUNTING

Concept Counting, as a technique for finding the number of a set.

Ability To count how many objects there are in a set.

Discussion of concept

Counting is a more sophisticated technique than is usually realised. When we say the number-names in order, the last name we say is always the total number of words we have said, e.g. 'One, two, three, *four*.' We have said four words, so if we pair each word with an object, this also tells us how many objects we have done this with. All the time we are talking about the latest total of objects, not the last object.

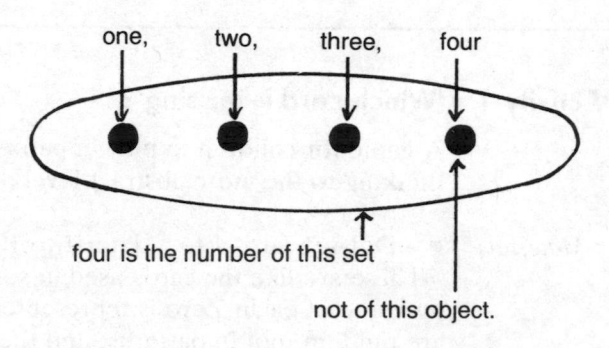

Counting is a multi-purpose technique. It can be used for finding the (cardinal) number of a given set; for making a set of a given number; for adding (by counting on); for subtracting (by counting back); for multiplying (by counting groups treated as units); and for dividing (using a similar method in reverse). So it is important that children get this right conceptually, from the start.

An additional difficulty arises from the fact that counting may also be used to find the ordinal number of an element in a set. To prevent confusion I think it is better omitted at this stage, until cardinal number is well established. When in due course ordinal numbers are introduced, they should be clearly distinguished from cardinals by using the words 'first', 'second'. . .

Activity 1 **Finger counting to 5**

An activity for a small group. Its purpose is to introduce finger counting with a good conceptual foundation. (See 'Discussion of activities'.)

What they do Begin with the left hand, palm downward. Start with the left little finger.
1. Touch the table with the little finger only.   Say 'One'.
2. Lift hand, and touch the table with the little and fourth fingers together.   Say 'Two'.
3. Lift hand, and touch the table with the little, fourth, and middle fingers together   Say 'Three'.

4. Lift hand, and touch the table with all four
fingers together   Say 'Four'.
5. Lift hand, and touch the table with all four fingers
and thumb together.   Say 'Five'.

Activity 2   Planting potatoes

An activity for a small group. Its purpose is to link finger counting with a
number rhyme.

What they do 1. They learn the following number rhyme, which you will recognise as
adapted from a children's counting-out rhyme. 'One potato, two
potatoes, three potatoes, four. Five potatoes, that's enough, so we will
plant no more.'
2. They then link it with finger counting, as in activity 1. From 'five
potatoes. . .' on, they keep all five fingers on the table.

**Discussion of
activities**

Counting on our fingers is so natural a technique that we almost certainly
derive our use of base 10 from the fact that we have 10 fingers (more
accurately, digits). The way children often finger count, however, there
is a danger that they will attach numbers to single fingers rather than to
sets of fingers. (See 'Discussion of concept.') The purpose of these
activities is to provide a good conceptual foundation to finger counting.

At this age, some children will have difficulties of co-ordination. But
finger counting in this way is so useful for adding by counting on,
subtracting by counting back, that it is worth introducing early and
practising regularly as it recurs in later networks. Other number rhymes
will be found in Num 2.1.

The counting activities in this network relate closely to those in
network Num 2, 'The Naming of Numbers', and I was for a while
undecided whether to put them into the latter network. In the end I
decided to put into this network counting activities in which the greater
emphasis is on the numbers themselves, their properties and inter-
relationships; and into Num 2 those in which the greater emphasis is on
the symbols (number-words and numerals). Counting thus keeps a place
in both networks, and helps to link them together.

OBSERVE AND LISTEN   **REFLECT**   **DISCUSS**

Num 1.5   EXTRAPOLATION OF NUMBER CONCEPTS TO 10

Concepts (i) The complete numbers from 1 to 10,
(ii) linked to their names.

Ability As for Num 1.4, with these larger numbers.

Discussion of concepts

The concepts of the numbers from 1 to 5 have been constructed and used so far mainly at a perceptual level. They have also been systematically related to the concepts of order, successor, counting in preparation for the use of counting to extend number concepts to larger numbers.

Activity 1   **Finger counting to 10**

An activity for a small group. Its purpose is to extend the ideas and method of finger counting up to 10.

What they do   The method just described extrapolates nicely to 10.
1. Touch the table with the left hand as for five, and with the right *thumb*.   Say 'Six'.
2. Left hand as before, right thumb and forefinger.   Say 'Seven'.
3. And so on, up to 10.

Activity 2   **Missing stairs, 1 to 10**

An activity for children to play in pairs. Its purpose is to help in extrapolating the ideas of a complete sequence of numbers in order to 10.

Materials   For each pair:
- 55 cubes of one colour.
- 10 cubes of a different colour.

What they do   This game is played in the same way as 'Missing stairs' in Org 1.5/1.

Activities 3 and 4   The first two activities from NuSp 1.1 should be used here. From now on, number track activities should be closely integrated with this and the other networks.

Discussion of activities

Physical activities, and mathematical language, are used in combination (modes 1 and 2) to expand the children's existing ideas of number. The connections with order, successor, number-names, are carefully preserved.

The earlier (1 to 5) version of 'Missing stairs' could be played largely at a perceptual level, though counting was certainly a help. Here in activity 2, counting becomes essential.

OBSERVE AND LISTEN   **REFLECT**   **DISCUSS**

Num 1.6   ZERO

Concepts (i)   Zero as the number of the null set.
(ii)   Zero as the number before one.

Abilities (i)   To attach this number to any example of the null set which they encounter.
(ii)   To extrapolate the counting sequence backwards past one to zero.
(*Note* Internationally, 'zero' is preferred to 'nought' because it cannot be confused with 'eight' over the telephone or by radio; but both are correct. 'Oh' is not correct, being the name of a letter.)

Discussion of concepts

Compare these questions and answers. (i) 'How many objects in this set?' 'None'. This is appropriate in the context of Org 1.6. But if we re-word the question as (ii) *'What is the number of* this set?', the correct answer is 'Zero'. To understand zero as a number involves more sophisticated thinking than any of the number concepts which the children have encountered so far, since it refers to the *absence* of any object in a set. The simplest way in which it can be presented is as described in Org 1.6 (the empty set). As soon as children begin counting backwards, zero can also be introduced as the number before one (i.e. after one when counting backwards). As well as being a number in its own right (albeit an unusual kind of number), zero acquires extra importance in place-value notation. When we write 30, the zero not only tells us that there are no units, but it changes the meaning of the 3 from 3 units (if written alone) to 3 tens (if followed by a zero). It is the only number in the present curriculum which is treated as a topic all by itself.

Activity 1   **'Which card is missing?' (Including zero)**

As already noted in Num 1.3/1, this game may be played with the inclusion of a blank card as soon as children have encountered the null set (Org 1.6). Its purpose is to introduce zero as the number of the null set.

Activity 2   **Finger counting from 5 to zero**

An activity for a small group. Its purpose is to introduce zero as the number before one.

What they do 1. Reverse Num 1.4/1 (Finger counting to 5), starting with five and finishing with one.
2. Repeat as in 1, but after touching the table with little finger only palm downward and saying 'one', turn the hand palm upwards showing an empty hand and saying 'zero'.

Discussion of activities

These activities are all helping children to form the concept of zero as a number by extrapolating their existing concept, derived from and until now restricted to, numbers of objects which they can see. This is mode 3 schema building: creativity. They are creating a new concept out of an existing schema.

The first activity is an easy one, since the blank card stands out from the others. Nevertheless, it comes in the context of cards with varying *numbers* of dots on them, so it prepares the way for the idea of the null set as having a number also. The concept of zero involves thinking, not 'This card doesn't have a number', but 'The number of dots is zero'. After this simple beginning, activity 2 makes the extrapolation explicit by putting zero into a sequence of counting numbers, and associating it simultaneously with no fingers touching the table, and an empty hand.

The next point is a subtler one. When we are extrapolating, the next objects have to be more objects of the same kind, e.g. what comes after these:

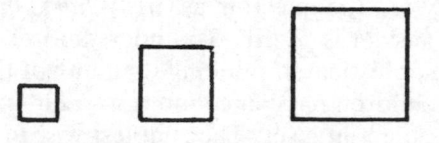

has to be another square, not a triangle, still less a letter of the alphabet. So when we extrapolate the sequence of numbers 5, 4, 3, 2, 1 . . . whatever comes next has to be a *number* of some kind.

So in these activities we have extrapolation of two distinct and complementary kinds. There is more here than meets the eye!

OBSERVE AND LISTEN   **REFLECT**   **DISCUSS**

Num 1.7   EXTRAPOLATION OF NUMBER CONCEPTS TO 20

Concept   The complete numbers from 11 to 20 in order, linked with their names.

Ability   As for Num 1.3, extended to these larger numbers.

Discussion of concept	This topic involves the formation of new concepts of what is now a familiar kind.

Activity 1   **Finger counting to 20: 'Ten in my head'**

An activity for a small group. Its purpose is to use the familiar activity of finger counting to continue the counting sequence to 20.

What they do   1. They begin by finger counting from 1 to 10, as in Num 1.5/1.
2. After reaching 10, they raise both their hands from the table and say 'Ten in my head'.

3. They then continue counting, 'Eleven' (left little finger), 'Twelve' (two fingers of left hand) and so on.
4. When the children have practised this, they form pairs and ask each other questions of two kinds.
   (a) Question: 'Show fourteen.'
       Answer: 'Ten in my head' and touches table with four fingers of left hand.
       Question: 'Show four.'
       Answer: 'None in my head', fingers as above.
   (b) Question: 'What number is this? I have ten in my head,' and touches table with all fingers and thumb of left hand, thumb of right hand.
       Answer: 'Sixteen.'
       Question: 'What number is this? None in my head' and touches table with all digits of left hand, thumb and first finger of right hand.
       Answer: 'Seven.'

Discussion of activity	This activity relates the new number concepts to physical materials and activities with which the children are already familiar. Activity 1 also relates the numbers 11 to 20 to a repetition of the same pattern as 1 to 10, which is specially useful since the spoken number-words do not follow a regular pattern. Fortunately the written numerals do.

OBSERVE AND LISTEN   REFLECT   DISCUSS

Num 1.8   ODDS AND EVENS

Concepts   Even numbers as
 (i)   numbers which can be made from twos.
(ii)   numbers which can be divided into two equal parts.
Odd numbers as
 (i)   numbers which cannot be made from twos,
(ii)   numbers which cannot be divided into two equal parts.

Abilities   (i)   To say whether any given number is odd or even.
(ii)   To test the accuracy of a statement of this kind.

Discussion of concepts	Physical objects have a variety of properties such as being hard, or red, or soluble in water. Numbers are mental objects, and these too have a variety of properties which we now begin to investigate. The concepts of even and odd numbers described under (i) and (ii) above indicate the two different beginnings which these concepts have. The final concepts are formed when a child recognises that these are two aspects of the same property.

Activity 1 'Yes or no?'

An activity for 2 children. Its purpose is to introduce the concepts of even/odd numbers as described in (i) above. (This activity was invented by a working group of teachers at a conference organised by the Inner London Education Authority.)

Materials
- 3 pockets joined together.*
- Number cards 1 to 10.
- 20 cubes of at least 5 different colours.

* This is made from thin card, and stapled as shown below.

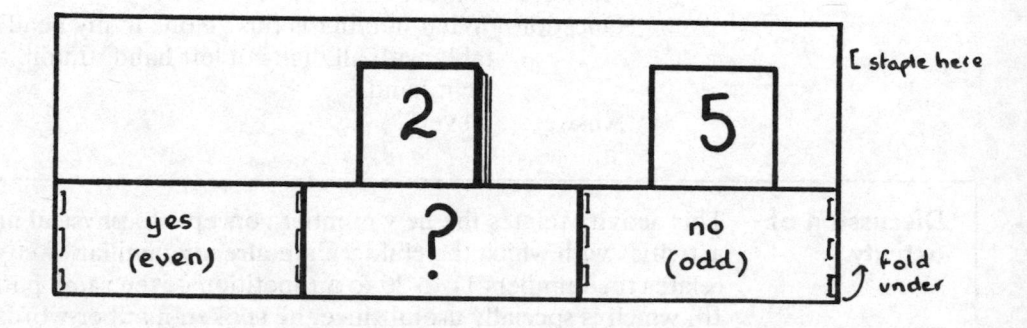

What they do
1. The number cards are shuffled and put in the centre pocket.
2. Player A has 10 single cubes.
3. Player B has 10 cubes joined in twos, each two of a different colour.
4. A takes a card from the ? pocket, and puts out that number of singles.
5. B then says either 'Yes, this number can be made with twos', and puts the correct number of twos; or 'No, this number cannot be made with twos'. At this stage, they may decide to check physically, by joining their cubes to form rods and seeing whether these are the same length. If A agrees with B's answer, they may think that this is not necessary.
6. The card is then put into the appropriate pocket.
7. When all the cards have been used, the children take them out of their respective pockets and look for a pattern.

Notes
(i) When B's twos are made into a rod, it is desirable for them to be still distinguishable. This is why B should have twos in several different colours.
(ii) At least for the first few times, children should test physically, so that they know exactly what is involved.
(iii) After a while, children can replace 'Yes' or 'No' with 'Even' or 'Odd'.
(iv) When children are confident with numbers from 1 to 10, they can play from 1 to 20.

Activity 2 'Can they all find partners?'

An activity for children to do by themselves. This uses the even/odd concepts predictively.

Materials
- Picture sets of children, varying between 5 and 20 in number.*
- Washable OHP markers.

* These should be on card covered in plastic film. At the top of each, write 'Can they all find partners?'

What they do
1. A child receives one of these.
2. He writes 'Yes' or 'No' after the question.
3. He then tests his prediction by drawing lines to join the children into pairs.
4. If his prediction was wrong, he corrects it.

Activity 3 'Odd or even?'

A game for children to play in pairs. Its purpose is to introduce aspects (ii) of the concepts of even/odd.

Materials 20 cubes.

What they do
Begin with the following preliminary explanation. Make two rods, say 6 and 7 cubes respectively. Break the 6 rod into two 3s, put these side by side. Say 'This is a different meaning for even. We can make a 6 into two rods of even length. This is another way of showing that 6 is an even number.' Break the 7 rod into a 3 and a 4, put these side by side, and say 'Now there's an odd one left over. 7 is an odd number'.
When they have grasped this, the children play as follows.
1. A makes a rod, puts it on the table and says to B (e.g.) 'Seven: odd or even?'
2. When B has answered, A gives him the rod so that he can test as described above.
3. If correct, B gets a point; if incorrect, he doesn't.
4. A and B change over, and steps 1 to 3 are repeated.
Play initially with 10 cubes, then extend to 20.

Discussion of activities

'Yes or No' begins with mode 1 schema building (physical experience), using materials which embody the concept of an even/odd number as one which can/cannot be made physically from pairs. At first they should test by mode 1 (prediction). If they have played the game long enough to have the concepts well established, they can test by mode 2: agreement based on a shared schema. If they do not agree, they will have to discuss, and probably appeal to mode 1 testing.

Activity 2, 'Can they all find partners?' embodies the same concept in different materials. Testing is by mode 1 (prediction).

Activity 3, 'Odd or even'? uses both mode 1 building (physical experience) and mode 1 testing (prediction).

The final stage is reached by mode 3 building, when children realise that activity 1 and activity 3 are two different physical results of the same mathematical property. Even is a higher order concept combining both aspects. If necessary you can help by this demonstration.

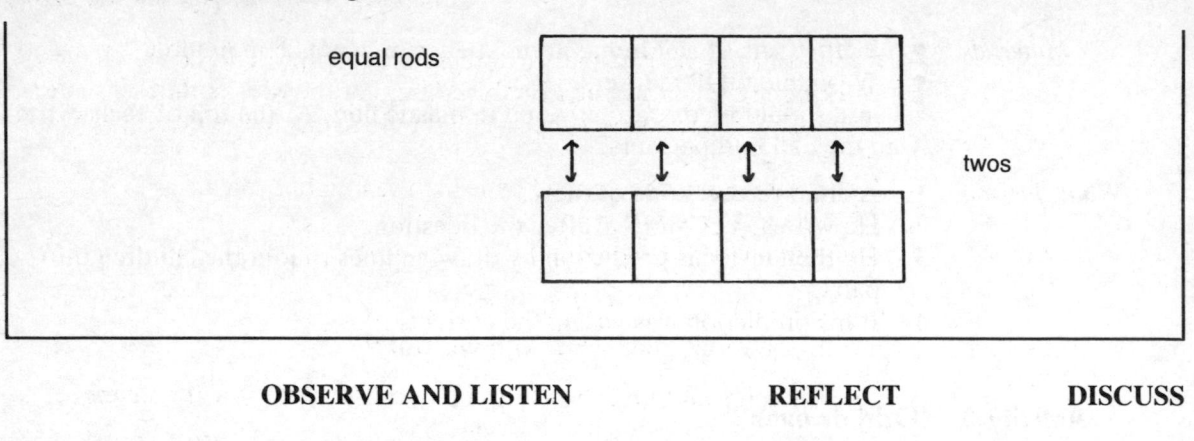

equal rods

twos

OBSERVE AND LISTEN   **REFLECT**   **DISCUSS**

Num 1.9   DOUBLING AND HALVING

Concepts   (i)   Doubling a number.
           (ii)   Halving a number.

Ability   Given an even number, to double or to halve it.

Discussion of concepts	Here we continue the parallel described in Num 1.8 between physical objects, and numbers regarded as mental objects. We can do things to physical objects, and what we can do depends on their nature. Similarly we can do things to numbers, again depending on their nature. All numbers can be doubled; only even numbers can be halved, so long as we are talking about whole numbers. To remind us simultaneously of the parallel between these, and also the difference, it is useful to talk about physical *actions* and mathematical *operations*. So doubling and halving are mathematical operations. Adding and subtracting, multiplying and dividing, are other examples of mathematical operations.

Activity 1   **'Double this, and what will we get?'**

A game for two children to play in pairs. It introduces children to the concept of doubling and to a simple method of multiplication.

Materials
- Cubes, 55 each (see step 1).
- A pack of cards 1 to 10.
- A number track 1 to 20.

What they do
1. Each makes a staircase from 1 to 10. It helps if the rods from 6 to 10 are made with 5 cubes of one colour and the rest of a different colour.
2. The pack of cards is shuffled and put face downwards.
3. A turns over the top card and puts it face upward, starting a new pile.
4. She then takes out the rod of that number from her staircase, and predicts the number of the rod which will result from joining this to the rod of the same number from B's staircase. Let them devise their own

methods if possible. If they are stuck, one good way to do this is by working in base 5, assisted by the colours of the rods, counting singles twice. E.g. if the rod is 7, he says 'Double five is ten, eleven, twelve, thirteen, fourteen.'

5. Her prediction is then tested by using the number track.
6. If correct, A scores a point.
7. They then change about.

Activity 2 **'Break into halves, and what will we get?'**

A game for children to play in pairs. Its purpose is to show the inverse relation between doubling and halving.

Materials
- 30 cubes in two different colours.
- Even number cards from 2 to 10.

What they do
1. Each child makes a 1 to 5 staircase of a different colour.
2. These are then joined to make a 2 to 10 staircase of even numbers, which shows clearly the doubles/halves relationship.
3. Explain that 'Break into halves' means 'Break into two matching parts', and demonstrate.

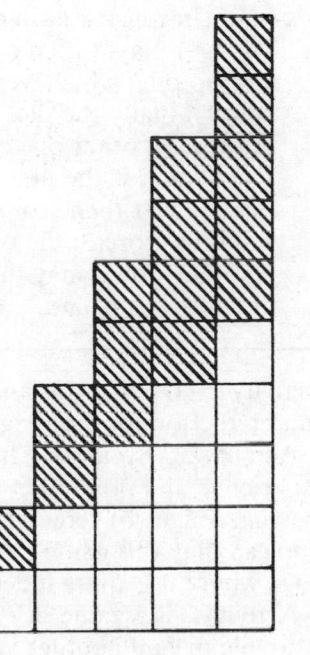

A doubles and halves staircase.

Stage (a)
4. Shuffle the cards and place face downwards.
5. Player A turns over the top card and puts it face upwards, starting a new pile.
6. If the number is (say) 6, she points to the 6 rod and says 'Half of 6 is 3'.
7. If B does not agree, they test physically by breaking the rod.

8. If B does agree, she awards A a point.
9. They then continue as above with B turning over the next card.
Stage (b)
As above, except that the staircase is covered with a sheet of paper, so A does not point to the rod, the paper is removed and they check visually or physically.

Activity 3 **Doubles and halves rummy**

A card game for up to four players. Up to six may play if a third pack of cards is introduced. Its purpose is to practise the concepts of halves and doubles of a given number, independently of physical materials.

Materials
- 2 double-headed number packs 1–20, without the odd numbers over 10.

Rules of the game
1. The packs are put together and shuffled. Five cards are dealt to each player.
2. The rest of the pack is put face down on the table, with the top card turned over to start a face upwards pile.
3. The object is to get rid of one's cards by putting down pairs of cards in which one is the half or double of the other.
4. Players begin by looking at their cards and putting down any pairs they can. They check each other's pairs.
5. The first player then picks up a card from either the face down or the face up pile, whichever she prefers. If she now has a pair, she puts it down. Finally she discards one of her cards onto the face-up pile.
6. In turn the other players pick up, put down a pair if they can, discard.
7. The winner is the first to put down all her cards. Play then ceases.
8. Each player then scores the number of pairs she has made. The winner will thus score 3, the others 2, 1, or 0.
9. Another round may then be played, and the scores added to those of the previous round.

Discussion of activities

Activity 1, 'Double this and what will we get?', uses physical experience and prediction for building and testing the concept of doubling.

Activity 2, 'Break into halves, and what will we get?', uses physical experience and prediction for building and testing the concept of halving. Stage (b) requires this to be done entirely mentally. Children who can play this game have developed the mathematical operation to a stage where it is quite independent of physical action.

Activity 3 is a game in which players have to realise that one number is double or half another. Whereas being odd or even is a property of a number itself, being double or half is a relationship with another number; so this activity takes children into a new area. This game will later be played with the same rules, but different mathematical relationships. An earlier game used here was called 'Halves and doubles snap'. I replaced it by the present activity 3 because I wanted one which did not involve speed of response.

OBSERVE AND LISTEN   **REFLECT**   **DISCUSS**

Num 1.10   EXTRAPOLATION OF NUMBER CONCEPTS TO 100

Concept   The complete counting numbers in order to 100, grouped in tens.

Abilities   (i)   To state the number of a given set from 1 to 100.
(ii)   To make a set of a given number from 1 to 100.

Discussion of concept	Here we are concerned, not with a totally new concept (such as being odd or even) but with increasing the examples which a child has of his existing concept of number. Order and completeness provide a framework to ensure that these new examples fit the established pattern. The key feature of the extrapolation is the idea that we can apply the process of counting, not only to single objects but to groups of objects, treating each group as an entity. So this topic links with all the topics in Org 1 (Set-based organisation) which are shown in the upper part of the network as leading to topic 16 (grouping in tens).

Activity 1   **Throwing for a target**

An activity for one player, two working together, or it may be played as a race between two players throwing alternately. Its purpose is to help children to extrapolate their number concepts up to 100, and to consolidate their use of grouping in tens.

Note   Before this activity, children should have completed Org 1.

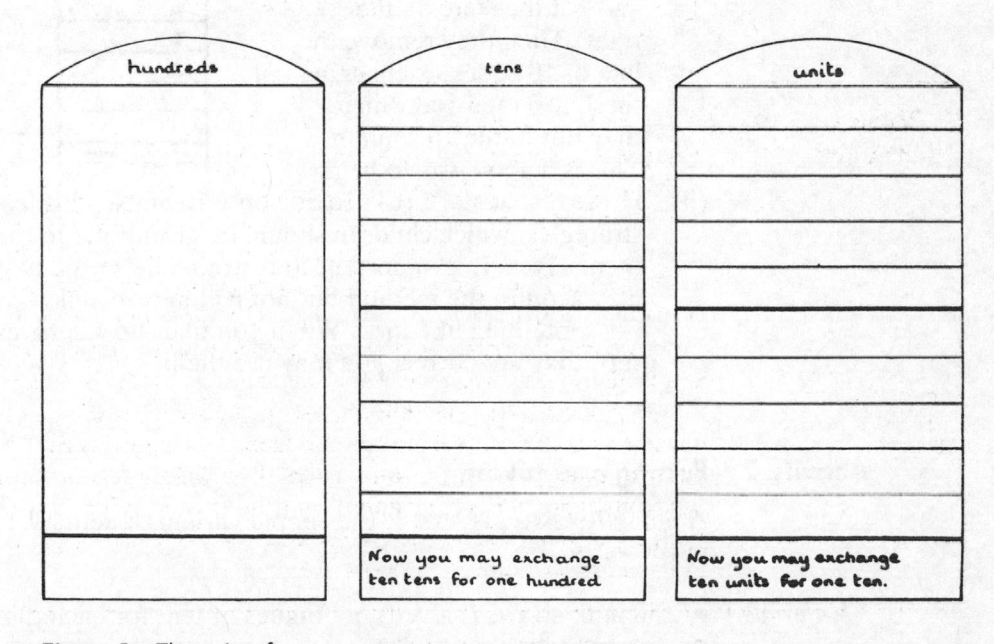

Figure 1   Throwing for a target.

Materials
- A game board, see figure 1.
- For stage 1, base 10 material.
- For stage 2, a variety of other materials as described below.
- 2 dice.
- Slips of paper on which are written target numbers, e.g. 137, 285. (It is best not to go above 300 at most, or the game takes too long.)

What they do   *Stage (a)*
1. The player throws the dice and adds the two numbers.
2. He puts down that number of units.
3. Each time he reaches 10 units he exchanges them for one 10, and likewise for tens.
4. He must finish with a throw of the exact number to reach the target number.
5. If the number required is 6 or less he uses one die only.

Stage (b)

To prevent children becoming too attached to a particular embodiment, this game should also be played with other suitable materials, such as lolly sticks in units, tens with a rubber band around, and ten bundles of ten. Milk straws cut in half are good. Also coins: pennies, 10p pieces, and £1 pieces.

Notes

(i) At stage (a) children will often put more than 10 units, and these should be available. E.g. starting with state on the left, and throwing 5, they put down 5 and get the state on the right. Then they remove the line of 10 cubes, exchanging these for a ten-rod which they put in the 10 column. This is a good way to begin.

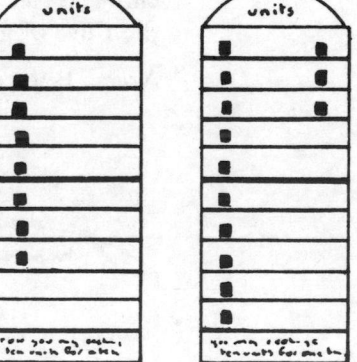

(ii) However, at stage (b) provide only 10 units. This leads to a variety of strategies, which children should be given time to discover for themselves. It is important to restrain one's urge to tell them, or they may acquire the method but not its interiority. I recommend that you say something like this: 'When you find short cuts, as soon as you are sure they are correct you may use them.'

Activity 2   Putting and taking

A game for two players. It is a simple variant of activity 1, with the same purpose.

Materials
- 50 milk straws (halved) in bundles of ten, for each player.
- 5 more tens.

- 10 units.
- 2 dice.
- A box to put spares in.

What they do
1. Each player starts with 50 straws, in bundles of 10. They agree which will put, and which take, each working separately with his own set of straws.
2. They throw the dice alternately.
3. The 'putter' begins and puts down the number of units shown by the total shown on the dice.
4. The 'taker' plays next and takes away the total shown when he throws the dice.
5. The 'putter' wins by reaching 100.
6. The 'taker' wins by reaching 0.
7. Exchanging of 1 ten for 10 units will be necessary whenever they cross a ten boundary upwards or downwards.
8. If the game is played with the same requirement as in activity 1, that the exact number must be thrown to win, this could prolong the game unduly. It is therefore probably best to agree that a throw which would take the number past 100 or 0 is also acceptable.

Discussion of activities

Activities 1 and 2 both use the now-familiar concepts of grouping in tens, and canonical form (see Org 1) to lead children on to 100. Although they are extrapolating their number concepts, which is schema building by mode 3, this extrapolation is also strongly based on physical experience (mode 1 building). This is an excellent combination.

An interesting feature here is that the physical experience by itself would not be sufficient to lead to the formation of these new concepts. A suitable schema is also needed which can organise this experience, and contains a pattern ready to be extrapolated by this experience. This has never been put better than by Louis Pasteur, when he said: 'Discoveries come to the prepared mind.'

OBSERVE AND LISTEN   **REFLECT**   **DISCUSS**

THE NAMING OF NUMBERS
in ways which help us to organise them and
use them effectively

Num 2.1   THE NUMBER WORDS IN ORDER (spoken)

Concept   At this stage, mathematical concepts are not necessarily involved.

Ability   To speak the number words in order.

Discussion of concept	Counting involves both saying (or thinking) the number words in order, and also making each word correspond to an object in the set to be counted, without omitting any and without counting any object twice. We begin by learning the number words, ready for use in this way.

Activity 1   **Number rhymes**

Activities for a small group. Their purpose is for children to memorise the number words in order, ready for their application in counting.

Materials   You will already know a number of these. Useful sources for other ones are:
One, Two, Three, Four compiled by Mary Grice, published by Frederick Warne.
Number Rhymes by Dorothy and John Taylor, published by Ladybird Books.
Counting Rhymes, edited by Clive Samsom, published by A. & C. Black.

What they do   1.   Everyone says the number rhymes together. This one uses the first five number-words only.

   One, two, three, four, five,
   Once I caught a fish alive,
   Why did you let it go?
   Because it bit my finger so.

2.   When these are well established, they can be linked with finger counting (see Num 1.4/1). For this they need something which goes more slowly. Here is one from Mary Grice's book.

   Peter taps with one hammer,
   One hammer, one hammer,
   Peter taps with one hammer,
   This fine day.

And so on up to five.

3. Here is a speedier one, adapted from the traditional counting-out rhyme.

One potato, two potatoes, three potatoes, four.
Five potatoes, that's enough, so we will plant no more.

4. Note that the relation between these and the finger movements is a truly counting one. E.g. 'Peter taps with three hammers' means three fingers tapping; 'three potatoes' means a total of three potatoes planted, corresponding to three fingers touching the table.

Discussion of activity	No new mathematical concept is being learnt here. This topic and the one which follows are concerned with memorising the number words, so that they are available for attachment to the number concepts acquired in other topics, e.g. Num 1.1. However, the correspondence between the memorised order, and the structural order of the complete sequence of numbers, is an important concept, and an invaluable tool for manipulating the number concepts. Much the easiest way to arrive at (e.g.) the number one more than seven is by knowing that it is given by the next word after seven, i.e. eight. This leads to adding by counting on, and subtraction by counting back. These topics thus link closely with the concepts learned in Num 1.4 (counting).

OBSERVE AND LISTEN   REFLECT   DISCUSS

Num 2.2   NUMBER WORDS FROM ONE TO TEN

Concept
Ability }   As already discussed in Num 2.1, continued to ten.

Discussion of concept	These are a continuation of the same kind as in Num 2.1.

Activity 1   **Number rhymes to ten**

One, two, three, four, five,
Once I caught a fish alive.
Six, seven, eight, nine, ten,
And then I let it go again.

This continues the rhyme already learnt. When the children are good enough at finger counting (see Num 1.4), it can be linked with finger counting to ten. Here is one from *Number Rhymes and Finger Plays* by E.R. Boyce and Kathleen Bartlett, reproduced here by permission of Pitman Publishing, London. I hope that Kathleen Bartlett will forgive me for changing 'housewives' to 'husbands' on alternate lines!

One busy housewife sweeping up the floor,
Two busy husbands polishing the door,
Three busy housewives washing baby's socks,
Four busy husbands winding up the clocks,
Five busy housewives washing out the broom,
Six busy husbands tidying the room,
Seven busy housewives cleaning out the sink,
Eight busy husbands giving puss a drink,
Nine busy housewives stirring up the stew,
Ten busy spouses with nothing else to do.

Discussion of activity	The discussion at the end of the previous topic applies equally well here.

OBSERVE AND LISTEN   REFLECT   DISCUSS

Num 2.3   SINGLE-DIGIT NUMERALS RECOGNISED AND READ

Concept   Written digits as having the same meanings as the spoken number words.

Abilities   (i)   Seeing a single digit, to say the corresponding number words.
         (ii)   Hearing a number word, to identify the corresponding written or printed numeral.
         (iii)   Later, to write these themselves.

Discussion of concept	A numeral is a symbol for a number. The digits are the single-figure numerals 0, 1, 2 . . . 9. So 574 is a three-digit numeral, standing for a single number. This distinction between numbers and numerals is not one which I would make explicit to the children, who use these ideas quite well intuitively: but it is as well to be clear about it ourselves. It is a particular case of the difference between the name of an object, and the object itself, which is hardly to be regarded as trivial.
	Myself, I regard any symbol for a number as a numeral, e.g., I would say that 4, Roman IV, the written word 'four', and also the spoken word 'four', are all numerals for the same number concept. Some may not agree with all of these, and it will be sufficient if we agree to use the term 'numeral' for written symbols such as 4, 7053, and later on ¾, 0.325.

We are so used to writing numbers (or rather, numerals) that we do not realise what a major step this is for children. Spoken words are naturally attached to ideas; doing the same with written symbols is like learning a new language.

Activity 1 Saying and pointing

An activity for a small group. Its purpose is to link spoken and written numerals.

Materials
- Numerals 1 to 10 written large on a card.

What they do
During the number rhymes, the teacher or a child points to the numerals as they are spoken.

Activity 2 'Please may I have . . .?'

A game for 4 to 6 children. Its purpose is to consolidate the connections between written numerals and spoken number-words.

Materials
- An even number of packs of number cards 1-5, at least as many packs as players.

Rules of the game
1. The cards are shuffled, and all are dealt to the players.
2. The object is to get rid of one's cards by putting down pairs with the same number (as we call it to the children).
3. After the deal, players look at their cards. If they have any pairs of cards with the same numeral, they put these down, face up.
4. They then play in turn, asking whoever they like for cards they need to make further pairs. E.g. 'Please, Sally, may I have a three?'
5. If Sally has a 3, she gives it. The asking player can then make a pair and put it down. If Sally hasn't a 3, she says 'Sorry'.
6. This continues in turns.
7. The winner is the first to put down all his cards, but the others continue and play out their hands.

Activity 3 Joining dots in order, to make pictures

This well-known activity, current in children's play materials for over a half a century, is excellent practice in using the written numerals in order.

Activity 4 Sets with their numbers

For children working on their own.

Materials
- Little rubber stamps of animals, or other pictures, that children can quickly put on paper.
- Pieces of paper cut up ready to make into pictures.
- Pencils.

What they do
1. The children make a set of a chosen number at one side of the paper.
2. They enclose them in a drawn set loop.
3. They then write the correct numeral against it, as shown below.
This might be allowed as a reward for having neatly copied a line of this numeral, on the grounds that before making a picture of this kind it is necessary to be able to write the numeral nicely.

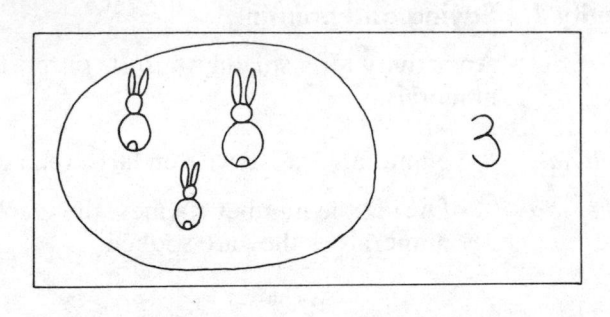

Activity 5   Sequencing numerals 1 to 10

A game for children to play in pairs. Its purpose is to give further practice in putting the first ten written numerals in order.

Materials ● . set of double-headed number cards, with numerals from 1 to 10.

What they do *Stage (a)*
1. The cards are spread out on the table face up.
2. The children co-operate in putting these in order.
Stage (b)
1. The cards are shuffled and dealt, five to each player. They look at their cards, and play whichever they choose.
2. One player puts down a card.
3. The other player, if she can, puts down a card in sequence.
4. The first player does likewise.
5. The winner is the player who first puts down all her cards.

Discussion of activities

The learning in this topic is more associative than conceptual. In Num 1 the spoken number words will have become associated with their number concepts at the same time as the latter were formed. The present topic is concerned with associating the written digits, the spoken words, and the concepts, all with each other. In the process, children will come to realise that the spoken sound and the mark on paper have the same meaning, e.g.,

Four
(spoken)

4
(written)

(thinks)
concept
4

The number concept 4 is a mental object and we cannot see or hear it.

Just as the words needed to be memorised in Num 1.1 and 1.2, so in the present topic the written symbols have to be memorised. But whereas with spoken words, the abilities to speak them and to recognise them are acquired simultaneously, it is different with the written symbols. Since learning to write the digits is so much more laborious than learning to speak them, the physical skill of writing them needs to be established independently of using them for mathematical purposes.

OBSERVE AND LISTEN   **REFLECT**   **DISCUSS**

Num 2.4   CONTINUATION OF COUNTING: 1 TO 20

Concept   The number names one to twenty.

Ability   To speak the number words in order, from one to twenty.

Discussion of concept

By now the children know that the words in counting rhymes also stand for numbers. So in this topic, they are also beginning to extend their range of number concepts, particularly if finger counting is linked with the number rhyme.

Activity 1   **Number rhymes to twenty**

An activity for a small group. Its purpose is to extend children's range of number names up to twenty. This can be linked with finger counting to twenty if the children work in pairs.

Materials   This is a good rhyme to begin with. For others, see the sources already quoted.

One, two, buckle my shoe.
Three, four, knock at the door.
Five, six, pick up sticks.
Seven, eight, lay them straight.
Nine, ten, a big fat hen.
Eleven, twelve, dig and delve.
Thirteen, fourteen, maids a-courting.
Fifteen, sixteen, maids in the kitchen.
Seventeen, eighteen, maids in waiting.
Nineteen, twenty, my plate's empty.

What they do   1.   The one on the left puts down fingers for the first decade.
2.   The one on the right continues from eleven to twenty. This links the words eleven, twelve . . . twenty, with ten and one fingers, ten and two fingers . . . ten and ten fingers (= two tens).

3. When this is well established, children can finger count to twenty on their own, lifting all their fingers after ten and starting again with left little finger at eleven. In this case the first ten are stored mentally. So they say: 'Ten in my head, eleven, twelve. . .'

Discussion of activity

'Eleven' and 'twelve' follow no pattern; and the pattern from thirteen to twenty is not consistent with the pattern from twenty onwards, which is a fairly consistent one thereafter. Also the spoken number-words do not correspond with the written numerals (thirteen is written as ten, three and so on) unless like the Arabs we read from right to left. So the learning in this activity is largely associative rather than conceptual.

OBSERVE AND LISTEN   **REFLECT**   **DISCUSS**

Num 2.5   COUNTING BACKWARDS FROM TWENTY

Concept Reversal of the counting sequence.

Ability To say the number words in order backwards, beginning with any number up to 20 and ending with zero.

Discussion of concept

As in several of the earlier topics, we are here mainly concerned with developing a verbal skill. This will later be linked with the concept of subtraction.

It is important to be able to start with any number.

Activity 1 Backward number rhymes

An activity for a small group. Its purpose is to teach children the number names in reverse.

What they do 1. Here is a nice one from Mary Grice's book. The name of a child goes in the space, a different child for each verse. Everyone says the number rhymes together.

> Five currant buns in the baker's shop,
> Big and round with sugar on top.
> Along came . . . with a penny one day,
> She/he bought a currant bun and took it away.

> Four currant buns (etc.)

> No currant bun in the baker's shop,
> Big and round with sugar on top.
> Along came . . . with a penny one day,
> She/he couldn't buy a bun and take it away.

If you like, this could be used with objects on a 'plate' representing buns.

2. Here is a backwards rhyme from ten, also from Mary Grice's book.

Ten little school boys went out to dine;
One choked his little self, and then there were nine.

Nine little school boys sat up very late;
One overslept himself, and then there were eight.

Eight little school boys travelling in Devon;
One said he'd stay there, and then there were seven.

Seven little school boys chopping up sticks;
One chopped himself in half, and then there were six.

Six little school boys playing with a hive;
A bumble-bee stung one, and then there were five.

Five little school boys going in for law;
One got in chancery, and then there were four.

Four little school boys going out to sea;
A red herring swallowed one, and then there were three.

Three little school boys walking in the zoo;
A big bear hugged one, and then there were two.

Two little school boys sitting in the sun;
One got frizzled up, and then there was one.

One little school boy living all alone;
He got married, and then there were none.

Other popular rhymes are 'Ten green bottles', and 'There were ten in a bed'. I have seen these successfully used with the children miming while they sung, each holding a number card.

Activity 2   Numbers backwards

A game for up to 6 children. Its purpose is to practise the skill of counting backwards.

Materials
- Number cards 0 to 20.
- Two or three lists of numbers 0 to 20.

Rules of the game   *Stage (a)* is played with the visual help of the number lists.
1. The number lists are put so that every player can see one of these right way up.
2. The cards are shuffled and put face down.
3. One of the players turns over the top card, puts it down face up, and says its number-word aloud, e.g. 'Eleven'.
4. The others in turn count 'Ten,' 'Nine', 'Eight', . . . 'Zero'.
5. The player who says 'Zero' is the one to turn over the next card, after which steps 3 and 4 are repeated.
Stage (b) is played as above, but without the help of the number lists.

Variation 1. One of the players turns over the top card as before, and puts it face up. She now starts counting at zero.
2. The others in turn clockwise count forwards until they reach the number shown.
3. Then they go into reverse, and count anti-clockwise from this number down to zero.
4. As before, the player who says 'Zero' turns the next card.
5. After a while they are likely to notice that this is always the same player. You might ask them whether this must always be so.

Discussion of activities	As with the earlier number rhymes, the learning in this topic is largely associative. However, in activity 1, some of the rhymes used do relate to diminishing the set by a one each time. In the future, counting backwards provides a valuable technique for subtraction. It can then be conceptualised in terms of taking away one object for each word spoken.

OBSERVE AND LISTEN   **REFLECT**   **DISCUSS**

Num 2.6   COUNTING IN TWOS, FIVES

Concept Sequences of number-words by which a set can be counted 2 at a time, or 5 at a time.

Ability To match these sequences with groups of 2 or 5 objects, and thereby to find the number of a given set.

Discussion of concept	Although 'one, two, three. . .' is the most basic counting sequence, by memorising others derived from this we acquire the means to handle number concepts in other ways. E.g., learning to count backwards provides a technique for subtraction. The sequences 'Two, four, six. . .' and 'Five, ten, fifteen. . .' provide a quicker way of counting large sets. The latter is also useful when working in base ten.

Activity 1 **Counting with hand clapping**

A group activity for any number of children. Its purpose is to teach the word-sequences themselves, in preparation for their use for counting.

What they do *Stage (a)*   Counting in twos.
1. They count aloud together, clapping hands on every multiple of 2, thus: 'One, *two*, three, *four*, five, *six*. . .'.
2. When they can do this, they whisper the 'in-between' words.
3. Next, they 'say in their heads' the in-between words.
4. Finally, without hand-clapping, they say 'Two, four, six, eight. . .'.

Stage (b)   Counting in fives.
As in stage (a), but for multiples of five, thus: 'One, two, three, four, *five*, six, seven, eight, nine, *ten*. . .'.

Activity 2   Counting 2-rods and 5-rods

A group activity. Its purpose is to link the verbal skill with the number concepts.

Materials   • Cubes

What they do   Stage 1
1. The children first make quite a lot of 2-rods.
2. They then count them, using the pattern acquired in the first stage of activity 1.
Stage 2
As in stage 1, but using 5-rods. Return to this activity when the children are able to count beyond 20.

Activity 3   Counting money, 2p and 5p coins

An activity for children working in pairs. Its purpose is to consolidate the skills which have been learnt, in a new and useful situation.

Materials   • 2p coins (plastic or genuine).
• 5p coins (ditto).
• Containers for these.
• Pencil and paper for each child.

What they do   Stage (a) uses 2p coins only.
1. One child takes a random set of coins, and decides on its value by counting in twos.
2. He writes down the result, which he does not show to the other child.
3. He gives this set of coins to the other child, who does likewise.
4. They compare results. If these are different, they check together until they reach a result which they agree as correct.
5. Steps 1 to 4 are repeated, starting with the other child.

Activity 4   Counting sets in twos and fives

An activity for a small group. Its purpose is to give further practice in these skills.
Return to this after Num 2.9, when children are able to count and record beyond 20.

Materials   For each child:
• A container in which is a set of objects between 20 and 100 in number.
• A slip of paper and a pencil.

What they do   1. The children each have a container of objects.
2. They tip these onto the table, and find the number of the set by counting in twos.

3. This they record on the slip of paper which they fold over and place on top of the objects which they return to the container.
4. The children then exchange containers, and again find the number of their sets, but this time they count in fives.
5. This result they write on the outside of the slip on paper.
6. Finally they compare these two numbers.
7. If these are different, then the children check together to try to reach a result which they agree as being correct.
8. The numbers of the sets used do not need to be exact multiples of 2 or 5. Singles left over are counted singly, e.g. '. . . thirty, thirty-five, thirty-six, thirty-seven'.

Discussion of activities	Activity 1 is a way of deriving two new counting sequences (counting in twos, fives) from the basic sequence which children already know. Only associative learning is involved here; but in activities 2, 3, and 4, the new counting sequences are related to number concepts which children have already. Activities 3 and 4 both use mode 2 testing (checking their own conclusions against each other's, with discussion if their results do not agree). In activity 3, mode 3 testing (internal consistency) is also involved: the number of a set is the same however we count it.

OBSERVE AND LISTEN   **REFLECT**   **DISCUSS**

Num 2.7   EXTRAPOLATION OF COUNTING PATTERN TO ONE HUNDRED

Concepts   (i)   The pattern of spoken number-words and written numerals.
(ii)   Their associated numbers, in physical embodiments.

Ability   To count from 1 to 100.

Discussion of concepts	From 20 onwards there is a clear pattern, so conceptual learning can now be brought in. This is a combination of two patterns. The first is that of the words for the sequence of tens: ten, twenty (meaning two-ty), thirty (three-ty), forty, fifty (five-ty), sixty, seventy, eighty, ninety. The second pattern links to this the existing sequence of number words from one to nine: twenty one, twenty two, twenty three, etc. Thus the whole pattern repeats, though not identically, for every new decade. This topic relates to Org 1.13 (grouping in tens), and Num 1.10 (extrapolation of number concepts to one hundred).

Activity 1   **Counting in tens**

An activity for a small group. Its purpose is to apply the technique of counting to groups of 10, and to learn the new number-names used for this.

Materials
- Ready-made 10-rods such as base 10 Dienes material; or ready-made bundles of milk straws.
- Tens and units tray (see activity 3).

What they do
1. One child puts these one at a time into the ten side of the tray, and all count in unison 'Ten, twenty, thirty. . . .'. Initially they will need help from you.
2. Afterwards they try to say the words themselves without being reminded.

Activity 2 Counting two ways on a number square

An activity for a small group. It could also be used as a class activity. Its purpose is to link the spoken words with the written numerals.

Materials
- A number square, 1 to 100, for each child, when working in groups.
- A number square on the blackboard when taken as a class activity.

What they do
Stage 1
Children count in unison down the left-hand column, saying, 'ten', 'twenty', 'thirty' . . . at the same time pointing to the corresponding numerals.
Stage 2
Children count vertically down a column, e.g. 'three, thirteen, twenty-three. . .'

This could also be done in turn round a group, either with each child saying a whole column, or with one number-name per child.
Stage 3
One child points while the others say the number. The pointer starts at the top edge and zig-zags (without jumping) as she likes until she reaches the bottom or the right-hand edge, e.g. 14, 24, 35, 45, 46, 47, 57, 67, 68, 69.

This could also be used for larger groups or for the class as a whole. In this case either the teacher, or one of the children, points to the numerals on the blackboard.

Activity 3 Tens and units tray

An activity for a small group. They must all be able to see the tray the right way round, with tens on the left. Its purpose is to consolidate children's understanding of the two counting patterns in combination, that in units and that in tens.

Materials
- Base 10 material, units and tens.
- Tens and units tray, as illustrated below. (A card may be used instead if desired.)

Tens	Units

What they do
1. Each child in turn puts in either a unit or a ten, whichever she likes.
2. At the same time she continues the counting sequence, either one more or ten more.
3. Round the group, a typical sequence might be: 'ten', 'eleven', 'twenty-one', 'thirty-one', 'thirty-two', 'thirty-three', 'forty-three'. . .

Discussion of activities

Activity 1 uses physical experience (mode 1) combined with communication from you (mode 2) to link the numbers of tens in the tray with their corresponding number-words.

The number square used in activity 2 is a good way of showing how the two patterns, in ones from 1 to 10 and in tens from 10 to 100, are combined to provide a counting pattern from 1 to 100. By counting in various ways based on this square, children will begin to establish this double pattern in their own minds.

Activity 3 connects this two-way counting pattern with the underlying mathematical concepts, these concepts being embodied in physical materials (ten-rods or ten-bundles, units) and physical actions. Putting one more ten corresponds to saying the next ten-word, putting one more unit corresponds to saying the next word used for units.

OBSERVE AND LISTEN   **REFLECT**   **DISCUSS**

Num 2.8   WRITTEN NUMERALS 20 TO 99 USING HEADED COLUMNS

Concept   That a particular digit can represent a number of units, tens, (and later hundreds. . .) according to where it is written.

Abilities   (i)   To match numerals of more than one digit with physical representations of units, tens, (and later hundreds. . .).
(ii)   To speak the corresponding number-words for numbers 20 to 99.

Discussion of concept

First, let us be clear about what is a digit. It is any of the single-figure numerals, 0, 1, 2, 3, 4, 5, 6, 7, 8, 9 (corresponding to the numbers we can count on our fingers). Just as we can have words of one letter (such as a), two letters (such as an), three letters (such as ant), and more, so also we can have written numerals of one digit (such as 7), two digits (such as 72), three digits (such as 702), and more.

The same numeral, say 3, can be used to represent 3 conkers, or shells, or cubes, or single objects of any kind. If we want to show which objects, we can do so in two ways. We can either write '3 conkers, 5 sea shells, and 8 cubes', or we can tabulate:

conkers	sea shells	cubes
3	5	8

Likewise the same numeral, say 3, can be used to represent 3 single objects, or three groups of ten, or 3 groups of ten groups of ten (which we call hundreds for short). We could write '3 hundreds, 5 tens, and 8 units'; or we could tabulate:

hundreds	tens	units
3	5	8

We are so used to thinking about (e.g.) 3 hundreds that we tend not to realise what a major step has been taken in doing this. We are first regarding a group of 10 objects as a single entity, so that if we have several of these we can count 'One, two, three, four, five . . . *groups of ten*'. Then we are regarding a *group of ten groups of ten* as another entity, which can likewise be counted 'One, two, three. . .'. And by the end of this network, we shall no longer be regarding these as groups of physical objects, but as abstract mental entities which we can arrange and re-arrange. We shall also have introduced a condensed and abstract notation (place value).

These two steps need to be taken one at a time. While the first, described above, is being taken, we need to use a notation which states clearly and explicitly what is meant. Headed column notation does this well.

Also, because the correspondence between written numerals and number words only becomes regular from 20 onwards, we start children's thinking about written numerals here where the pattern is clear. The written numerals 11-19 are also regular, but their spoken words are not, so these are postponed until the next topic.

Activity 1 — Number targets

A game for as many children as can sit so that they can all see the tray right way up; minimum 3. It follows on from 'Tens and units Tray' (Num 2.7/3), which was the last activity described. Its purpose is to link the spoken number words, just learnt, with the corresponding written numerals.

Materials
- Tens and units tray.*
- Target cards.**
- Pencil and headed paper for each child.**
- Base 10 material, tens and units.***

* The same as for 'Tens and units tray' (Num 2.7/3)
**See illustrations overleaf. See also note (iii).
*** This game should be played with a variety of base 10 material such as milk straws or lolly sticks in units and bundles of ten, multibase material in base ten.

What they do
1. The target cards are shuffled and put face down.
2. In turn, each child takes the top card from the pile. He looks at this, but does not let the others see it.
3. Before play begins, 2 tens are put into the tray. (This is to start the game at 20.)

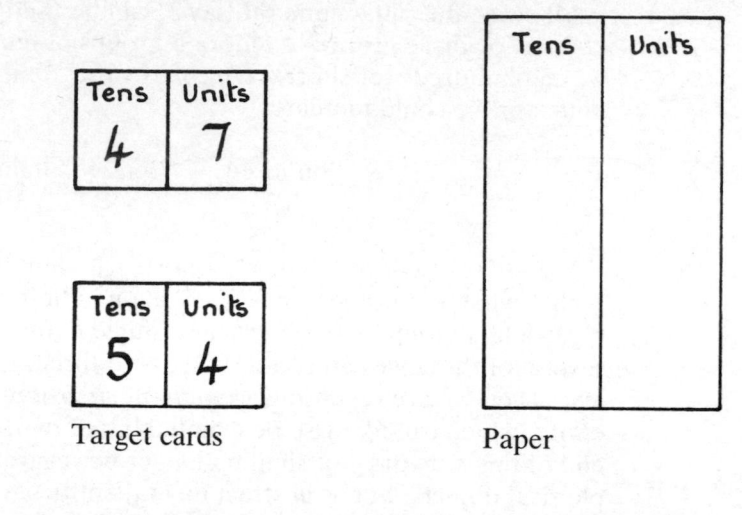

Target cards   Paper

4. The objective of each player is to have in the tray his target number of tens and units.
5. Each player in turn may put in or take out a ten or a unit.
6. Having done this, he writes on his paper the corresponding numerals and speaks them aloud in two ways; e.g.

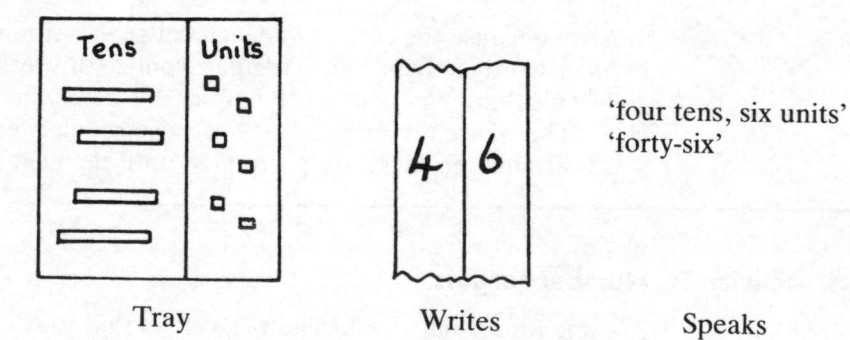

Tray   Writes   Speaks

'four tens, six units'
'forty-six'

7. In the above example, if a player holding a 47 target card had the next turn, he would win by putting down one more unit. He would then show his target card to show that he had achieved his target.
8. Since players do not know each others' targets, they may unknowingly achieve someone else's target for them. In this case the lucky player may immediately reveal his target card, whether it is his turn next or not.
9. When a player has achieved a target, he then takes a new target card from the top of the pile, and play continues.
10. The winner is the player who finishes with most target cards.

Notes (i) If one side of the tray is empty, a corresponding zero must be written and spoken; e.g.,

'four tens, zero units';
'forty'.

and also

 'zero tens, seven units';
'seven'.

(ii) Players are only required to write the numbers they themselves make. It would be good practice for them to write every number, but we have found it hard to get them to do it.

(iii) Several sets of target cards are provided in which the numbers are reasonably close together, both the tens and the units. If they are too far apart, the game may never end.

Variation It makes the game more interesting if, at step 5, a player is allowed two moves. For example, he may put 2 tens, or put 2 units, or put 1 ten and take 1 unit, etc. This may also be used if no one is able to reach his target.

Activity 2   Number targets beyond 100

When children are familiar with numbers greater than 100, they can play this game with suitable modifications using targets in hundreds, tens and units.

Discussion of activities

In preparation for place-value notation, it is important for children to have plenty of practice in associating the written symbols and their locations with visible embodiments of hundreds, tens, units and in associating both of these with the spoken words. In this topic 'location' means 'headed column'; in Num 2.10 it will mean 'relative position'.

So that their conscious attention is free to concentrate on the meaning of what they are doing, children should before beginning this activity be able to write the digits 0, 1 . . . 9 without too much effort. This is a copying exercise, not in itself a mathematical one.

This activity uses concept building by physical experience (mode 1). The social context provided by a game links these concepts with communication (mode 2) using both written and spoken symbols.

OBSERVE AND LISTEN   **REFLECT**   **DISCUSS**

Num 2.9   WRITTEN NUMERALS FROM 11 TO 20

Concept   The written numerals 11-19 as having the same meanings as the number-words with which they are already familiar.

Abilities   (i)   To match the numerals 11-19 with the spoken number-words.
(ii)   To match both with physical embodiments of these numbers.

Discussion of concept

The discussion of Num 1.8 applies equally here. However, the clear and regular correspondence which we find from 20 onwards, e.g.:

2 tens,   7 units
twenty   seven
27

does not apply from 11-19. E.g. although 1 ten, 2 units is written (as we would expect) 12, it is spoken not as 'onety two' but as 'twelve'. And 1 ten, 7 units is written (as we would expect) 17, but the spoken form is backwards, seventeen. So the present topic contains, implicitly, the notion of irregularity – departure from an expected pattern.

Activity 1   Seeing, speaking, writing 11-19

A teacher-led activity for a small group. Its purpose is to relate the number-words spoken but not written down in Num 1.7/1 to the written numerals 11-19.

Materials   • Tens and units tray.
• Base 10 material.
• Paper and pencil for yourself.
1.   You put in

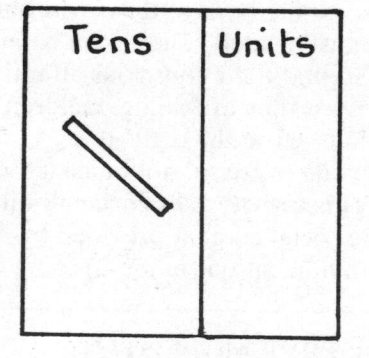

2.   Write

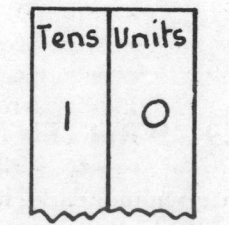

3.   Say: 'one ten, zero units. Ten.'
4.   Put in

100

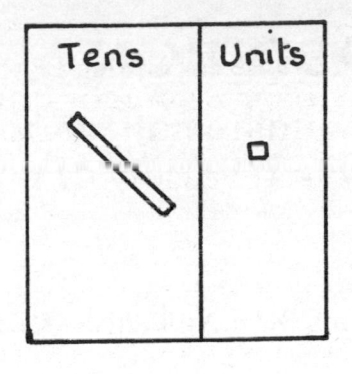

5. Write

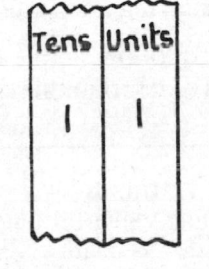

6. Say: 'One ten, one unit. Eleven.'
7. Carry on through the teens. (So you don't put in another ten.)
8. Soon the children will join in. You might point out that if these followed the same pattern as 21, 31 . . . we would talk about onety-one, onety-two, etc., and explain that in olden times people hadn't thought about it carefully: so these names got attached, and have 'stuck'.

Activity 2 Number targets in the teens

The same number targets game as in the topic just before this (Num 1.8/1) should now be played, starting with the tens and units tray empty.

Materials As for (Num 2.8/1) except:
- Target cards now 11 to 19.

Discussion of activities

The written numerals 10-19 follow the same pattern as those from 20 on, so these concepts are acquired by extrapolation (Mode 3 schema building). However, the spoken number-words do not follow this pattern, and do not correspond well to the numerals even from 13 on. ('Thirteen', 'fourteen' . . . reads from right to left.) Children will however be already familiar with the spoken number-words, and the activity now links these to the numbers in physical embodiments (tens and units tray), and to the written numerals.

OBSERVE AND LISTEN   **REFLECT**   **DISCUSS**

ADDITION

A mathematical operation which corresponds
with a variety of physical actions and events

Num 3.1 ACTIONS ON SETS: PUTTING MORE (Total < 10)

Concepts   (i)   Sets as operands.
(ii) Putting more as actions.
(iii) Starting and resulting numbers.

Abilities (i)   To follow simple instructions for actions with sets.
(ii) To describe these actions and their results.

Discussion of concepts

In Org 1, from topic 2 onwards, we developed the idea of a set as
something which, though made up of separate objects, could also be
thought of as a single entity. In Org 1.3 for example, we compared sets
to decide which had the larger number, and in Org 1.4 we ordered sets
by their numbers.

In the present topic, we consider sets as something on which we can
perform (physical) actions: for short, sets as operands. The actions in
this case are putting more objects into the set; as a result of which, we
finish with a set having a larger number. This is a very everyday affair –
it happens whenever we put biscuits on a plate. Nevertheless, as we shall
see in topic 2, it is the foundation for two important mathematical
concepts.

A general name for objects on which actions or operations are
performed is 'operand'. We do not need to teach children this term, but
it is convenient to have it available for our own use.

Activity 1   **Start, Action, Result (do and say)**

An activity for two to four children. Its purpose is to introduce the
concepts described above.

Materials
- An SAR board (see figure 2).
- Start cards 1-5 (later 0-5) which say (e.g.) 'Start with a set of 3'.
- Action cards 1-5 (later 0-5) which say (e.g.) 'Put 2 more', 'Increase it by 5', 'Make it 4 larger'.
- Result cards numbered from 1-10 (later 0-10).
- Objects such as counters, shells, buttons, to put in the set loop.
- A reversible card. On side one is written
  'Find the card to show your result. Say what you did, and the result.'
  On side two is written
  'Predict the result.'

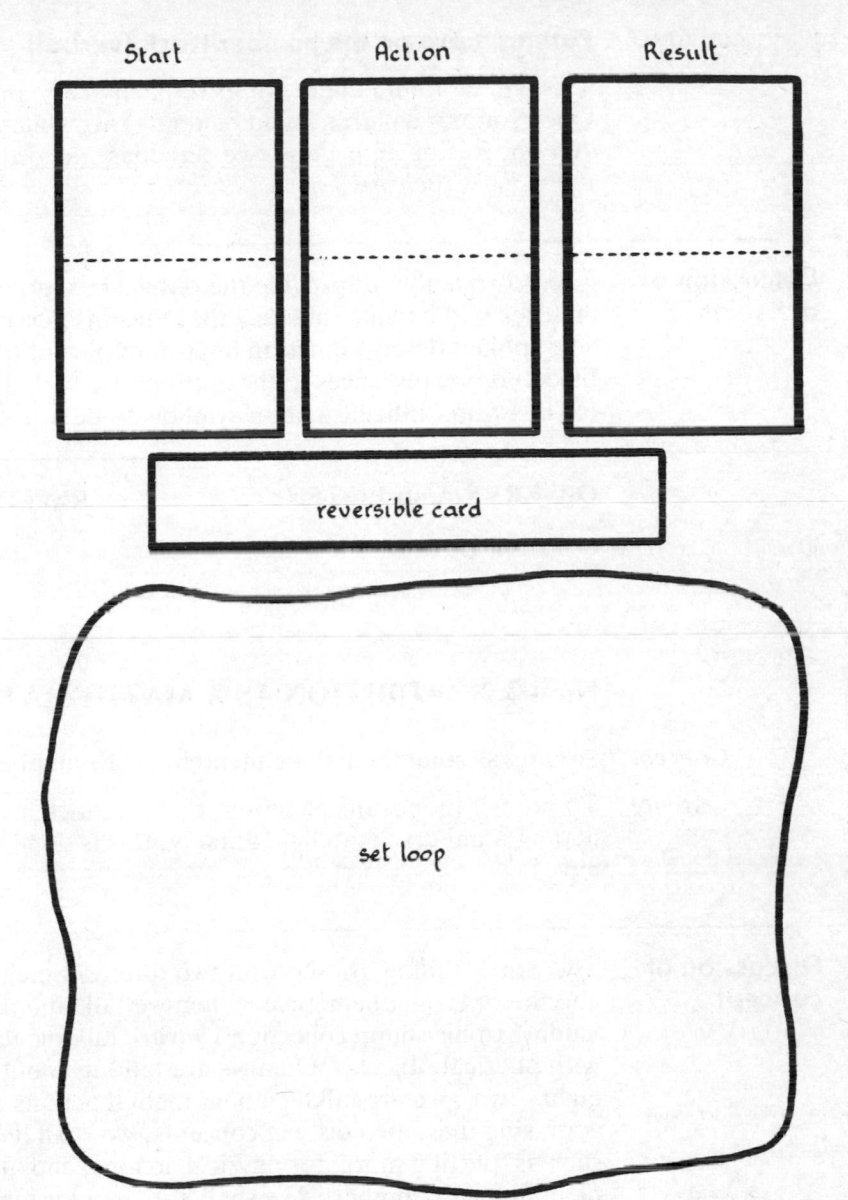

Figure 2 SAR board

What they do
1. The cards are shuffled and put face down in the upper part of their spaces on the SAR board.
2. The reversible card is put in its space with side one showing.
3. One child turns over the top start card into the space below, and puts a set of the required number into the set loop.
4. Another child then turns over the action card, and puts more objects into the loop as instructed. Note that at this stage we do not talk about adding.
5. He then finds the appropriate result card to show the number of the resulting set.
6. Finally he describes to the others what he did, and the result.

103

Activity 2 Putting more on the number track (verbal)

This will be found under NuSp 1.3, activity 1, and should be used here. One group of children could be doing this while another is doing 'Start, Action, Result'. For these two activities, the order does not matter. (This is not usually the case.)

Discussion of activities	These two activities provide the physical experiences from which children will begin to abstract the concepts described in the next topic. The spoken description is an important part of the activities, since it links these experiences to the appropriate verbal symbols, in preparation for the more difficult written symbols to be introduced in topic 3.

OBSERVE AND LISTEN   REFLECT   DISCUSS

Num 3.2 ADDITION AS A MATHEMATICAL OPERATION

Concept Adding as something done mentally, with numbers.

Ability To predict the results of actions on sets which involve putting more, by adding numbers mentally. (Initially, this is done with help from physical aids.)

Discussion of concept	The word 'adding' is used with two different meanings, one everyday and the other mathematical. When we talk about 'adding an egg', 'adding to his stamp collection', we are talking about physical actions with physical objects. When we are talking about 'adding seven', 'adding eighty-two', we are talking about mental actions on numbers. To avoid confusing these two distinct concepts, we shall hereafter use other words such as 'putting more' for physical actions, and 'adding' for what we do mentally with numbers. We shall also avoid using 'action' for the latter, and use 'operation' instead. The distinction we are making is therefore between physical *actions* and mathematical (i.e. mental) *operations*. Adding is thus a mathematical operation. Other mathematical operations are subtraction, multiplication, division, factorisation. . . . May I mention also that these others are not 'sums'? A sum is the result of an addition.

Activity 1 Predicting the result (addition)

This is a direct continuation of Num 3.1/1, 'Start, Action, Result' (do and say). It can be played by two children, or two teams. Its purpose is to teach children to use the (mental) operation of addition for making simple predictions.

Materials
- As for Num 3.1/1, 'Start, Action, Result' (do and say).
- Pencils.
- Stage (b) requires a handkerchief or bag for hiding the objects.

What they do   *Stage (a)*
1. The SAR board and the start and action cards are put out as before. The reversible card is put below the Result space with side two showing.
2. Player A turns over the top 'start' card, and puts a set of the required number in the loop.
3. Player B turns over the top 'action' card, after which she must predict the result and choose the appropriate card from the results pack. She puts this in the 'result' space.
4. Finally she puts down more shells (or whatever) and physically checks her prediction.

Stage (b)
1. The first card is turned as in stage (a), but this time the objects are put into a bag or under a handkerchief.
2. The second card is turned and the indicated number more are put with the first set.
3. A prediction is made as before, and tested physically by emptying the bag or lifting the handkerchief.

Activity 2   'Where will it come?'

This will be found at NuSp 1.3/2, and should be used here.

Activity 3   Stepping stones

A board game for 2, 3, or 4 children. Its purpose is to give further practice at adding, in a predictive situation.

Materials
- Game board (see figure 3).
- Die, 1 to 6.
- Shaker.
- Markers, one for each child. (Little figures are good, which do not hide the numbers.)

Rules of the game
1. Players start from the near bank, which corresponds to zero.
2. Players in turn throw the die, add this number to that on the stone where they are, and move to the stone indicated. E.g., a player is on stone 3, throws 5, so moves to stone 8. When starting from the bank, they move to the stone with the number thrown.
3. If that stone is occupied, she should not move since there is not room for two on the same stone.
4. If a player touches her marker, she must move it. If this takes her to an occupied stone, she falls in the water and has to return to the bank.
5. The exact number must be thrown to reach the island.

Note   This will be used again in Num 4.2 as a subtraction game, to get back from the island.

Figure 3 Stepping Stones

Activity 4 Crossing

This will be found at NuSp 1.3/3, and should be used here.

Discussion of activities	In activity 1, there is an important progress to be made from *counting all* to *counting on*. At first, children need to count the first set, then the set added, and finally to count *all* the objects to get the total. Later, they may become able, after counting the first set, to count *on* the number of the second set to get the total. At the simplest stage, this involves realising that having already counted the first set, it is not necessary to do so again, since this number can be used as starting point for counting the enlarged set. This applies when the two sets are present physically

and visibly. Counting on mentally is a much more sophisticated technique. To add (say) 5 and 3 now involves, first holding 'five' in one's head, and then saying 'six, seven, eight' while also thinking 'one, two, three'.

This would be very difficult without the help of some method such as finger counting to keep track of the 'one, two, three,' and children should be encouraged to use this. (Please see Num 1.4/1, Num 1.5/1, for descriptions of the recommended method of finger counting.)

Another way of counting on is by using a number track or number line. With this, you find your starting number, and count on saying (or thinking) 'one, two, three,' while pointing to 6, 7, 8. This is different from the methods described earlier, since it uses the number track to show the running total. You don't speak the answer, but your finger ends up pointing to it.

Of these two, the number track is perhaps easier to do, but it is harder to interpret. Children often make mistakes because they say 'one' while pointing to the starting number instead of its successor: in this example, pointing to 3 instead of 4. Or they may take the last word they speak as the total, rather than the number pointed to. Both techniques should be learnt, but I suggest that finger counting be well established before using the number track.

OBSERVE AND LISTEN　　　　**REFLECT**　　　　**DISCUSS**

Num 3.3　NOTATION FOR ADDITION: NUMBER SENTENCES

Concept　　The use of written number sentences of these two forms

$$3 \xrightarrow{+2} 5 \text{ and } 3 + 2 = 5$$

for representing the operation of addition, and its result.

Abilities　　(i)　To write number sentences describing actions of 'putting more' with physical materials.

(ii)　To use number sentences for making predictions about the results of physical actions, and to test these predictions.

Discussion of concept　　The arrow notation for addition corresponds well to its meaning:

start	operation	result
3	$\xrightarrow{+2}$	5

The part representing the operation looks different from the parts representing start and result, which is good. It may be read verbally as:

'three,　　add two　　result five.'

I prefer 'add' to 'plus', since 'add' is the name of the operation, while 'plus' is the name of the symbol.

   If you prefer the familiar alternative form $3 + 2 = 5$ it may be used here; but I recommend its postponement until children have learnt about addition as a binary operation, in topic 7.

Activity 1   Writing number sentences for addition

Form (a). This is an activity for two to four children. Its purpose is to introduce children to written number sentences, used here for recording.

Materials
- SAR board as used in Num 3.1/1, and all other materials.
- Start cards and action cards which include parts of a number sentence, as illustrated below.
- Reversible card. On one side is written,
  'Write a number sentence to show what you did'.
  On side two is written,
  'First write a number sentence showing what you predict the result will be. Then test your prediction'.
- Pencil and paper for each child.

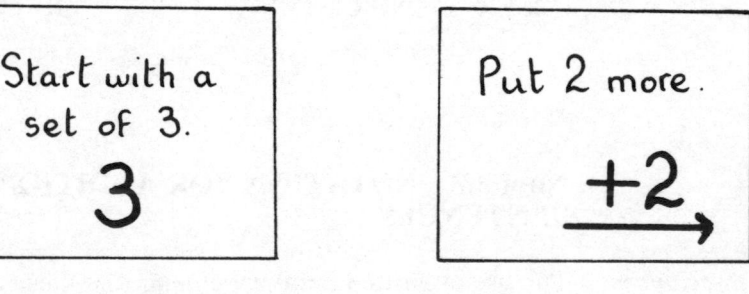

What they do
1, 2, 3, 4 are as in Num 3.1/1.
5.   After doing the action, the instruction on the card is followed. In the above example, each child would therefore write:

$$3 \xrightarrow{+2} 5$$

6.   They compare what they have written.

Form (b)   As in Num 3.1/2, the same activity may usefully be done here using cubes and a number track instead of a set loop.

Activity 2   Write your prediction

This is a predictive version of activity 1.

Form (a)

Materials
- As version (a) for activity 1.

What they do
1. The reversible card now shows side two.
2. Each start and action card is turned over as before.
3. Each child copies the first two parts of the number sentence, and completes it by doing the addition mentally (using aids such as finger counting, number track, as desired).
4. Finally they check their predictions by using the physical materials, e.g., if a child turns over these cards

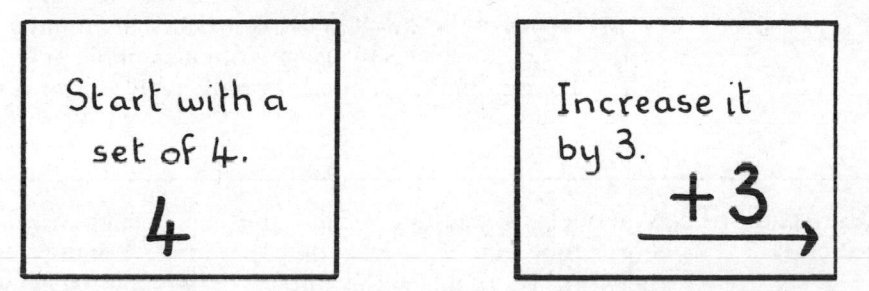

he writes $4 \xrightarrow{+3}$

Then he completes the number sentence $4 \xrightarrow{+3} 7$

Finally he puts four objects into the set loop, then 3 more, and counts the total.
5. It might be of interest for another child to check the prediction.

Form (b) The same activity may usefully be done using cubes and a number track instead of a set loop.

Discussion of activities

In activity 1, children are learning what is meant by 'write a number sentence', by copying examples of these. The number sentences are written after the physical manipulations, so that the concepts are already there and ready to be attached to the written symbols. It is a concept-building and symbol-linking activity. The concepts involved here are not only the mathematical operation of addition, but the fact that the number sentence can represent both a physical (making a set, putting more) and a mental activity (adding).

In activity 2, the combination of written symbols and associated concepts is used to make a prediction. In this case it is a simple one, but essentially this is the same kind of use that mathematics is put to in the adult world. Does our bridge stay up, does our aircraft find its destination? This is the crunch, and it depends partly on whether someone 'got his sums right'.

The notation is highly condensed, which is one of its strengths: by using it one can handle a lot of information. It also carries the risk that its meaning can easily become detached and lost. Hence the importance of continually relating it to physical experience.

OBSERVE AND LISTEN   **REFLECT**   **DISCUSS**

Num 3.4   NUMBER STORIES: ABSTRACTING NUMBER SENTENCES

Concept   Numbers and numerical operations as models for actual happenings, or for verbal descriptions of these.

Abilities

(i)   To produce numerical models in physical materials corresponding to given number stories, to manipulate these appropriately, and to interpret the result in the context of the number story.

(ii)   Later, to do this by using written symbols only.

(iii)   To use number sentences predictively, to solve verbally given problems.

Discussion of concept

A model is something which represents in simpler form something else, e.g. a tube map is a model on paper of the London Underground network. By reducing the amount of detail and leaving out non-essentials, it enables us to think and plan more easily and effectively. Mathematical models are mental models, though we use physical aids such as cubes, written symbols, to help us to get hold of them. They are a very versatile and useful kind with applications as different as shop-keeping and communication satellites. Hence their importance in the world today.

The idea of a mathematical model is quite an abstract one, and will become clearer as more examples are encountered. The activities in this topic provide some examples to start with.

Activity 1   **Personalised number stories**

An activity for 2 to 6 children. Its purpose is to connect simple verbal problems with physical events, linked with the idea that we can use objects to represent other objects.

Materials

• Number stories of the kind in the example over the page. For some stories you will need 2 versions, one with pronouns for girls, the other with pronouns for boys. These can be on different sides of the same card.

• The name of each child on a card or slip of paper.

• Three separate sets of number cards on different coloured cards:
   Start cards 1-5
   Action cards 1-5 (later 0-5)
   Result cards 1-10.

• Objects such as bottle tops, conkers, shells, counters.

• Paper and pencils.

What they do   (*apportioned according to how many children there are*)

1.   A number story is chosen. The name, start, and action cards are shuffled and put face down.

2.   The top name card is turned over and put in the number story.

3.   Another child then turns over the top start card, and puts it in the appropriate space.

4. Another child then turns over the top action card, and puts it in the appropriate space.
5. The number story now looks like this. Depending on children's reading ability, it may be useful for you to read it aloud for them.

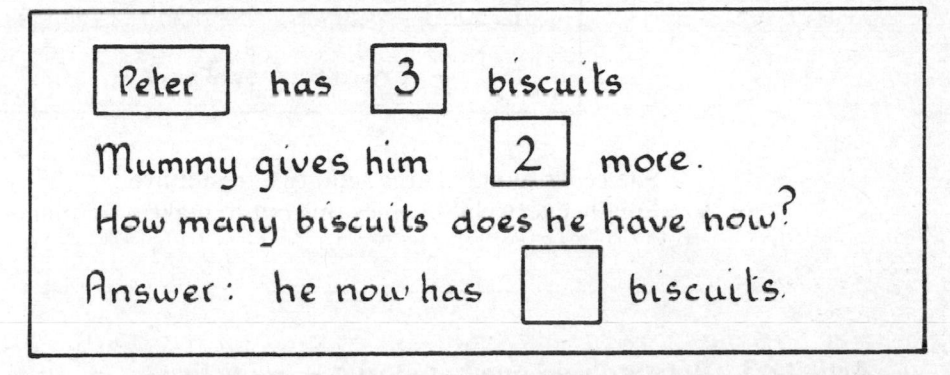

6. The named child then takes over, describing aloud what he is doing while the others check. (E.g.) 'We haven't any biscuits, so what can we use instead?' (Puts down bottle tops.) 'These are the 3 I start with.' (Puts down 2 conkers.) 'I've put 2 more. Now I have 5 altogether.' It is a good idea to use different objects for the biscuits mummy gives him, to keep the two sets distinct. You could suggest that these are a different kind of biscuit.
7. Finally another child puts the correct number card in the result space to complete the number story.

Activity 2   Abstracting number sentences

An extension to activity 1 which may be included fairly soon. Its purpose is to teach children to abstract a number sentence from a verbal description.

Materials   • As for activity 1, and also:
   • Number sentence card as illustrated below.

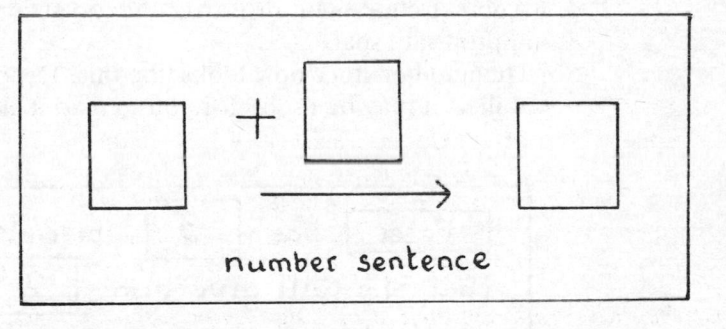

What they do   Steps 1 to 7 are as in activity 1.
8. You, or a child, then says 'Now we make a number sentence recording what happened.' She puts the number sentence card below the story card, then moves the three number cards from the story card to the number sentence card as shown here

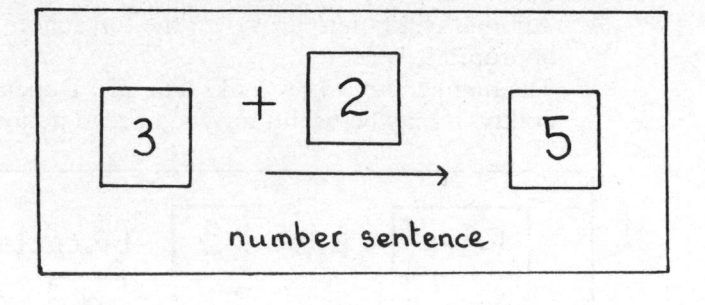

She reads aloud 'Three, add two, result five'.
9. Finally every child copies this out to make a permanent record.

$$3 \xrightarrow{+2} 5$$

Activity 3   Personalised number stories – predictive

An activity for 2 to 6 children. It combines activities 1 and 2, in predictive form.

Materials
- Number stories of the new kind shown in step 5. These now require a prediction.
- The name of each child on a card or a slip of paper.*
- 2 sets of number cards: start cards 1-5, and action cards 1-5 (later 0-5).*
- Objects such as bottle tops, conkers, shells, counters.*
- Slips of paper to fit answer space.
- Pencil and paper for each child.

* These are the same as for activity 1.

What they do   (*apportioned according to how many children there are*)
1. A number story is chosen. The name, start, and action cards are shuffled and put face down.
2. The top name card is turned over, and put in the appropriate space in the number story.
3. Another child then turns over the top start card, and puts it in the appropriate place.
4. Another child then turns over the top action card, and puts it in the appropriate space.
5. The number story now looks like this. Depending on children's reading ability, it may be useful for you to read it aloud for them.

Peter has 3 biscuits. Mummy says that she will give him 2 more if he can tell her how many he will have then. What should he say?
Answer: he should say "I shall have [ ] biscuits".

6. The named child now has to answer the question by writing and completing a number sentence, explaining as he does so, e.g.

Says	Writes
'I have 3 biscuits.'	3
'I get 2 more.'	$3 \xrightarrow{+2}$
'3, add 2, result. . .'	$3 \xrightarrow{+2} 5$

'So I'll say, "I will have 5 biscuits." '

7. Peter then writes the resulting number on a slip of paper and puts it in the appropriate space to answer the question in the number story.

8. Meanwhile the other children write the same number sentence, as in step 9 of activity 2.

9. Finally one of the other children tests the prediction by using the physical materials, describing what she is doing while the others check. E.g. (with appropriate actions). 'I'm using these bottle tops and conkers in place of biscuits. These are the 3 he started with. Now he gets 2 more. There are now 5 altogether. So, Peter gave the correct answer.'

Discussion of activities

'We don't have any biscuits here, so what can we use instead?' introduces children to *modelling*, already discussed at the beginning of this topic. This idea, that something can be used to represent something else, is a very important one. Also important is what we incorporate in the model, and what we leave out. So far as the model is concerned, it doesn't matter whether the story is about biscuits, or marshmallows, or balloons; and the model would be the same for Jane and her auntie as for Peter and his mummy. From this we see (i) how general a mathematical model is, and thus how versatile; (ii) how great is the abstraction involved when going from a number story to a mathematical model. It is because of the latter that children so often find it difficult to come up with the right model. 'Please Miss, is this add or multiply?'

This is why the process of modelling is here treated with such thoroughness. In activities 2 and 3, the abstractive process is shown visibly when the numbers are removed from the story card and put out by themselves. The terms 'number story' and 'number sentence' also call attention to the relation between the described happening, and its model.

A very important feature of the present plan of development is having the children move first from verbal problems to physical representations of the objects, numbers, and actions described in the number story, and from the latter to the mathematical statement, not directly from words to mathematical symbols.

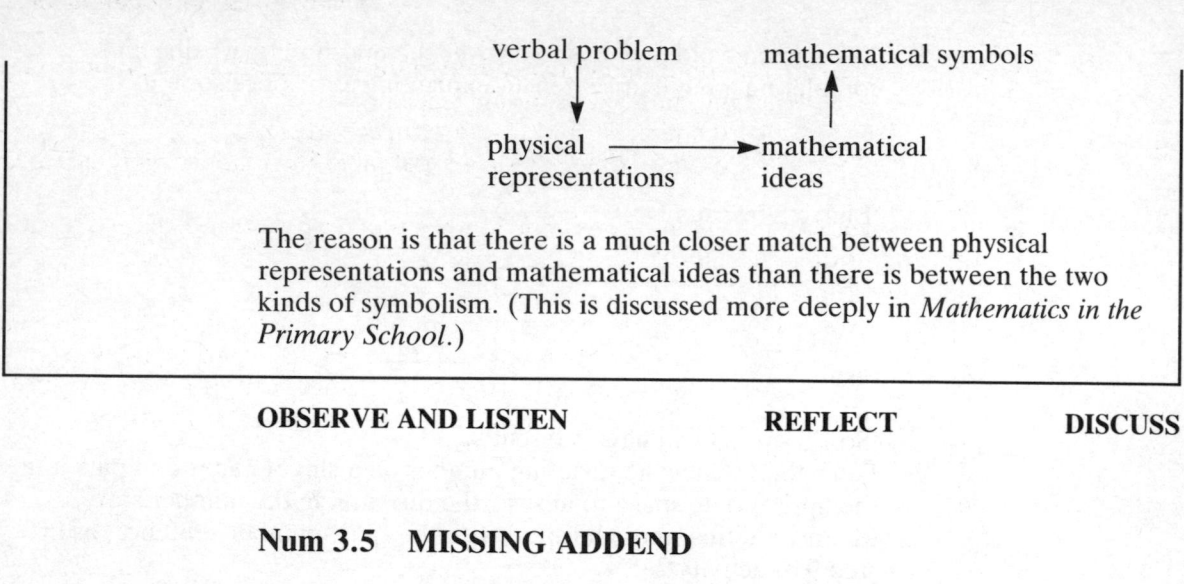

The reason is that there is a much closer match between physical representations and mathematical ideas than there is between the two kinds of symbolism. (This is discussed more deeply in *Mathematics in the Primary School*.)

OBSERVE AND LISTEN   **REFLECT**   **DISCUSS**

Num 3.5   MISSING ADDEND

Concept   Missing Addend.

Abilities   To find missing addends
  (i) in physical representations
  (ii) in number sentences
  (iii) in number stories.

Discussion of concept	A missing addend is the answer to a question such as 'Four and how many make seven?' Or

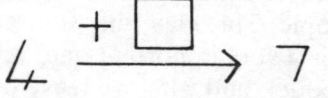

Or 'Peter had four biscuits. His mummy gave him some more, and then he had seven. How many did his mummy give him?'

Activity 1   **'How many more must you put?'**

A teacher-led activity for a small group. Its purpose is to introduce the concept of missing addend in a physical representation.

Materials
- SAR board as used in Num 3.1/1.
- Start cards 1-5 (later 0-5).
- Result cards 6-10 (ordinary number cards).
- Reversible instruction card. Side one reads
 'How many more did you put to get this result?'
Side two reads
 'How many more will you have to put to get this result?'
- Objects
- Pencils, slips of paper.

What they do   1. The SAR board is put out with Start and Result packs in position, as in previous activities. The reversible card is put below it, with side one showing for continuation (a), side two for continuation (b). A name is picked and put in the appropriate space.

2. A 'Start' card and a 'Result' card are turned over.

3. Objects are put into the set loop according to the number on the 'Start' card.

The activity may then be continued either practically or predictively, according to which side up the instruction card is.

(a) *Practically*

4. Additional objects are put until the required total is reached.

5. This action is then recorded on a slip of paper, using arrow notation. This is used to fill the Action space on the SAR card. If the newly put objects are different from the starting ones, this makes it easier to distinguish them.

6. The SAR board will finally look like this.

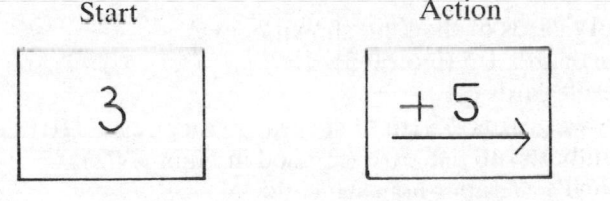

written by child

(b) *Predictively*

4. Using finger counting on, or any other technique he likes, the child answers the question on the instruction.

5. He records his prediction on the slip of paper and puts it into the Action space, e.g.,

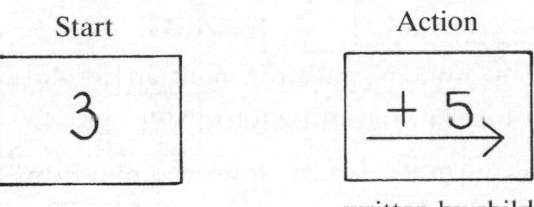

written by child

6. The prediction is then tested practically as in (a).

Activity 2 Secret adder

A game for a small group. It requires the same thinking as activity 1(b), but without any support from physical materials.

Materials None.

Rules of the game
1. One child thinks of a number to be added, which he does not tell the others.

2. The others in turn speak a number, and the 'secret adder' responds by adding his number and giving the results.

3. The first to deduce the number being added takes over as 'secret adder'.

115

E.g.
Player: 'Three'. Secret adder: 'Seven'.
Next player: 'One'. Secret adder: 'Five'.
Same player: 'You're adding four'. Secret adder: 'Correct'.

4. Using only numbers up to 5 (to give totals up to 10) this is quite an easy game – especially when one of the players thinks of saying 'Zero'. (They may then discuss whether this should, by agreement, be excluded.) When they can add beyond 10, the use of numbers below 5 can be excluded. This gives good practice in adding past 10.

Activity 3　Personalised number stories: what happened?

An activity for a small group. Its purpose is to apply what was learnt in activity 1(b) to the solution of number story problems.

Materials
- Story cards of the kind shown below.
- Start cards 1-5 (later 0-5)
- Result cards 6-10
- Answer cards 0-5 (to fit spaces in story), or OHP marker.
- Number sentence card (as used in Num 3.4/2).
- Pencil and paper for each child.

What they do　This activity is like activity 1, but a number sentence is used to record their predictions, as in the following example. The same number story is used here to make the variation stand out more clearly.

> Peter had 3 biscuits. While he was out of the room his mummy put some more on his plate. When he came back he found he had 7 .
> How many more did his mummy give him?
> Answer: his mummy gave him ☐ more.

1. The story card is made ready as in earlier activities, with numbers in the Start and Result spaces and a name in the name space.
2. Each child writes a number sentence with an oblong to show where it is incomplete, thus:

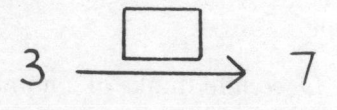

They may use the number sentence card as a guide to help them to do this.

3. Each then writes a number in the oblong to complete the number sentence.

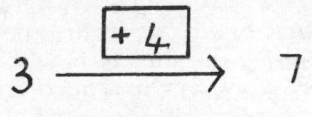

$$3 \xrightarrow{\boxed{+4}} 7$$

They use any method they like. Finger-counting is useful, but if they have any difficulty, the use of physical materials as in activity 1 should be encouraged.

4. They compare results. If these disagree, there is discussion and if necessary the use of physical materials.

5. Finally the agreed answer is put in the answer space on the story board, using either an answer-card or an OHP marker.

Discussion of activities	Finding a missing addend is harder than finding a result. In the latter case our thinking goes forward: from start, through action, to result. This topic asks children to back-track: from start and result, back to discover what action would produce that result. (Here, at least, they know that the action was one of putting more, corresponding to adding. In later forms of this problem, it might correspond to any mathematical operation). They are thus being asked to use their existing knowledge and abilities in a new way. This adaptability, which is a key feature of intelligence, is brought into use all the time in the present approach. The present topic exercises it to the full.

OBSERVE AND LISTEN   REFLECT   DISCUSS

Num 3.6   ADDING PAST 10

Concept   Adding when the sum is greater than 10, but not greater than 20.

Ability   To do everything in topics 1-5 (except missing addends), with results greater than 10 but not greater than 20.

Discussion of concept	This is the first step from quite small number operations, which can easily be handled in physical embodiments, towards operations with large numbers for which physical embodiments offer little or no help. For addition, base 10 material continues to be useful right into the thousands. But for multiplication, even of numbers no bigger than (say) 17×13, children have to be able to think in abstract symbols. As a beginning for this transition this topic uses physical materials and symbols together.

Activity 1   **Start, Action, Result over ten**

For a small group. This activity is similar to the earlier version of Start, Action, Result (Num 3.1/1). By now, however, children are familiar with recording, so it does not need to be treated as a separate stage.

Materials
- SAR board (see figures below).*
- Start cards 5-9.**
- Action card 5-9.**
- Base 10 material, tens and units.
- Paper and pencil for each child.

* Note that SAR boards vary between different activities.

** If all the numbers from 1-10 are used, only a minority of results will be over 10.

What they do
1. The Start and Action cards are shuffled and put in position as usual, and the top two cards turned over.

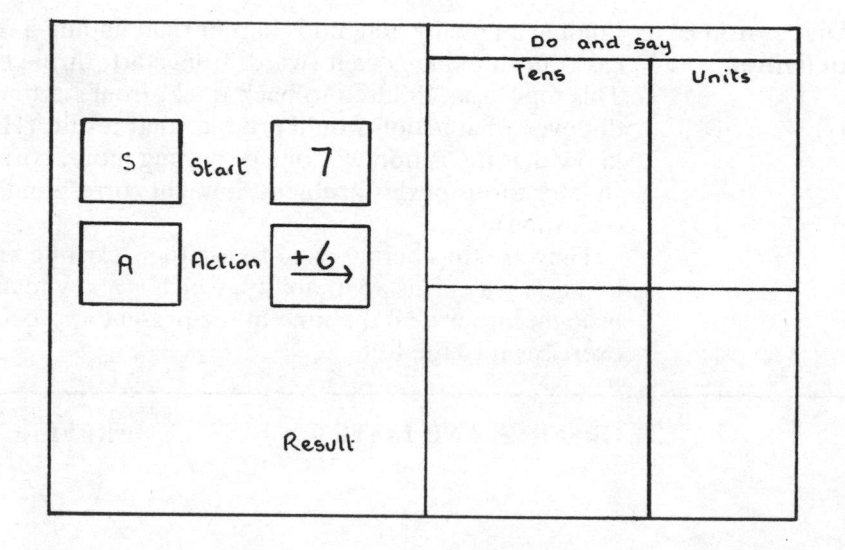

2. Unit cubes are put down as shown on these cards by one of the children, who describes what she is doing and what it corresponds to on the SAR board. E.g. 'The Action card means "Put 6 more".' Each child records this on her own paper, which she first rules into headed columns. The board, and records, will now appear as below.

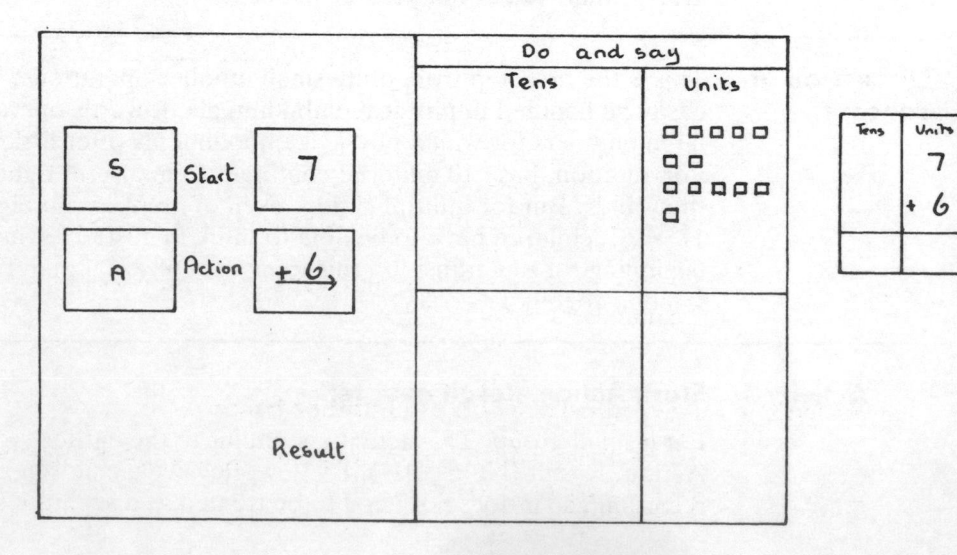

3. The next stage is shown below.

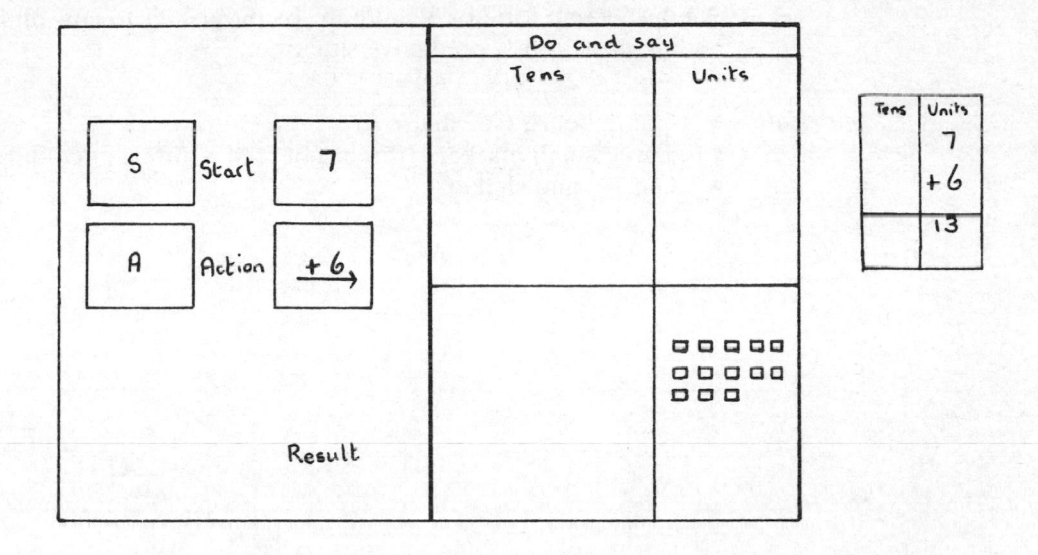

4. Finally, 10 of the units are exchanged for a 10-rod. This is transferred to the tens column. The children again record this individually.

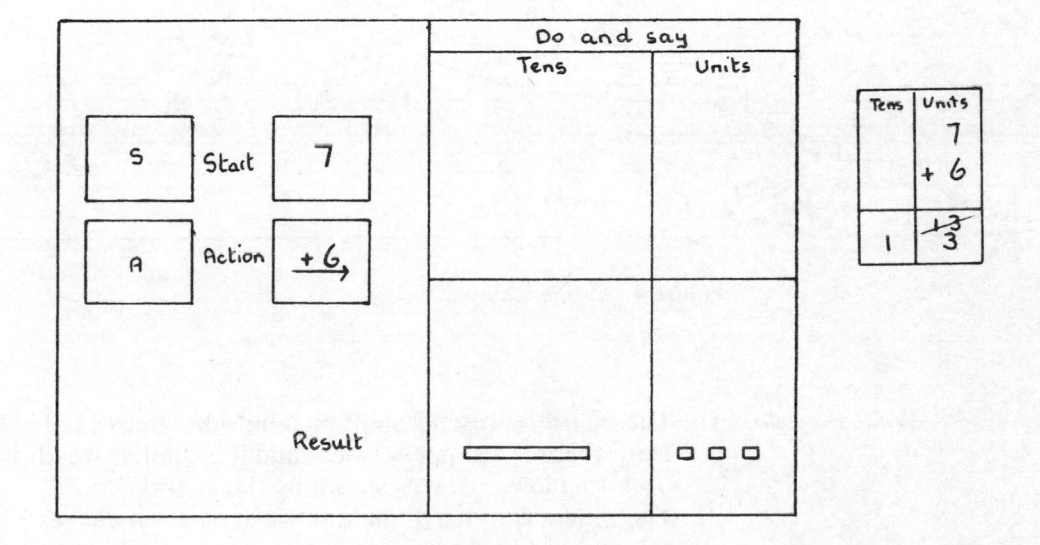

5. Children compare their final results. There should be no difference, but if there is, they will need to repeat the process and check each step together.

6. The board is cleared, and steps 1 to 5 are repeated with different numbers.

Activity 2 Adding past 10 on the number track

This activity, which will be found as NuSp 1.3/4, should be used here as a preliminary to activity 4.

Activity 3 Slippery Slope

A board game for 2 or 3 children. Its purpose is to consolidate the skill of adding past 10 in a predictive situation.

Materials
- Game board (see figure 4).
- Three small markers (three cubes) of a different colour for each player.
- Die 1-6 and shaker.

Figure 4 Slippery slope.

What they do
1. The board represents steps up a hillside. Steps 11, 12, 13 are missing. Here there is a slippery slope, and if a climber treads here she slides back to a lower step as shown by the arrows.
2. The object is to reach the top. Each player manages 3 climbers, represented by markers.
3. Players in turn throw the die, and move one of their climbers that number of steps up. They begin at START, which corresponds to zero.
4. A climber may not move upwards to a step which is already occupied. Overtaking is allowed.
5. Players may choose not to move. However, if a climber has been touched, it must be moved (but see also step 6).
6. If a climber is touched and the move would take her to an occupied step, she must return to the start.
7. If a climber slides back to an occupied step, any climber already on that step is knocked off and must return to the start.
8. The exact number must be thrown to finish.

Activity 4   Adfacts practice

An activity for children to play in pairs, as many as you have materials for. They can use this in odd times which might otherwise be wasted. Its purpose is to practise the recall of all their addition facts (often called 'number bonds').

Materials
- 10 sets of addition cards, with 10 cards in each set, from 1 + 1 to 10 + 10.
- One linear slide rule for each pair. (This is described fully in NuSp 1.6, page 225.)

What they do
1. In each pair, one child has in her hand a single pack of cards, shuffled and face down. The other has on the table the linear slide rule.
2. Child A looks at the top card in her hand and tries to recall this result. Child B then checks by using the linear slide rule.
3. If A's answer was correct, this card is put on the table. If incorrect, it is put at the bottom of the pile in his hand so that it will appear again later.
4. A continues until all the cards are on the table. This method gives extra practice with the cards she got wrong.
5. Steps 1 to 4 are repeated until A makes no mistake, and her hand is empty.
6. The children then change roles, and repeat steps 1 to 5.
7. Steps 1 to 5 are, then or at other times, repeated with a different pack until all the packs are known.
8. Next, the game may be played with two packs mixed.
9. The final stage is to mix all the packs together. Each child then takes from these a pack of mixed cards, and repeats steps 1 to 5 with this pack.
10. This activity should be continued over quite a long period, gradually introducing new packs. A good way to practise is little and often.

Activity 5   Adfacts at speed

A game for up to 6 children. Its purpose is further to consolidate children's recall of addition results. This game may be introduced for variety before children have completed activity 4, using the packs which they have learnt so far.

Materials
- Addition cards: all the packs which they have learnt, mixed together.
- A linear slide rule.
- Adfacts board (see figure 5).

Rules of play
1. All, or nearly all, the cards are dealt to the players. Each should have the same number, so when the remaining cards are not enough for a complete round, they are put aside and not used. The adfacts board is put on the table between them.
2. The players hold their cards face down. In turn they look at their top card (e.g. 7 + 4) and put it in the appropriate space on the adfacts board (in this case 11). It does not matter if there is a card in that space already – the new card is then put on top.

= 1	= 2	= 3	= 4	= 5
= 6	= 7	= 8	= 9	= 10
= 11	= 12	= 13	= 14	= 15
= 16	= 17	= 18	= 19	= 20

4 + 3

Adfacts cards to fit spaces

Figure 5   Adfacts board.

3. The others check. If it is wrong, they tell her the correct answer and she replaces the card at the bottom of the pack.
4. If she does not know, she asks and someone tells her. She then replaces the card at the bottom of the pack.
5. Any disagreements are settled by using the linear slide rule.
6. Play continues until all have put down all their cards. If there are no mistakes, all will finish in the same round. Those who do make mistakes, or do not know, will be left with cards in their hands to put down in subsequent rounds.
7. If one player finishes a clear round ahead of the others, she is the winner.

Variation   If a stopwatch is available, this game may also be played as a race. To make it a fair race, each player needs to be using the same pack. This suggests various forms, e.g.,
Form (a)   A single pack, of a table to be consolidated or revised.
Form (b)   Several packs mixed.
Form (c)   (For advanced players) All packs from twos to ten, making 90 cards in all.
The rules for all forms are the same:
1. One player acts as starter and timekeeper.
2. The others in turn see how quickly and accurately they can put down all their cards.
3. Those not otherwise involved check for accuracy, *after* all the cards have been put down.
4. For each incorrect result, 5 seconds are added to the time. (This figure may be varied according to the skill of the players.)

5. The winner is the player with the fastest time after correction for errors.

Activity 6   Predictive number sentences past 10

An activity for a small group. It develops the skills which will be used in activity 5 and gives practice in all combinations of numbers, with a majority crossing past ten.
It may also be played as a group game.

Materials
- Start cards 5-9.
- Action card 1-9.
- Some cubes with which they can check their calculations if needed.
- Pencil and paper for each child.

What they do
1. The two packs are shuffled and put face down on the table.
2. The top 'start' and 'action' cards are turned and put side by side. Each child then writes a number sentence and completes it, as in the example below.

Start card   Action card   Number sentence

Start with   Increase it $8 \xrightarrow{+5} 13$
a set of 8.   by 5.

3. Finally, they compare results. If there is disagreement they should use physical material to verify.

Activity 7   Explorers

Another board game, for two or three players. Its purpose is to consolidate addition skills, especially those past ten and in the teens.

Materials
- Game board (see figure 6).
- Die 1-6 and shaker.
- Markers: up to 3 per player.

Rules of the game
1. Each player manages one, two, or three explorers, according to number and experience of players.
2. The explorers have to find their way from the start, through the forest and desert, to the Lost City.
3. They go forward according to the number thrown on the die by the players in turn.
4. In the forest, positions 1, 2, 3, 4, 6, 7 may be occupied by only one explorer. The rest camp (5) has room for all who come.
5. The oases likewise have room for as many as arrive. The missing numbers are in the trackless desert, where there is no landmark to

Figure 6 Explorers

show where you are. Explorers may only move to the numbers shown on the board. Thus, an explorer at 6 could only move to 7, 11, or 12 (by throwing 1, 5, or 6). A player at 13 could move to 16, 17, 18 (throw of 3, 4, or 5). The exact number must be thrown to reach the Lost City (20).

6. A player may choose not to move. However, a piece must be moved if touched. The penalty for a false move (to an occupied location in the forest, or to a number in the trackless desert) is to return to START if before 5, and otherwise to be rescued and taken back to the forest rest camp to recuperate. (This rule may be relaxed while learning the game.)

7. The winner is the first player to get all his explorers to the Lost City. Play may however continue until all have arrived.

Discussion of activities	Activities 1-5 in this topic provide a similar progression to that in earlier topics, but more rapidly since children are now extrapolating concepts which should already be well established.

Activity 1 makes a beginning with what will become the conventional way of recording, with a close parallel shown visually between the physical materials and the symbols. This is mode 1 concept building. Activity 2 also provides strong physical support, in this case from the number track. Adding by use of the number track is probably easier than the method used in activity 1. However, it does not easily extrapolate, whereas the base 10 material provides very well for extrapolation to hundreds and thousands. In this activity, the 'teens' notation is used since children will certainly have encountered it, albeit without fully understanding its rationale.

Activity 3, 'Slippery Slope', also involves adding with the help of a number track. Visual support is still provided, but a predictive element has been introduced, with the purpose of planning which is the best piece to move. Steps 5, 6, 7 are bad ones to linger on, whereas 10 maximises the number of throws which will take one past the slippery slope. This game can be played at different levels of sophistication.

Activity 4 gives practice in the newly developed skills, and relates these to the notation which children already know. In activities 3 and 5 we see in microcosm a key activity of intelligence: comparing alternative plans before deciding which to put into action.

The numbers in Activity 5 require plenty of calculations past ten and in the teens. A false move in the desert leads to additional calculations. There is now less visual support. Finger counting using 'Ten in my head' (Num 1.7/1) should be freely used as long as it is needed. |

OBSERVE AND LISTEN   REFLECT   DISCUSS

Num 3.7   COMMUTATIVITY

Concepts   (i)   Commutativity.
(ii)   Non-commutativity.

Ability   To recognise whether a given action or operation is commutative or non-commutative.

Discussion of concepts	Although these two additions are different, the result is the same.

Start	*Operation*	*Result*
3	$\xrightarrow{+5}$	8
5	$\xrightarrow{+3}$	8	

125

Children are also familiar with the vertical notation.

$$\begin{array}{r} 3 \\ +\ 5 \\ \hline 8 \end{array} \qquad \begin{array}{r} 5 \\ +\ 3 \\ \hline 8 \end{array}$$

The following means the same as the above.

$$3 + 5 = 8 \qquad\qquad 5 + 3 = 8$$

Whichever way we write it, if the numbers to be added are interchanged the result is the same. This is expressed by saying: *addition is commutative*. To us this may seem obvious. But commutativity does not always hold: it is not true for subtraction. When it does hold it can be very useful. If we know that addition is commutative for all pairs of numbers, we have only half as many addition facts to remember.

This distinction between commutative and non-commutative operations also applied to many physical actions. Here are some examples.

Commutative

Put sock on left foot, put sock on right foot.

Open textbook, open exercise book.

Put apple into bowl, put orange into bowl.

Non-commutative

Put on shirt, put on tie.

Undress, get into bath.

Pick up telephone, dial the number.

Activity 1   Introducing commutativity

A teacher-led discussion for 2, 4, or 6 children working in pairs. A suggested sequence is given below, which you can adapt to follow up leads given by the children themselves.

Materials   For each pair:
- Multilink or Unifix cubes, ten each of two colours.
- A card number track 1-20.
- Paper and pencil.

Suggested sequence for the discussion

1. Children work in pairs alongside, so that they see everything the same way up.
2. Write a pair of number sentences such as

$$5 \quad \xrightarrow{\ +\ 2\ }$$

$$2 \quad \xrightarrow{\ +\ 5\ }$$

3. Tell the children to show what these mean with cubes on the number track. They should use one of their colours for the 'start' number, the

other for the 'action' number. One child in each pair does the first sentence, the other does the second.

4.   Ask 'What do you notice?' There are two points which need to be put into words, either now or at subsequent repetitions of steps 3 and 4.
     (i)   The numbers are the same in both sentences, but interchanged.
     (ii)   The result is the same in both cases.
'It doesn't make any difference if you change the numbers about' is a reasonable beginning, but doesn't bring out that the *same* result is being obtained by a *different* path. So it is better to say 'It doesn't make any difference *to the result* if the two numbers are interchanged.'

5.   Tell each pair of children to write another pair of number sentences like the first, but using different numbers.

6.   Repeat steps 3, 4.

7.   Repeat steps 5 and 6 until they decide that this will always be so, whatever the numbers.

8.   This can be confirmed quite nicely by using two paper sleeves over the rods

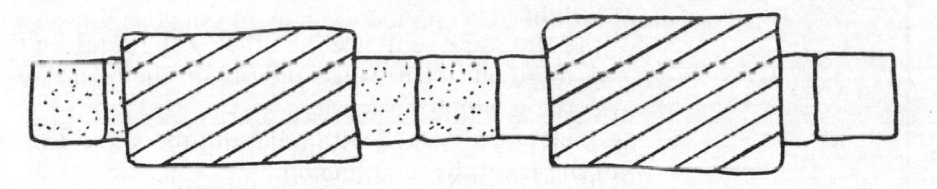

Say, 'Now we can't see what the numbers are'.
Turn it around. Ask 'What can we say about this?'

9.   Say that there is a shorter way of saying that (whatever was their formulation). We say 'Adding is *commutative*'.

Activity 2   Introducing non-commutativity

A continuation of the discussion in activity 1. Its purpose is to prevent children from thinking that all operations are commutative.

Materials   As for activity 1, as and if needed.

Suggested sequence for the discussion

1.   Explain that this idea also applies to everyday action. You can use the examples given in the discussion at the beginning of this topic, or invent your own.

2.   Ask the children for further examples, and discuss these.

3.   Ask whether they think that all pairs of actions are commutative. Use the given examples of non-commutative actions, or some of your own, until they can recognise whether an example is commutative or non-commutative.

4.   Ask the children for further examples, and discuss these.

5.   Ask whether they think that subtraction is commutative or non-commutative. Suggest that they try some particular cases, e.g.

$$5 \xrightarrow{\;-2\;}$$

$$2 \xrightarrow{\;-5\;}$$

127

(*Note*   If the two numbers are the same, then of course we can interchange them and the result is the same. If this arises, explain that we only say that an operation is commutative if it is always true whatever the numbers are.)

Activity 3 Using commutativity for counting on

A continuation of the discussion in activity 2. Its purpose is to show children one of the uses of commutativity.

Materials
- Pencil and paper for each child and for the teacher.
- Number track 1-10 for each pair of children.

Suggested sequence for the discussion
1. Write an incomplete sentence in which the first number is much smaller than the other, such as 2 + 7 =
2. Ask them all to copy this and obtain the result by counting on from 2. In each pair one should use the number track, the other finger counting.
3. Write the same sentence the other way round, in this case 7 + 2 =
4. Ask them all to copy this, and obtain the result by counting on from 7.
5. Ask them which was easier.
6. Repeat steps 1 and 2 with other numbers, but this time just ask them to get the result by counting on.
7. Did they make it easier for themselves by counting on from the larger number? If so, the point has been taken. If not, steps 3, 4, 5 may be repeated.
8. Continue until all have realised the advantage of starting with the larger number when counting on.
9. Consolidate by returning to the points made in activities 1 and 2: that this only works because addition is commutative. Check that they remember what this means, expanded into a sentence.

Activity 4 Commutativity means less to remember

A continuation of the discussion in activity 3. Its purpose is to show children another of the applications of commutativity.

Materials
- Pencil and paper for each child, and for the teacher.

Suggested sequence for the discussion
1. Write an incomplete number sentence, such as 9 + 5 = . Ask them all to copy this and complete it.
2. Write the same sentence the other way round, in this case 5 + 9 = . Ask them to copy and complete this.
3. Ask how many worked this out again. Some may have realised that they didn't need to.
4. Repeat steps 2 and 3 until all have realised that if they know one result, they know the other.
5. Consolidate by making the point that this means that they only have about half as many addition facts to remember. (Slightly more than half, since there is no saving when the two numbers to be added are equal.)

Discussion of activities

Though commutativity is quite an abstract idea for children at this stage, I have included it for several reasons. First, it is useful, as activities 3 and 4 make clear. Second, children seem to grasp it fairly easily if given concrete examples. Third, unless it is made explicit and discussed, we cannot also make explicit that subtraction is not commutative. While the idea remains at an intuitive level, children are liable to generalise it incorrectly.

Discussion of related concepts

There are related topics which I did not include in the discussion at the beginning of this topic, since I did not wish to make it too heavy. One of these is the distinction between unary and binary addition. Although these are different mathematically, I think that from the children's point of view it is better to treat them as the same. However, it may be as well for teachers to be aware of the distinction in case of need; here is a short explanation.

At a practical level, there is not a lot of difference between these two.

A. Start with a set of 3 apples in a bowl.

Put 5 more.

Result a set of 8 apples in a bowl.

B. Start with a set of 3 apples in a bowl,

Put these all

Result, a set of 8 apples in the bowl.

into

another bowl.

and a set of 5 apples in a different bowl.

Mathematically, A corresponds to unary addition, in which

we start with a number,	do an operation on it	and the result is another number.
3	$+5$	8

B corresponds to binary addition, in which

We start with a pair of numbers,	do an operation on this pair	and the result is another number.

$$3, 5 \quad \xrightarrow{\;+\;} \quad 8$$

Number sentences for the first are written like this, as we already know.

$$3 \xrightarrow{\;+5\;} 8$$

When 'modern mathematics' came into vogue, a number of school texts introduced this notation

$$(3,5) \xrightarrow{\;+\;} 8$$

for the second. This is entirely correct mathematically, and a good notation at more advanced levels. But I do *not* recommend its use for young children, to whom parentheses ( ) mean multiplication. I suggest that instead, we simply

drop the arrow from

$$3 \xrightarrow{\;+5\;} 8$$

and write

$$3 + 5 = 8$$

as a convenient and widely accepted notation for both. This saves having to decide whether, in a particular case, we mean unary or binary addition;

and it lends itself readily to adding in columns, when we come to hundreds, thousands etc.

$$\begin{array}{r} 3 \\ +5 \\ \hline 8 \end{array} \qquad \begin{array}{r} 362 \\ +574 \\ \hline \end{array}$$

OBSERVE AND LISTEN   **REFLECT**   **DISCUSS**

[Num 4]   SUBTRACTION

Taking away, Comparison, Complement, Giving change.

Num 4.1   ACTIONS ON SETS: TAKING AWAY

Concepts   (i)   Sets as operands.
(ii) Taking away as actions.
(iii) Starting and resulting numbers.

Ability   To relate the physical action of taking away to the starting and finishing numbers of a set.

Discussion of concepts	This topic closely parallels Num 3.1, and it will be useful to re-read the discussion of concepts given there.

Activity 1   **Start, Action, Result (do and say)**

An activity for 2, 3, or 4 children. (Parallels Num 3.1/1.) Its purpose is to introduce the take-away kind of subtraction in a physical form.

Materials
● SAR board (as used in Num 3.1/1).
● Reversible card.
● Start cards 5-10; e.g. 'Start with a set of 8.'*
● Action cards 1-5 (later, 0-5); e.g. 'Take 2 away'.*
● Result cards 0-10. Just the numerals, 0-10.*
● Objects to put in the set loop: e.g. counters, shells, buttons.
* Similar to those used in Num 3.1/1, but with different writing.

What they do
1.   The cards are shuffled and put face down in the upper parts of their spaces.
2.   The reversible card is put in its place with side 1 showing.
3.   One child then turns over the top start card, and puts a set of the required number into the set loop.
4.   Another child then turns over the top action card, and takes away the indicated number of objects.
5.   Then she finds the appropriate result card to show the number of the resulting set.
6.   Finally she must describe to the other children what she did, and the result. E.g. 'I started with a set of seven shells. I took away three. The result is a set of four shells.'
7.   Simplified wording is acceptable to start with, but the aim should be something near the above.

Activity 2 Taking away on the number track (do and say)

This will be found under NuSp 1.4/1, and should be used here. Some children can be doing this while the others do activity 1. In this case the order does not matter, although usually it does.

Discussion of activities

These two activities provide the physical experiences from which children will begin to expand the important concept of mathematical operation to include subtraction. Again, the spoken description of what they have done is an important part of the activities, since it links these experiences to the appropriate language. This not only serves as preparation for the more condensed written symbols which come in Topic 3, but makes a link with the word problems which children will encounter later on.

   These activities closely parallel those at the beginning of the addition network, Num 3, and use many of the same materials. There, children were learning new activities, but the concept (addition) is an easier one than here. Now that they are learning the more difficult concept of subtraction, we start with a familiar situation.

OBSERVE AND LISTEN   **REFLECT**   **DISCUSS**

Num 4.2   SUBTRACTION AS A MATHEMATICAL OPERATION

Concept   Subtraction as a mental operation.

Ability   To predict the result of 'taking away' actions on sets, by mentally subtracting (using physical aids initially).

Discussion of concept

As in the case of addition, we need to make a distinction between the actions we do in the physical world, and their corresponding mental operations. (It will be useful here to re-read the discussion in Num 3.2.)

   Subtraction is, however, a more difficult concept than addition. In its fully developed form (Topic 8) it is a mathematical model for not one but four physical counterparts: taking away, comparing two sets numerically, giving change, and complement. (See the dependency network for Num 4.) This has two consequences for teaching. One is that we should use the word 'subtract', not 'take away', for the mathematical operation. 'Take away' is all right when we are in fact taking away, but to talk about 'taking away' when what we are doing is comparing is bound to cause confusion. The other is that subtraction should be introduced rather later than is often done, so that they arrive at this topic when they already have good support from their work on the number line (NuSp 1.7 and the topics leading up to this). In this topic, subtraction is a unary operation, done on a single number, e.g.,

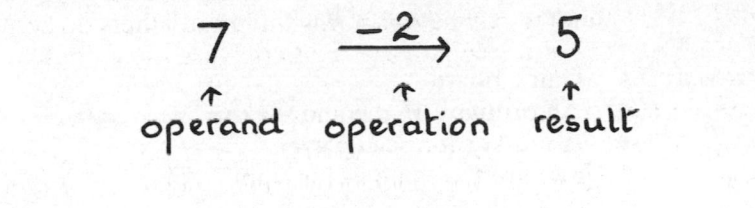

Activity 1   Predicting the result

An activity for 2 children, or 2 teams. Its purpose is to use the new concept to predict physical outcomes.

Materials
- SAR board.
- Reversible card.*
- Start cards 5-10.*
- Action cards 1-5 (later 0-5).*
- Result cards 1-10.
- Objects to put in the set loop; e.g. counters, shells, buttons.*

* These are the same as for Num 4.1/1.

What they do

Version (a)
1. The cards are shuffled and put face down in the upper part of their spaces. The reversible card now shows side two.
2. Player A (or a player from team A) turns over the top start card and puts a set of the required number into the loop.
3. Player B (or a player from team B) turns over the top action card, after which he must predict the result and put the correct result card in the result space.
4. Player A then physically checks this prediction by taking away the indicated number of objects and counting the resulting set.

Version (b)
1. The cards are shuffled and put face down in the upper part of their spaces.
2. In this version, the start card is turned as in (a), but this time the objects are put into a bag or under a handkerchief.
3. Then the action card is turned, and the indicated number of objects is taken out.
4. Finally the prediction is tested physically by emptying the bag or lifting the handkerchief.

Activity 2   What will be left?

A number track activity for 2 children, or 2 teams. It will be found at NuSp 1.4/2.

Activity 3   Returning over the stepping stones

A game for 2, 3, or 4 children. Its purpose is to introduce the idea of subtraction as counting back.

Materials
- Game board.*
- An ordinary 16 die and shaker.*
- A marker for each player.*

* These are the same as for Num 3.2/3.

Rules of play
1. Each player is represented by a marker. He starts on the island, and tries to get back to the bank.
2. Players in turn throw the die, and may then move back that number of stepping stones.
3. A player may not move to a stone which is occupied.
4. If a player touches his marker, he must move it. If it turns out that this would take him to an occupied stone, he falls in the water, misses his next turn, and returns to the island.
5. A player may decide not to move.
6. The exact number must be thrown to reach the bank.
7. The winner is the first player to return to the bank.

Activity 4   Crossing back

A number track activity for 2, 3, or 4 children. It will be found at NuSp 1.4/3.

Discussion of activities

As in the previous topic, these activities closely parallel those in the corresponding topic of Num 3; and for the same reason.

This is the next stage of developing subtraction as a mathematical operation: that is, as a mental activity which is done independently of physical action, and may be used to predict the results of action. A good way to learn this is by counting back with the help of finger counting. (Please see Num 1.4/1 and Num 1.6/2 for the recommended method of finger counting.) With practice, this is replaced by the use of known number facts.

Activity 3, 'Returning over the stepping stones', is intended to emphasise the need to 'Look before you leap', or calculate before you move. In the adult world, the result of miscalculation may be more serious.

The discussion in Num 3.2 may usefully be re-read at this stage.

OBSERVE AND LISTEN   **REFLECT**   **DISCUSS**

Num 4.3   NOTATION FOR SUBTRACTION: NUMBER SENTENCES

Concept   The use of written number sentences of these two forms

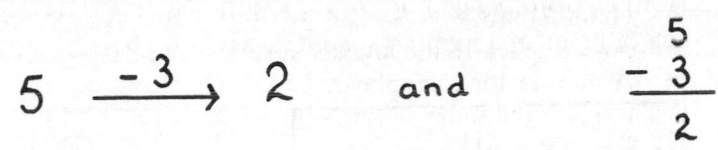

for representing the operation of subtraction, and its result.

Abilities   (i)   To write number sentences describing actions of 'taking away' with physical materials.

(ii)   To use number sentences for making predictions about the results of physical actions, and to test these predictions.

Discussion of concept

As in addition, the arrow notation corresponds well to its meaning:

start   operation   result

$$5 \qquad \xrightarrow{\;-2\;} \qquad 3$$

This should be read verbally as:

'five,   subtract two,   result three'.

The term 'take away' should not be used here, for two reasons. (1) It refers to the physical action, not the mental operation: what we do with our hands, not what we do in our head. (ii) It ties the subtraction concept to this particular physical embodiment, whereas we need to expand it to include comparison, giving change, and complement as well. (See 'Discussion of concept' in Num 4.2.)

Activity 1   Number sentences for subtraction

An activity for 2, 3, or 4 children. Its purpose is to introduce a written notation for subtraction, initially as a record of something which has been done.

Materials
- SAR board.*
- Reversible card.**
- Start cards 5-10 which say (e.g.) 'Start with a set of 5.'***
- Action cards 1-5 (later 0-5) which say (e.g.) 'Make it 1 less', 'Decrease it by 2', 'Take away 3'.***
- Result cards 0-10.*
- Objects to put in the set loop.*

* These are the same as for Num 4.1/1 and Num 4.2/1.
** On side one is written 'Write a number sentence to show what you did.
On side two is written 'First write a number sentence showing what you
predict the result will be. Then test your prediction.'
*** The start and action cards are different. They now include the
components of a number sentence, as shown here.

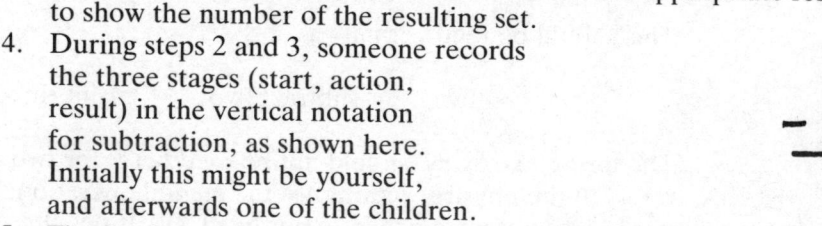

What they do   *(apportioned according to how many children there are)*
1. The cards are shuffled and put face down in the upper parts of their
    spaces.
2. One child then turns over the top start card, and puts a set of the
    required number into the set loop.
3. Another child then turns over the top action card, and takes away the
    indicated number of objects. Then she finds the appropriate result card
    to show the number of the resulting set.
4. During steps 2 and 3, someone records
    the three stages (start, action,
    result) in the vertical notation
    for subtraction, as shown here.
    Initially this might be yourself,
    and afterwards one of the children.

$$\begin{array}{r} 5 \\ -\ 2 \\ \hline 3 \end{array}$$

5. Finally the number sentence which has been constructed is also written,
    and read aloud.

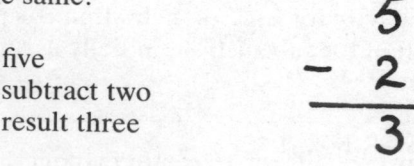

five   subtract two   result three

The vertical number sentence is also read aloud, and you explain that
both mean the same.

five
subtract two
result three

$$\begin{array}{r} 5 \\ -\ 2 \\ \hline 3 \end{array}$$

6. The cards used are replaced at the bottom of the piles, and steps 2 to 5
    are repeated.

Activity 2   Predicting from number sentences

An activity for 2 children, or 2 teams. Its purpose is to teach them to use written number sentences predictively.

Materials   The same as for activity 1, except that the result cards are replaced by pencil and paper for each child.

What they do   1.   The cards are shuffled and put face down in the upper part of their spaces.
2.   Player A (or a player from team A) turns over the top start card and the top action card.
3.   Player A (or another from team A) then copies out the incomplete number sentence shown on the cards, e.g.

$$7 \quad \xrightarrow{-4}$$

and completes it, in this case

$$7 \quad \xrightarrow{-4} \quad 3$$

4.   Player B (or a player from team B) meanwhile does the same calculation in the vertical notation; e.g.

first   and then

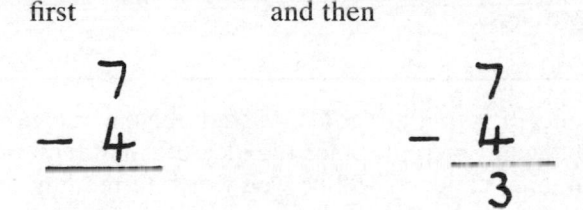

$$\begin{array}{r} 7 \\ -\ 4 \\ \hline \end{array} \qquad \begin{array}{r} 7 \\ -\ 4 \\ \hline 3 \end{array}$$

5.   These predictions are then compared. If they are different, no alteration is made at this stage.
6.   Finally the prediction is tested by putting the required number of objects in the set loop, taking away the number of objects shown by the action card, and counting the result. At this stage if one of the written predictions was wrong, it is corrected.

Discussion of activities   In activity 1, the children are making the transition from 'Do and say' to 'Do and record.' At this stage purely mental calculations are as easy as (or easier than) those using pencil and paper. When the numbers get more difficult, written notation is an important help in keeping track of what we are doing. Initially, however, the recording itself is an additional task rather than a help, so it needs to be learnt in a situation where the rest of what they have to do is familiar.

In activity 2, recording is replaced by calculation. That is, the result of the pencil and paper work is used to predict a physical result. This is a major use of mathematics in the adult world, and at any age it is satisfying to find one's prediction to be correct.

In both activities, horizontal and vertical notation are used alongside each other. Both have their advantages, and this helps children to learn another very general concept, that the same meaning can be expressed in more ways than one. Also, to acquire an important general ability – not to be put off if they see the same idea written in different ways.

OBSERVE AND LISTEN   **REFLECT**   **DISCUSS**

Num 4.4   NUMBER STORIES: ABSTRACTING NUMBER SENTENCES

Concept   Numbers and numerical operations as models for actual happenings, or for verbal descriptions of these.

Abilities   (i)   To produce numerical models in physical materials corresponding to given number stories, to manipulate these appropriately, and to interpret the result in the context of the number story: first verbally, then recording in the form of a number sentence.
(ii)   To use number sentences predictively, to solve verbally given problems.

Discussion of concept   The concept is that already discussed in Num 3.4, now being expanded to include subtraction. Since the idea of a mathematical model is of central importance, it will be well worth re-reading the discussion at the beginning of Num 3.4.

Activity 1   **Personalised number stories**

An activity for 2 to 6 children. Its purpose is to connect simple verbal problems with physical events, linked with the idea that we can use objects to represent other objects.

Materials   • Number stories of the kind in the example following. For some stories you will need two versions, one with pronouns for girls, the other with pronouns for boys. These can be on different sides of the same card.
• The name of each child on a card or slip of paper.
• Two separate sets of number cards on different coloured cards:
    start cards 5-10,
    action cards 1-5 (later 0-5).
• Slips of paper on which to write the results (to fit the spaces on the story board).

- Objects such as bottle tops, conkers, shells, counters.
- Paper and pencils.

What they do   (*apportioned according to how many children there are*)

1. A number story is chosen. The name, start, and action cards are shuffled and put face down.
2. The top name card is turned over and put in the number story.
3. Another child then turns over the top start card, and puts it in the appropriate space.
4. Another child then turns over the top action card, and puts it in the appropriate space.
5. The number story now looks like this.

```
┌─────────────────────────────────────────────────────┐
│                                                       │
│   [Peter]  has  [7]  cherries on his                 │
│                                                       │
│   plate.   He eats  [3]  of them.                    │
│                                                       │
│   Now he has  [ ]  cherries left on                  │
│                                                       │
│   his plate.                                          │
│                                                       │
└─────────────────────────────────────────────────────┘
```

   As with Num 3.4, it may be helpful if you read this over for them.

6. The named child then takes over, describing aloud what he is doing while the others check. (E.g.) 'We haven't any cherries, so we'll use these acorn cups instead.' (Puts down 7 acorn cups.) 'These are the 7 I start with.' (Takes away 3 acorn cups.) 'Now I've eaten 3. There are 4 left.'
7. Finally another child writes the result on a slip of paper and puts it in place to complete the number story.

Note   We use acorn cups rather than acorns because they don't roll.

Activity 2   Abstracting number sentences

An extension to activity 1 which may be included fairly soon. Its purpose is to teach children to abstract a number sentence from a verbal description.

Materials
- As for activity 1, and also:
- Arrow card as illustrated over.

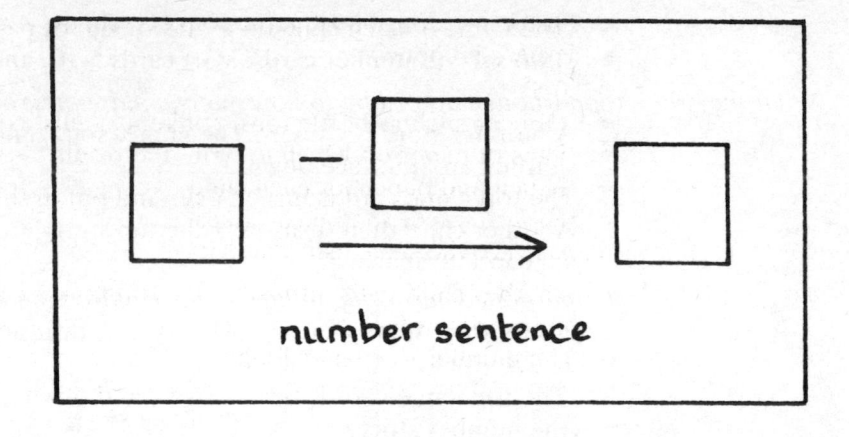

number sentence

What they do   1-7 as for activity 1.

8.   A child then says 'Now we make a number sentence recording what happened.' He puts the number sentence card below the story card then moves the three number cards from the story card to the number sentence card as shown in figure 53.

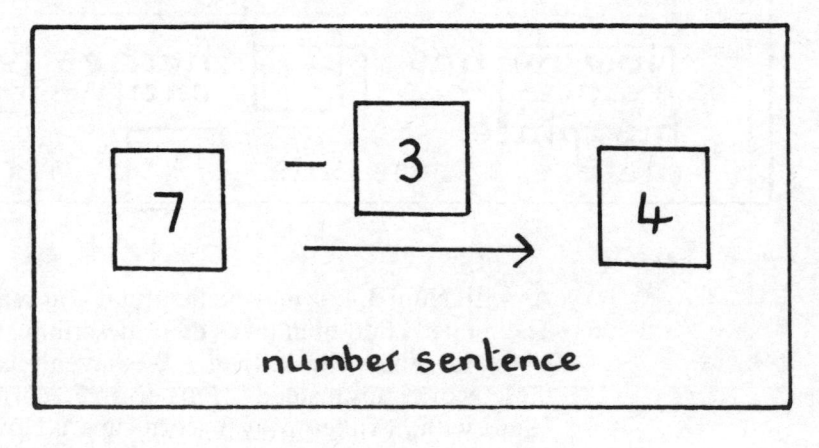

number sentence

He reads aloud 'Seven, subtract three, result four'.

9.   Finally every child writes this in both horizontal and vertical notations.

$$7 \xrightarrow{-3} 4 \qquad \qquad \begin{array}{r} 7 \\ -\ 3 \\ \hline 4 \end{array}$$

Note   The word 'subtract' is used in step 8 because we are here referring to the mathematical operation, not the physical action.

Activity 3   Personalised number stories – predictive

An activity for 2 to 6 children. It combines activities 1 and 2, in predictive form.

Materials   • Number stories of the new kind in the example over the page. These now require a prediction.

- The name of each child on a card or slip of paper.*
- Two sets of number cards: start cards 5-10, and action cards 1-5 (later 0-5).*
- Objects such as bottle tops, conkers, shells, counters. . .*
- Slips of paper on which to write the result.
- Pencil and paper for each child.
- Slips of paper to fit answer space.*

* These are the same as for activity 1.

What they do   (*apportioned according to how many children there are*)

1. A number story is chosen. The name, start, and action cards are shuffled and put face down.
2. The top name card is turned over, and put in the appropriate space in the number story.
3. Another child then turns over the top start card, and puts it in the appropriate place.
4. Another child then turns over the top action card, and puts it in the appropriate space.
5. The number story now looks like this.

Frances has 7 cherries on her plate. She eats 3 of them. How many cherries will be left on her plate? Answer: ___ cherries.

6. The named child now has to answer the question by writing and completing a number sentence, explaining as she does so. E.g.

Says	*Writes*
'I have 7 cherries.'	7
'I eat 3.'	$7 \xrightarrow{-3}$
'7, subtract three, result. . .'	$7 \xrightarrow{-3} 4$

'So I'll have 4 cherries left on my plate.'

7. The named child then writes the resulting number on a slip of paper and puts it in the appropriate space to answer the question in the number story.
8. Meanwhile the other children write the same number sentence in vertical notation, as in step 9 of activity 2.

9. Finally one of the other children tests the prediction by using the physical materials, describing what she is doing while the others check. E.g. (with appropriate actions). 'I'm using these bottle tops in place of cherries. These are the 7 she started with. Now she eats 3. These are the ones left: 4. So, Frances gave the correct answer.'

Discussion of activities

The activities in this topic parallel those in Num 3.4. The differences are (i) that subtraction replaces addition; that the third and fourth activities in Num 3.4 are here condensed into a single activity, Num 4.4/3. It will therefore be useful at this stage to re-read the discussion of activities at the end of Num 3.4.

Activity 1 is for building the concept of subtraction by mode 1, physical experience. It also uses again the idea that something can be used to represent something else – the concept of modelling.

Activity 2 also uses mode 1, in this case for building the concept of abstracting – in this case physically 'pulling out' the number sentence from the number story.

Activity 3 combines what has been learnt in activities 1 and 2, and also the following further steps:

(i) From schema building to schema testing. A number sentence is used to make a prediction, which is then tested.

(ii) The mathematical operation, in this case subtraction, is now done *before* the action, and so becomes independent of action.

(iii) This involves a change from recording something which has just been done physically to putting *thoughts* on paper. These thoughts are the operation of subtraction.

Once again, there is more here than is immediately apparent. And when we do look below the surface and analyse what is involved, once again we realise how much it is that we are expecting children to learn; and hence, the importance of providing them with the right learning situations and materials.

OBSERVE AND LISTEN   **REFLECT**   **DISCUSS**

Num 4.5   NUMERICAL COMPARISON OF TWO SETS

Concepts (i) Numerical difference between two sets, combined with the relationship 'is greater than' or 'is smaller than': e.g. 'This set is 3 greater than that set'.

(ii) Difference between two numbers, as in (i).

Abilities (i) To be able to say which of two sets, or two numbers, is the larger; and by how many.

(ii) To express this comparison in the alternative way, i.e. which is the smaller, and by how many.

(iii) To be aware of the equivalence of these two statements.
(iv) To use the general notation for subtraction.

Discussion of concepts

In this topic and the two which follow, we introduce contributors to the overall concept of subtraction which are quite different from that derived from 'taking away'. These do not involve any kind of taking away, but are varieties of comparison, of which the present one is the simplest.

Activity 1 **Capture**

This will be found at NuSp 1.4/4, and should be used here.

Activity 2 **Laying the table**

An activity for six children. Its purpose is to introduce numerical comparison of two sets in a practical everyday situation.

Materials
- Plastic knives, forks, spoons, plates, cups, saucers. There should be at least 8 of each, and not all the same number.
- 6 cards, on which are written '4 knives', '2 plates', etc. Every number from 1 to 6 should be used.

What they do
1. The cards are shuffled and put face down.
2. The first child turns over the top card, e.g. '4 knives', and takes 4 knives which she puts in front of her.
3. The other children in turn do likewise, turning over the top card and taking the given number of utensils. This concludes the first round.
4. To begin the second round, the first child says (e.g.) 'We are 6 children and there are only 4 knives, so we need 2 more'. So he takes 2 more knives.
5. The other children in turn do likewise.
6. Finally they lay the table. If their subtractions have been correct, each child should have one utensil of each kind, six in all.

Note The description here is for six children. Fewer may play, in which case each takes a card, but some cards will not be used.

Activity 3 **Diver and wincher**

A game for two children. Its purpose is to use numerical comparison at a mental level, to achieve goals in a physical situation.

Materials
- A model of a salvage boat as shown in figure 7 complete with diver. The diver and rope* are made so that she can be pulled up or lowered down. The depth scale at the side is in fathoms, and can be hidden by a flap. A harder version may also be provided which covers all the water, including the diver. This corresponds more closely to the actual situation.
- A 1-9 die and shaker.

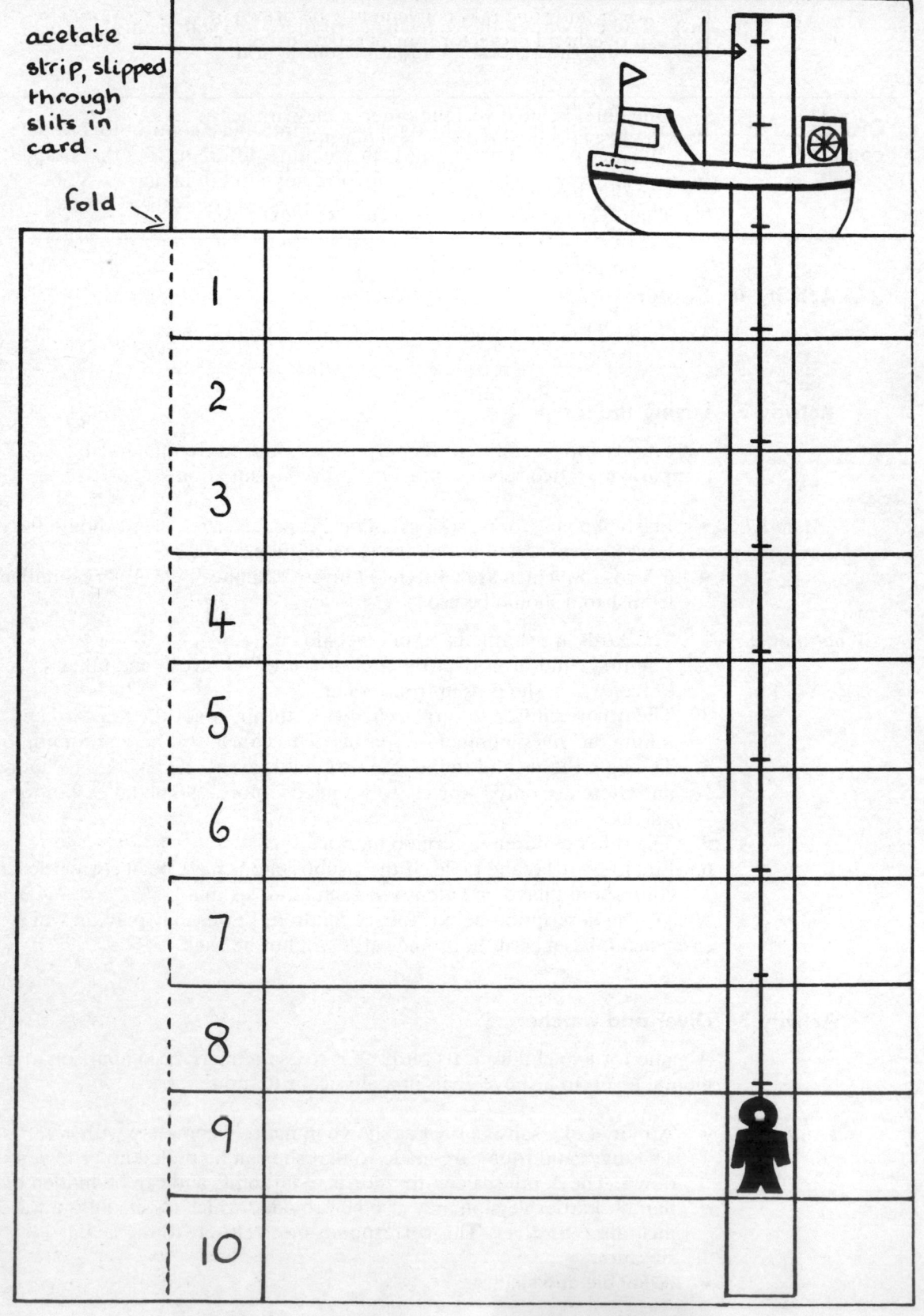

acetate
strip, slipped
through
slits in
card.

fold

1

2

3

4

5

6

7

8

9

10

Figure 7 Diver and Wincher.

* The diver and rope may conveniently be drawn on a strip of acetate cut from an overhead projector transparency, using a non-washable marker.

Rules of play

1. One child is the diver; the other is the wincher on the boat, who winches her up and down as requested.
2. The diver throws the die and starts at the level indicated: say, level 3. The depth scale is then covered.
3. The diver throws again, to decide her next level: say, level 7. To get there she calls to the wincher 'I'm at level 3 and I want to go to 7. Please give out 4 fathoms'.
4. The wincher does this, counting aloud '1, 2, 3, 4 fathoms; there you are.'
5. The diver then checks by uncovering the depth scale. (You can explain that she has a depth gauge on her wrist, operated by water pressure.) The depth gauge is then covered again.
6. The diver throws again, say 2. She calls 'I'm at level 7 and I want to get to 2. Please haul in 5 fathoms.'
7. The wincher does this, counting as before 'Hauling in, 1, 2, 3, 4, 5 fathoms; there you are.'
8. The diver checks her depth.
9. They continue thus for a while, and then change occupations.

Note A fathom is 6 feet, and is a measure still used for measuring depth by seamen. For this game a metre is too small a unit.

Activity 4 Number comparison sentences

An activity for 2 children. Its purpose is to teach two ways of writing a number sentence about the difference between two numbers, and to help them to realize that these are equivalent.

Materials
- Instruction board (see Vol. 1a).
- 3 packs of number cards 1-10:
  2 single-headed, of the same colour,
  one of a different colour which is double-headed with numerals at the bottom.
- 20 objects for counting, e.g. shells, cubes, bottle tops. . .
- Pencil and paper for each child.

What they do Note To follow this explanation, you need the full size instruction board which is on the photomaster.

1. The children sit opposite each other with the instruction board between them. At this stage, the flap at each end is turned under, so that it is not yet visible. Each has a single-headed number pack.
2. The double-headed number pack is put between them, face down. Each child turns over a card from this pack, and they agree which

spaces on the instruction board to put them in.

3. Each then follows the instructions facing her. (First time through, the teacher may read these with the children following.) The number for the difference is taken from their separate (single-headed) packs. They arrive at this answer by whatever method they like: e.g., by using the counting objects, by counting on or counting back with or without the help of finger counting.

4. To prevent one from simply copying the other, the cards for the difference may be put face down initially and turned over when both are down.

5. They should finish having written something like this on their papers.

$$7 > 2 \text{ diff } 5$$
$$2 < 7 \text{ diff } 5$$

6. If they disagree, they discuss and if necessary use physical objects.

7. The board is cleared, turned around, and steps 1-4 are repeated. The double-headed number cards should be replaced randomly in the pack.

Activity 5   Subtraction sentences for comparisons

An activity for two children. This is an extension of activity 4, to be included when you judge that the concepts of activity 4 are well established. Its purpose is to establish the comparison of numbers as one kind of subtraction, using the general notation for subtraction.

Materials • As for activity 4, except that on the instruction board the hinged flap at each end, previously turned under, is now brought into view. It reads:

> Write a subtraction sentence which means the same, like this:
>
> Larger number − smaller number = difference

What they do   1. to 5. The same as in activity 4.

6. They then follow the new instructions, finishing with something like this:

$$7 > 2 \text{ diff } 5$$
$$2 < 7 \text{ diff } 5$$
$$7 - 2 \ = 5$$

7. They should then read all three sentences aloud:

'7 is greater than 2, and the difference is 5'
'2 is less   than 7, and the difference is 5'
'7 subtract   2,   equals   5'

Discussion of activities

Since this topic introduces the comparison aspect of subtraction, which is quite different from the taking-away aspect, there are 5 activities to introduce and consolidate this concept.

The first is a number track activity, using length as a clearly visible difference between the sets. Moreover, the sets to be compared are both sets of the same objects, in this case cubes. Here we have mode 1 schema building.

Where the sets are of different objects, number is not the most obvious way to compare. For example, if we compare a set of 6 children and a set of 4 knives, the difference between children and knives is much more obvious (and more important!) than that between 6 and 4. Once again we note how abstract mathematics is compared with other everyday thinking. In this activity we use a common daily occurrence in which the difference between children and tableware is taken for granted, and the goal of one-to-one correspondence (each child has one of each object) a fairly obvious one. Unlike activity 1, the comparison is made mentally and the outcome is used for prediction-mode 1 scheme testing.

Activity 3 is a straightforward embodiment of the number track concept, numerically comparing present position and desired position. Prediction is again involved.

Activity 4 has two purposes. The first is to introduce recording. The second is thereby to make fully conscious, and crystallise, an idea which may already be present intuitively. This is, that if set A is numerically greater than set B, then set B is less than set A. And the number by which A is greater than B is the same as the number by which B is less than A.

Stated verbally, this seems long-winded. The mathematical notation says it in just 5 symbols. This is the new line introduced by activity 5. Looked at the other way, we see again how condensed is the mathematical statement, and how necessary to build up its interiority by a variety of activities. This final line relates the comparison aspect of subtraction to the notation already in use for the take-away aspect. It thus begins the process of combining these into a single concept.

OBSERVE AND LISTEN   **REFLECT**   **DISCUSS**

Num 4.6   COMPLEMENTARY NUMBERS

Concept The remaining part required to make a given whole.

Ability To state numerically the complement of any part relative to a given whole.

Discussion of concept

This concept forms a good bridge between the addition and subtraction networks.

It fits into the addition network if we call it missing addend: e.g.,

$$5 + \square = 8$$

It fits into the present (subtraction) network, if we ask e.g.,

What is the difference between 5 and 8?

Counting on is a good method for both of these. Both relate to the comparison aspect of subtraction rather than the 'take away' aspect.

Activity 1   The handkerchief game*

A game for children to play in pairs. (More can play together, but there is more involvement with pairs.) Its purpose is to build the concept of complementary numbers in a physical situation which allows immediate testing.

*   I first saw this game played at a school in Georgia, USA. It was taught to the children by Dr Leslie Steffe, University of Georgia.

Materials
- Handkerchief.
- 10 or more small objects such as shells, bottle caps, acorn cups etc.
- Number cards 5-10.

Rules of play
1. The game is introduced by having one child put out ten small objects. (Suppose that shells are used.) The other children check the number.
2. The children are asked to hide their eyes while a handkerchief is placed over some of the shells.
3. The players are told to open their eyes and are asked, 'How many shells are under the handkerchief?'
4. They check by removing the handkerchief.
5. The children then play in pairs, covering their eyes in turn.
6. Repeat, using other numbers of objects. For numbers other than 10, the children will need some kind of reminder of how many there are altogether, so, before putting down the handkerchief, a number card is put down for the total number.

Activity 2   'Please may I have?' (complements)

A game for four or six children. Its purpose is to take the concept to a mental and symbolic level.

Materials
- Four-way cards (see diagram) each showing a number from 6 to 10 (and each in a different colour).

- Double-headed number cards:
  6 pack: 4 sets (1, 2, 3, 3, 4, 5) same colour as four-way 6 card.
  7 pack: 4 sets (1, 2, 3, 4, 5, 6) same colour as four-way 7 card.
  8 pack: 3 sets (1, 2, 3, 4, 4, 5, 6, 7) same colour as four-way 8 card.
  9 pack: 3 sets (1, 2, 3, 4, 5, 6, 7, 8) same colour as four-way 9 card.
  10 pack: 3 sets (2, 3, 4, 6, 7, 8) 2 sets (1, 9) 2 sets (5), same colour as four-way card.

Rules of play
1. One of the four-way cards is put centrally, face up. Suppose this is the 7 card.
2. All the cards from the pack matching the four-way 7 card are dealt to the players.
3. The object is to put down pairs of complementary cards, i.e. which add up to (in this case) 7.
4. Play begins with all players putting down pairs of complementary cards which they have been dealt. They put these down face up.
5. Turns are taken clockwise, starting with the player on the left of the dealer.
6. To collect more pairs of complementary cards, they ask other players for cards they want. E.g., a player who has a 2 might ask, 'Please, Andrew, may I have a 5?'
7. If Andrew has a 5 he must give it. Otherwise he says 'Sorry', and the turn passes to the next player.
8. The cards which a player asks for are the complements of cards which they already hold. So when the player in the example in step 6 has asked for a 5, the others can then deduce that he holds the complement of 5, namely 2.
9. The player who puts down all his cards first scores 2 bonus points. Play continues until all pairs of complementary numbers are put down.
10. Players score 2 points for each pair.
11. The game is then repeated using a different central card.

Discussion of activities

Activity 1 introduces the idea of complement in a physical embodiment. Children first see the whole set, and then part of it, from which they have to deduce the part they cannot see. They are able immediately to test the correctness of their deduction.

Activity 2 may be played at two levels of sophistication. The first involves no more than using the new concept at a mental and symbolic level. The second is explained in step 8: the children should be allowed to discover this for themselves.

Counting on is a good way of doing both, and finger counting (see Num 1.5/1) should be encouraged and if necessary revised.

OBSERVE AND LISTEN   **REFLECT**   **DISCUSS**

Num 4.7   GIVING CHANGE

Concept   Paying a required amount by giving more and getting change.

Abilities   (i)   To give the correct change.
(ii)   To check that one received the correct change.

Discussion of concept

This is another contributor to the comparison aspect of subtraction. In this case, the larger number is the amount tendered, the smaller number is the cost of the purchase, and the difference is the change.

Activity 1   **Change by exchange**

An activity for 3 or 4 children (not more). Its purpose is to 'spell out' with the coins themselves what is happening when we give or receive change.

Materials   • Play money.
• A 'till' (tray with partitions).
• Pictures on cards representing objects for sale, with prices marked, all less than 10p.

What they do   1.   One child acts as shopkeeper, the rest as customers.
2.   The customers start with 30p, made up of two 10p, one 5p, two 2p, one 1p. The shopkeeper has plenty of 1p, 2p, 5p coins.
3.   The shopkeeper sets out her wares. If there is not enough table space for all the goods, some may be kept 'in the stock room' and put out later.
4.   The customers in turn make their purchases one at a time.
5.   To start with, they pay with exact money. When they no longer have the exact money for their purchases, they pay by giving more and getting change.
6.   Suppose that a customer asks for a 6p apple, and hands a 10p coin to the shopkeeper.
7.   The shopkeeper says 'I have to take 6p out of this, so I need to exchange it.' She puts the 10p coin into his till and takes out 10 pennies. (With experience, a combination of 5p, 2p, and 1p coins will be used.)
8.   Spreading these smaller coins out, she then says 'I'm taking this 6p for your apple' and does so. 'The rest is your change: 4 pence.'
9.   The shopkeeper gives the apple and the 4p change to the customer, who checks that she has received the right change.

Activity 2   **Change by counting on**

A continuation from activity 1, for 3 to 6 children. (May be included or bypassed, at your discretion.) Its purpose is to relate the method of giving change which children will often have encountered in shops to its mathematical meaning, by putting it between activities 1 and 3.

Materials   The same as for activity 1.

What they do   1-4 are the same as in activity 1.
5. The method of giving change is now different. Assume as before that the customer has handed a 10p coin to the shopkeeper for a 6p apple. The shopkeeper goes to the till and picks up coins to make the total up to 10p, saying to herself '7, 8, 9, 10'. These coins may be single pennies, or any combination of 2p and 1p coins.
6. She says to the customer '6p for your apple,' and then while counting the change into the customer's hand '7, 8, 9, 10'.

Note that with this method, the amount of the change is not explicitly stated or written.

Activity 3   Till receipts

A continuation from activity 2, for 3 to 6 children. Its purpose is to relate the kind of subtraction involved in giving change (comparison) to the conventional notation for subtraction.

Materials   ● The same as for activities 1 and 2, and also:
● A pad of till receipts. (See illustration below.)

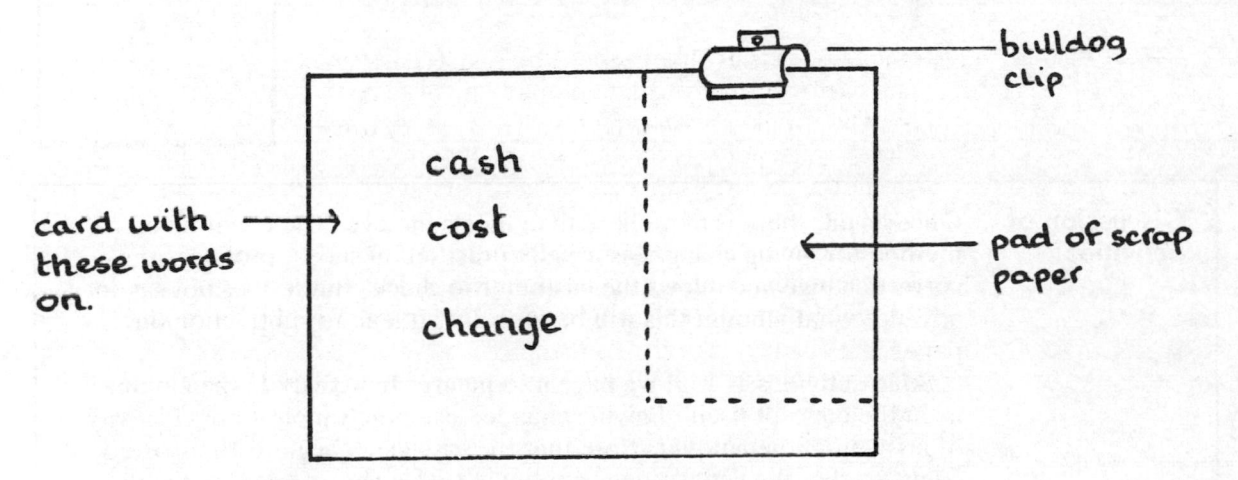

What they do   1,2,3,4. are as in activity 1.
5. Having arrived at the right change by any means he likes, the shopkeeper then writes for the customer a till receipt.

6. She shows it to the customer
    like this, before removing
    it from the pad and handing
    it to the customer.

$$
\begin{array}{r}
\text{cash} \quad 10 \\
\text{cost} \quad -6 \\
\hline
\text{change} \quad 4
\end{array}
$$

7. This is what the customer
    receives, together with her
    purchase and change.

$$
\begin{array}{r}
10 \\
-6 \\
\hline
4
\end{array}
$$

Discussion of activities

Once again, there is more here than meets the eye. The counting on method for giving change, as usually practised in shops, produces the correct change and allows the customer to check. But it does not say in advance what amount this will be, nor does it lead to subtraction on paper.

So in activities 1, 2, 3, we have a sequence. In activity 1, the emphasis is on the concept itself of giving change, using the simplest possible way of arriving at the amount. Note that the customers begin with assorted coins, so that the activity does not begin with giving change, but with paying in the direct way. Giving more and receiving change is then seen as another way of paying the correct amount. We found that when this approach was not used, some children continued to give change even when the customer, having collected the right coins by receiving change, then paid the exact amount! This shows how easily habit learning can creep in instead of understanding, and also how important it is to get the details right in these activities. Activity 2 uses counting on as a method for first producing the correct change, and then allowing the customer to check. Finally, activity 3 transfers this to paper and makes explicit the amount of change which the customer should receive. It also relates this new aspect of subtraction to the notation with which children are already familiar. This helps to relate it to the overall concept of subtraction.

OBSERVE AND LISTEN   **REFLECT**   **DISCUSS**

Num 4.8   SUBTRACTION WITH ALL ITS MEANINGS

Concept   Subtraction as a single mathematical operation with 4 different aspects.

Ability   To relate the overall concept of subtraction to any of its embodiments.

Discussion of concept

In this topic we are concerned with re-capitulating the 4 earlier aspects of subtraction: taking away, comparison, complement, and change. Finally, in activity 5, these are fused together into a concept of subtraction from which can be extracted all of these particular varieties.

Activity 1   **Using set diagrams for taking away**

A teacher-led discussion for a small group. Its purpose is to relate the take-away aspect of subtraction to set diagrams.

Materials   • Pencil and paper for all.

Suggested sequence for the discussion

1. Write on the left of the paper: $\begin{array}{r} 8 \\ -\ 5 \\ \hline \end{array}$

2. Say and draw (pointing first to the 8, then the 5):

    'This says we start with 8.'

    'This says we take away 5.'
    Cross out the 5 to be taken away.

3. Write the result, 3.
4. Review the correspondences between the number sentence and the starting set, the action (crossing out), and the result.

$\begin{array}{r} 8 \\ -\ 5 \\ \hline 3 \end{array}$

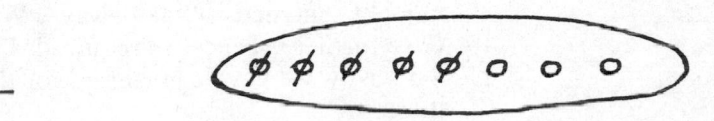

5. Let the children repeat steps 1 to 4 with another example. Use vertical notation, as above.
6. Give further practice if needed.

Activity 2   **Using set diagrams for comparison**

A teacher-led discussion for a small group. Its purpose is to relate the comparison aspect of subtraction to set diagrams, and thereby to what they have just done.

Materials   • Pencil and paper for all.

Suggested sequence for the discussion

1. Write as before.

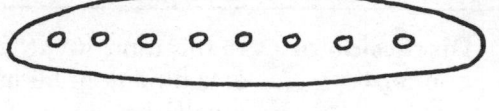

2. Say, 'This subtraction can have another meaning, besides taking away.' Here we have two numbers, the larger one above.
3. Draw these on the right of the subtraction sentence.

4. Ask (pointing): 'How many more are there in this set, than this?'
5. If they answer correctly, say 'Let's check.' Draw lines like this and say (pointing) 'These 5 lines show where the sets are alike, so these 3 without lines show where they are different.'

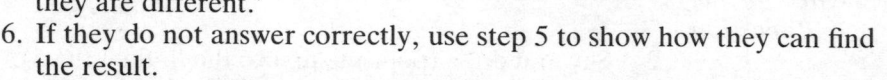

6. If they do not answer correctly, use step 5 to show how they can find the result.
7. Either way, write the result in the subtraction sentence.
8. Review the correspondences between the number sentence, the two sets, the action (comparison), and the result.

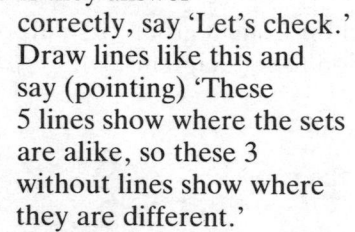
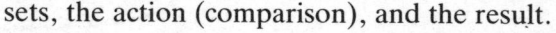

9. Explain: 'We've not been taking away, so we shouldn't read the number sentence as "take away". We say "8, subtract 5, result 3".'
10. Give further practice, as required. Use vertical notation only.
11. Say, 'Now we have 2 meanings for this subtraction sentence.' Review these.

Activity 3   Using set diagrams for finding complements

A teacher-led discussion for a small group. Its purpose is to relate the complement aspect of subtraction to set diagrams, and thereby to what they did in activities 1 and 2.

Materials
- Pencil and paper for all.
- Red and blue felt tips.

Suggested sequence for the discussion

1. Write, and draw in pencil.

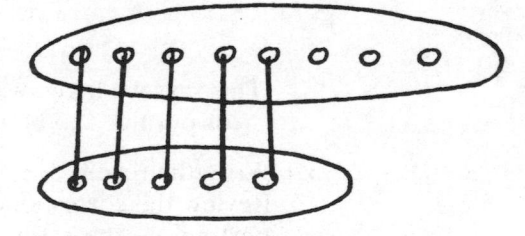

2. Say, 'Here is another meaning. We're told that these are all to be coloured red or blue. If five are coloured red, how many blue?'
3. If (as we hope) they say 'Three', check by colouring. If not, demonstrate.
4. Say, 'If we didn't have red and blue felt tips, what could we do instead?'
5. Accept any sensible answers, and contribute the suggestion below. Tell them that they may continue to use their own way if they like.

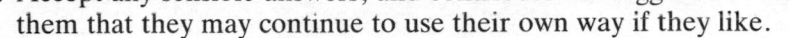

6. Invite other meanings, e.g. 8 children, 5 girls, how many boys?
7. Review the correspondences between the number sentence, the whole set, and the two parts of the set.

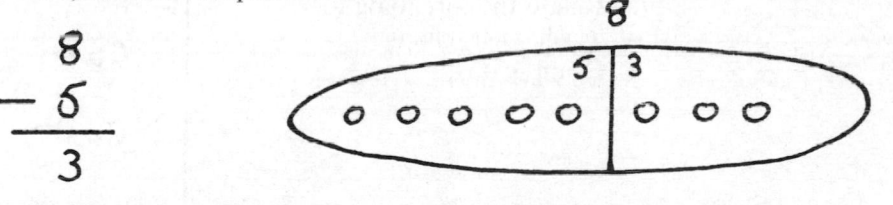

8. Remind them that the larger number has to be above. This time the larger number is the whole set, the next number is one part, and the last number is the other part.
9. Give further practice, as required. Use vertical notation only.
10. They now have 3 meanings for the subtraction sentence. Review these.

Activity 4   **Using set diagrams for giving change**

A teacher-led discussion for a small group. Its purpose is to relate the 'cash, cost, change' aspect of subtraction to set diagrams, and thereby to what they did in activities 1, 2, and 3.

Materials • Pencil and paper for all.

Suggested sequence for the discussion

1. Write, on the left of the paper:

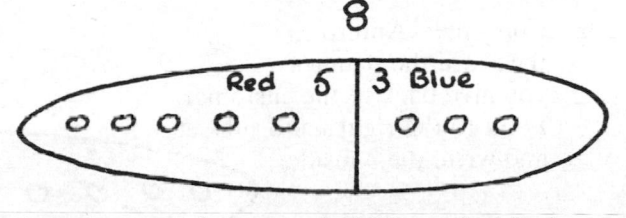

2. Say, 'There's just one more meaning we can give this. Suppose you are a shopkeeper, and a customer gives you 8p for an apple. But the apple only costs 5p. What money will you give him back?'
3. Assuming that they answer correctly, say, 'Yes. Now let's check.'
4. Draw.

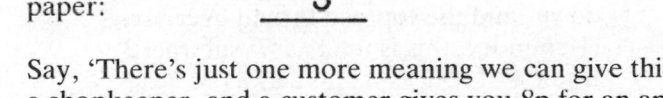

5. Say, 'these are
    the 5 pennies for
    the apple,' and
    draw the partition
    line. Write the 5 inside.

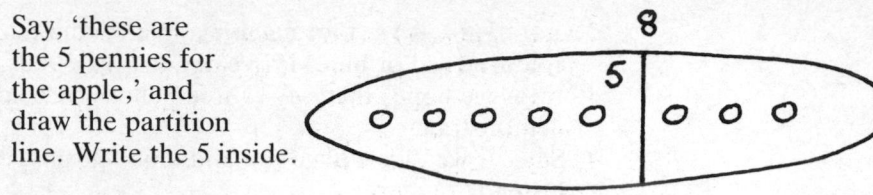

6. Continue: 'And so
    these are the pennies
    you give back to the customer.'
    Point to the right-hand sub-set
    and write the 3 inside.

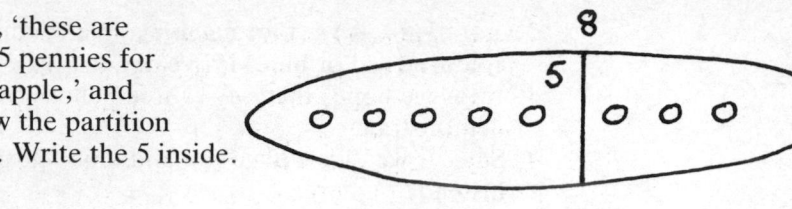

7. Relate the foregoing to
    'Cash, cost, change'
    (Num 4.7/3).

Cash	8
Cost	− 5
Change	3

8. Give further practice, as required.
9. Review all 4 of the meanings they now have for subtraction.

Activity 5   Unpacking the parcel

A game for up to 6 children. Its purpose is to consolidate children's understanding of the 4 different aspects of subtraction.

Materials   • Parcel cards, of two kinds:
        (a) as illustrated in step 1.
        (b) as illustrated in step 6.
      • A bowl of counters.

Rules of the game   1. The first set of parcel cards is put face
    down, and the top one turned over.
    (Reminder: this is read as '7, subtract 3,
    result 4', NOT as '7, take away 3. . .'.)

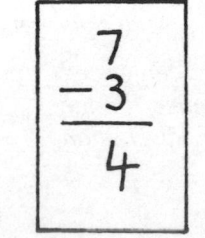

2. Explain that this has a number of different meanings which can be
    'taken out', one at a time, like unpacking a parcel.
3. The children take turns to give one meaning. If the others agree, he
    takes a counter.
4. There are four different mathematical meanings, as in activities 1, 2,
    3, 4.

5. An unlimited number of situational meanings can also be found, and
   these can become repetitive, e.g. if someone says,
   '7 boxes, 3 empty, so 4 have something in them,'
   and someone else then says,
   '7 cups, 3 empty, so 4 have something in them,'
   this is so little different as to be hardly worth saying. If the rest of the
   group unanimously think that an example is of this kind, they might
   reject it even though correct. This might lead to discussion as to what is
   acceptable as a genuinely different meaning.

6. 'Parcels' like
   this one have
   even more
   possible meanings, e.g.,

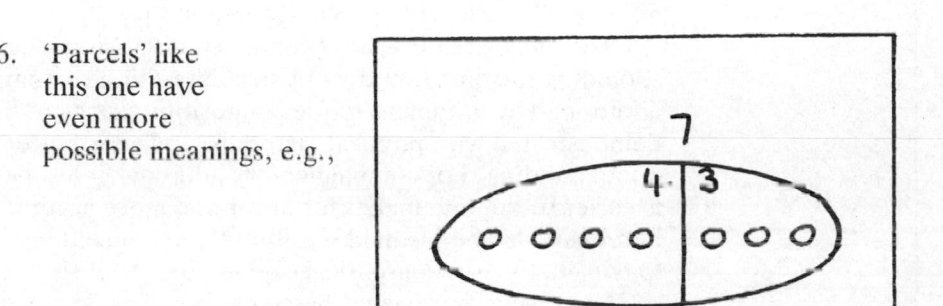

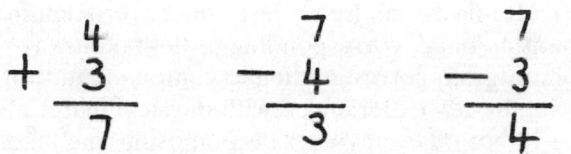

   with 4 different meanings for each of the subtractions.
7. This activity involves much concentration of mathematical meaning,
   and children should return to it at intervals until all 4 aspects are
   mastered. Children find the part-whole relationships harder than the
   take-away and comparison aspects of subtraction.

Discussion of activities	In this topic we have a good example of the highly abstract and concentrated nature of mathematical ideas. Hence its power, but hence also the need for very careful teaching.
	In the 4 topics which lead up to this one, the 4 different aspects of subtraction are introduced separately, with the use of materials to provide a less abstract approach. In the present topic these are brought together by using set diagrams, which again provide a less abstract symbolism than the purely numerical symbols whose use, with full understanding, is the final learning goal.
	In activity 5, the children are learning explicitly something about the nature of mathematics, namely its concentration of information. We ourselves have been taking notice of this from the beginning.

OBSERVE AND LISTEN   **REFLECT**   **DISCUSS**

Num 4.9   SUBTRACTION OF NUMBERS UP TO 20, INCLUDING CROSSING THE 10 BOUNDARY

Concept   Expansion of the subtraction concept to include larger numbers.

Ability   To subtract numbers up to 20, including examples which involve crossing the 10 boundary.

Discussion of concept	'Crossing the 10 boundary' means calculations like $12 - 3$, $14 - 6$, $17 - 9$. All subsequent examples which involve regrouping, such as $52 - 4$, $82 - 36$, $318 - 189$, depend on this.

'Crossing the 10 boundary' means calculations like $12 - 3$, $14 - 6$, $17 - 9$. All subsequent examples which involve regrouping, such as $52 - 4$, $82 - 36$, $318 - 189$, depend on this.

Over the years there has been much discussion whether children should be taught to subtract by decomposition or complementary addition. The argument for decomposition has been that it can be demonstrated with physical materials, and so is better for teaching with understanding. For complementary addition, it has been claimed that it is easier to do, and makes for faster and more accurate calculations. The latter can also be justified sensibly, though it seldom is: 'borrowing' and 'paying back' is a nonsensical explanation.

The present approach is based on the physical regroupings which the children have learnt in Org 1, and the concept of canonical form which comes in both Org 1 and Num 2. It has several advantages:

(i)   It is mathematically sound.

(ii)   It allows children to use whichever technique they find easier: counting back, corresponding to the take-away aspect of subtraction, or counting on, corresponding to complementation. Both of these they have already experienced with physical materials. Taking away across the 10 boundary involves decomposing one larger group into 10 smaller groups; complementing involves putting together 10 smaller groups into one larger group. Either way, re-grouping and canonical form are the key concepts.

(iii)   The same technique (changing out of or into canonical form) is also good for adding, multiplying, and dividing.

The present topic is preparatory to the full technique, which follows in Num 4.10. It teaches what we do after changing out of canonical form.

Activity 1   Subtracting from teens: choose your method

A teacher-led activity for up to 6 children. Its purpose is to show them two ways of subtracting across the tens boundary, help them to see that these are equivalent, and choose which method they prefer.

Materials   • Two sets of number cards, in different colours. One set is from 10–19, the other is from 0 to 9.
• Subtraction board, as illustrated below.

What they do

1. Before starting, it would be useful for you to read the discussion of finger counting in Num 1.4/1 and also Num 1.5/1 and 1.7/1.
2. The subtraction board is put where all the children can see it the same way up. Both sets of cards are shuffled and put face down, near the board, with the teens set on the left.
3. The top card from each pack is turned over, and put one in each space on the board to give (e.g.)

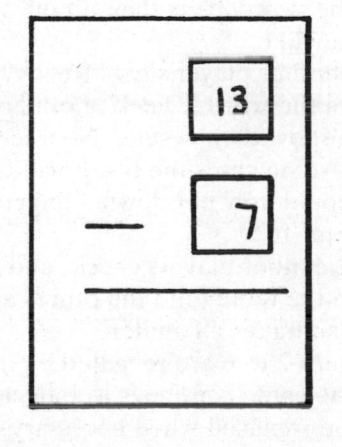

4. Demonstrate the two ways of doing this using finger counting.
   (a)   Counting back. 'We start at 13 and count back to 7, putting down one finger each time. 12 (one finger down), 11, 10, 9, 8, 7 (six fingers down). The difference is 6.' They all do this.
   (b)   Counting on. 'We start at 7 and count on to 13, putting down one finger each time. 8 (one finger down, 9, 10, 11, 12, 13 (six fingers down). The difference is 6.' They all do this.
5. Note that
   (i)   we use the word 'difference' in both cases to link with this aspect of subtraction.
   (ii)   We do *not* put down a finger for the starting number.
   (iii)   This method gives (as intended) a mixture of examples in which some do and some do not involve crossing the tens boundary.

159

6. With another pair of numbers, half the children arrive at the difference by counting back, and half by counting on. They should all have down the same number of fingers.
7. Step 5 is repeated until the children are proficient.
8. Tell them that having tried both, they may use whichever method they prefer from now on. They may like to discuss the reasons for their preference.

Activity 2 Subtracting from teens: 'Check!'

A game for 4 or 6 children, playing in teams of 2. Its purpose is to give them fluency in subtracting across the tens boundary.

Materials
- Number cards 10-19 and 0-9.*
- Subtraction boards.*
- A bowl of counters.
* The same as for activity 1.

What they do
1. Subtraction board 1 is put where all can see it the same way up. Both sets of cards are shuffled and put near the board, with the teens set on the left.
2. In the first team, each player turns over the top card from one of the packs and puts it on the board, the teens card being on the left.
3. The two players then do the subtraction independently by any method they like.
4. Another player says, 'Ready? Check!'
5. On the word 'Check', both layers immediately put fingers on the table to show their results. No alteration is allowed.
6. In some cases the result will be over 10. Example: 15 − 2. Both players should now put down 3 fingers, saying '10 in my head'. (See Num 1.7/1.)
7. The other players check, and if both have the same number of fingers on the table (and the others agree that this is the correct answer), this team takes a counter.
8. Steps 2 to 6 are repeated by the next team.
9. The game continues as long as desired, the number cards being shuffled and replaced when necessary. All teams should have the same number of tries.
10. The winners are those with the most counters.

Activity 3 Till receipts up to 20p

A continuation from Num 4.7/3, for 3 to 6 chilren. Its purpose is to consolidate their new skill in a familiar activity.

Materials
- Play money. The customers each have one 20p and two 10p, also one 5p, two 2p, and one 1p. The shopkeeper has a good assortment of all coins.
- A tray with partitions, used as a till.
- Pictures on cards representing objects for sale with prices marked, ranging from (say) 3p to 19p.

- Base 10 material, units and ten-rods.

What they do
1. to 7. The same as in the earlier version of 'Till receipts' (Num 4.7/3), except that the prices range all the way up to 19p.
8. Customers may now purchase several objects at a time, provided only that the total is below 20p. They may also give a 20p coin to pay for (e.g.) an object costing only 4p.
9. At any time when children have difficulty in writing the till receipts or checking them, they should help themselves by using base 10 material as in activity 1. They may also use the counting on method of Num 4.7/2.

Activity 4   Gift shop

A game, continuing on from the previous activity, for 3 to 6 children.

Materials   The same as for activity 3, together with a notice as illustrated in step 9. Its purpose is further to consolidate their new skills, and extend these to subtraction other than from multiples of 10.

Rules of play
1. to 8. The same as in activity 3.
9. However, the shopkeeper also displays a notice:

> YOUR PURCHASE FREE
>
> if I give the wrong change.

10. If a customer thinks she has received incorrect change, the other customers also check. If it is agreed that the change was incorrect, the shopkeeper must give the customer her purchase free. The cash is returned to the customer, and the change to the shopkeeper.
11. If this happens 5 times the shopkeeper goes broke, and someone else takes over the shop. (The number of mistakes allowed to the shopkeeper should be adjusted to the children's ability.)
12. To make things more difficult for the shopkeeper, customers may pay with whatever amounts they like. E.g., they could hand over 17p for an object costing 9p. (This rule should not be introduced until the children have learnt the rest of the game.)

Discussion of activities   It will be noticed that the activities of this topic do not begin with the use of physical materials, in spite of the importance which in general we attach to these. Base 10 material is good for teaching the exchange of 1 ten for 10 units, but they already have plenty of experience of this. It is also good for teaching conversion into and out of canonical form, and this too is done in earlier contributors to the present topic. It lends itself well to teaching subtraction in its 'take-away' form, but not nearly so easily to the comparison and complementation forms. The latter are easier to do mentally, since counting forward is easier than counting back. So the approach in this topic relies on the foundations laid by Mode 1 schema-building in earlier topics, and uses finger counting as a transitional technique which applies equally well to either aspect of subtraction. This will fall into disuse as children gradually learn, and use for subtraction, their addition facts.

These are followed by the application of these new techniques in familiar activities. The last activity, 'Gift shop', introduces a penalty for the shopkeeper if he makes too many mistakes, and a reward for the customer who detects a mistake. It is not only in this game that a shopkeeper who cannot do his arithmetic finds himself in difficulties!

OBSERVE AND LISTEN   **REFLECT**   **DISCUSS**

Num 5.1   ACTIONS ON SETS: COMBINING ACTIONS

Concepts   (i)   The action of making a set.
     (ii)   The action of making a set of sets.
     (iii) Starting and resulting numbers.

Abilities   (i)   To make a given number of matching sets.
     (ii)   To state the number of a single set.
     (iii) To state the number of matching sets.
     (iv)   To state the total number of elements.

Discussion of concepts

Multiplication is sometimes introduced as repeated addition. This works well for the counting numbers, but it does not apply to multiplication of the other kinds of number which children will subsequently encounter; so to teach it this way is making difficulties for the future. This is one of the reasons why so many children have problems with multiplying fractions, and with multiplying negative numbers. The concept of multiplication which is introduced in the present topic is that of combining two operations, and this continues to apply throughout secondary school and university mathematics. And as a bonus, the correct concept is no harder to learn when properly taught.

In the present case, we are going to multiply natural numbers. A natural number is the number of objects in a set, and we start with the concept as embodied in physical actions.

First action: make a set of number 5.
Second action: make a set of number 3.

To combine these, we do the first action

and then apply the second action to the result (make a set of 3 sets of 5).

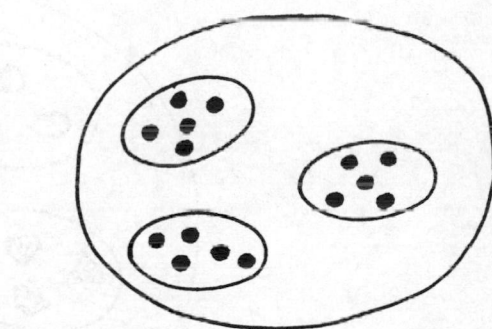

This is equivalent to making a set of number 15.

At this stage, there is not a lot of difference between this and adding together 5 threes, just as near their starting points two diverging paths are only a little way apart. But in the present case one of these paths leads towards future understanding, while the other is a dead end.

So instead of the sequence 'Start, Action, Result' used in the addition and subtraction networks, we shall be using the sequence 'First action, Second action, Combined result'. Later in this network we shall discuss notations for this.

Activity 1   Make a set. Make others which match

An activity for up to 6 children. Its purpose is to introduce the concept of multiplication in a physical embodiment.

Materials
- 5 small objects for each child. These should be different for each child, e.g. shells, acorns, bottle tops. . .
- 6 small set ovals.*
- Large set loop.

* Oval cards, about 6 cm by 7.5 cm.

See illustrations for steps 1 and 3.

What they do
1. The first child makes a set, using some or all of his objects. A small set oval is used for this. It is best to start with a set of fairly small number, say 3.

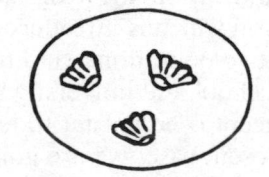

2. Everyone makes a set which matches this, i.e. has the same number. They too use set ovals and then check with each other.
3. All the sets are put in the set loop to make one combined set, which is counted.

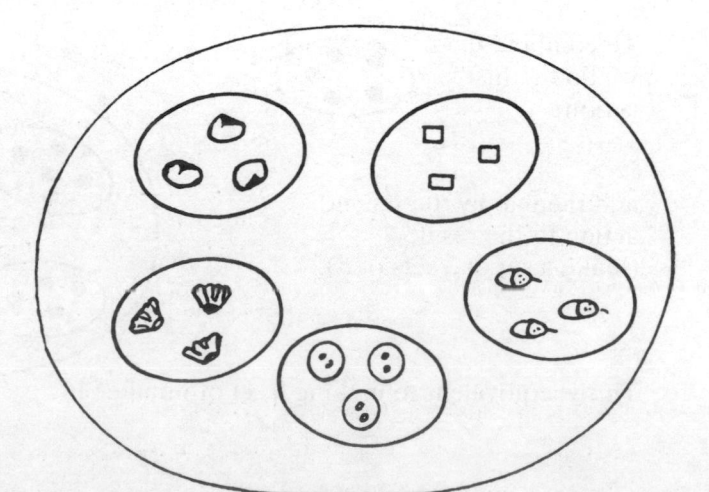

4. With your help, they say (in their own words) what they have done. E.g. 'Vicky made a set of 3 shells. We all made matching sets, so we made 5 sets of 3. When we put these together, there were 15 things altogether.' Or 'We made 5 sets of 3, making 15 altogether.' Or '5 sets, 3 in each, makes 15.'

5. The children take back their objects and steps 1 to 4 are repeated.

6. To give variety of numbers, sometimes only some of the children should make matching sets. E.g. everyone on this side of the table, or all the boys, or all the girls.

Activity 2　Multiplying on a number track

An activity for up to 6 children. Its purpose is to expand the concept of multiplication to include larger numbers. The use of a number track saves the time and trouble of counting the resulting sets.

Materials
- A number track 1 to 60 (2 cm spaces suggested).
- 10 cubes of one colour for each child (2 cm cubes suggested).
- Actions board, see figure 8.
- First action cards 2 to 10, e.g.
   'Each make a rod with 7 cubes'
- Second action cards 1 to 6, e.g.
   'Join 4 rods'
- Slips of paper to fit Combined Result space on Actions board.
- Pencil.

What they do
1. The pack of first action cards and second action cards are shuffled and put face down.
2. The top first action card is turned over, and put face up on top of the pack.
3. Each child makes a rod as instructed. The rods are then pooled for general use.
4. The top second action card is turned over, and put face up on top of the pack.
5. The number of rods indicated is taken, and joined together on the number track.
6. The result is recorded on a slip of paper, which is put in the space on the combined result card.
7. The second action card used is put face up at the bottom on the pile. Steps 3 to 6 are then repeated using the same first action card. This saves re-making the rods every time.
8. When a face-up second action card is reached, this means that all of this pack have been used once. The pack is then shuffled and put face down again.
9. Steps 2 to 7 are then repeated with the next first action card.

Activity 3　Giant strides on a number track

An activity for up to 6 children. Its purpose is to begin the process of freeing children's concept of multiplication from dependence on physical objects.

165

ACTIONS BOARD

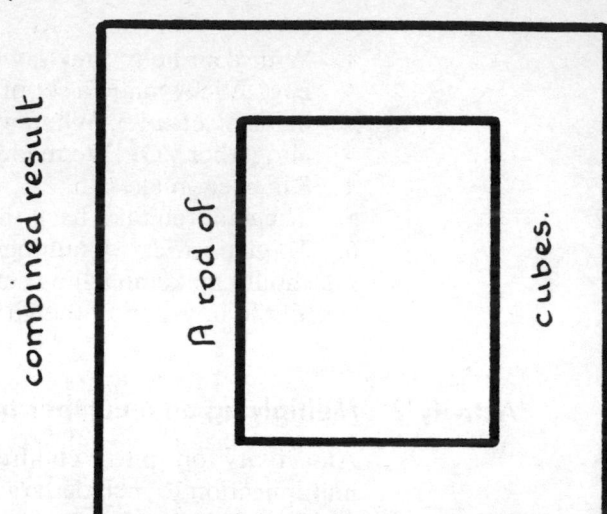

combined result

A rod of

cubes.

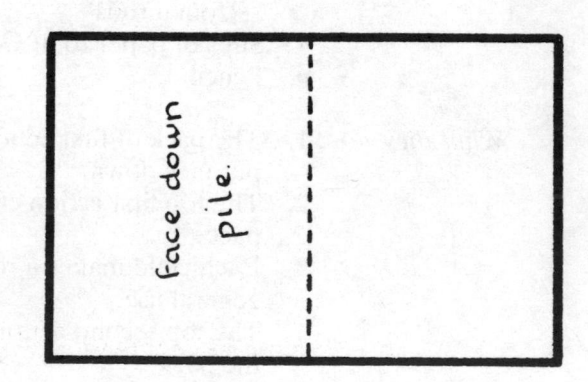

second action

face down
pile.

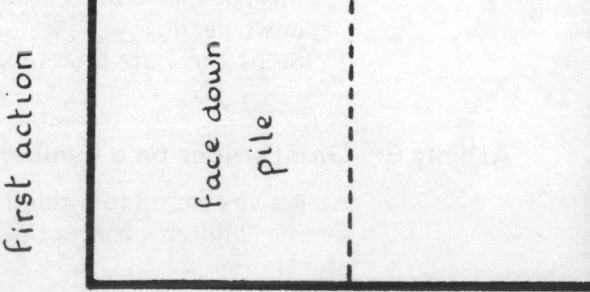

first action

face down
pile

Figure 8 Actions board for multiplying on an number track.

Materials
- A card number track 1 to 50.
- Activity board, see figure 9.
- Length-of-stride cards 2 to 5.*
- Number-of-strides cards 2 to 10.*
- Blu-Tack.
- Pencil and paper.

* Single-headed to fit the dotted spaces on the activity board. Each pack should be of a different colour.

What they do
1. The two packs are shuffled and put face down in their respective dotted spaces on the activity board.
2. The top card in each pile is turned over.
3. Suppose that each stride is 3 spaces, and they take 7 strides.
4. One child puts down 'footprints' on the number track (small blobs of Blu-Tack) at spaces 3, 6, 9 and so on, representing strides each of 3 spaces. The others help by making the blobs for him, and also checking that they are put in the right spaces.
5. This continues until (in this case) 7 strides have been taken. The last footprint will be in space 21.
6. Another child records 21 on a strip of paper, which is put in the last space on the board.
7. The cards are then replaced face down at the bottom of the pile, and steps 2 to 6 are repeated.

Discussion of activities

The first two activities embody, as physical actions, the concept of multiplication as described at the beginning of this topic. In activity 1, the first action is making a set of (say) shells, and the second action is making a set of matching sets. In activity 2, the first action is making a rod out of unit cubes, and the second action is making a rod using a given number of these rods. In activity 3, this is repeated at a slightly more abstract level. The last activity also makes a start with relating multiplication to number stories. The first action is making a stride of a given number of spaces, and the second action is making a given number of strides.

All of the activities in the present topic use mode 1 schema building. No mental calculations, and no predictions, are yet involved. Very simple recording is introduced in activities 2 and 3, in which the children do not have to do any writing themselves.

OBSERVE AND LISTEN **REFLECT** **DISCUSS**

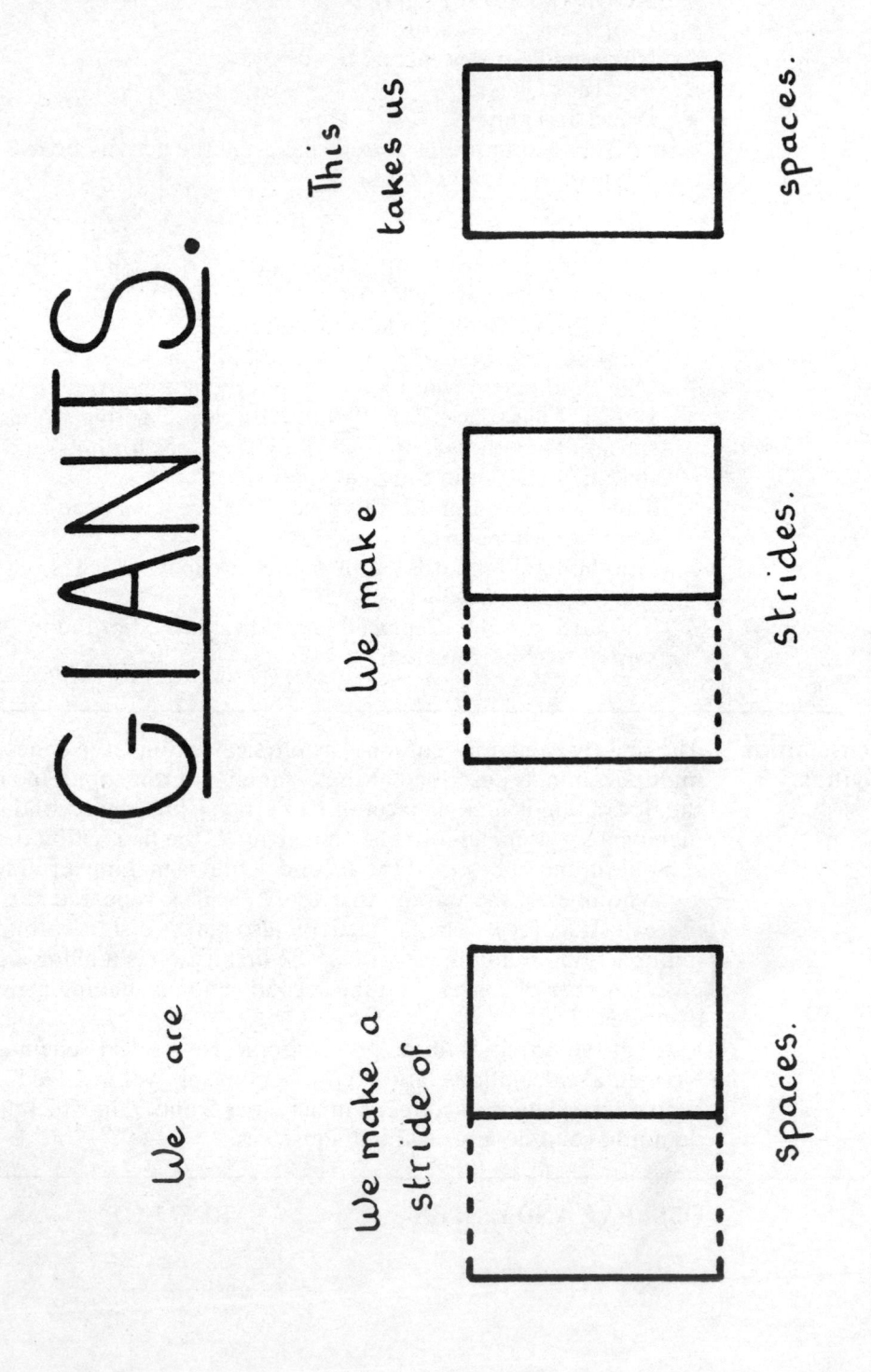

Figure 9 Giant strides on a number track.

Num 5.2 MULTIPLICATION AS A MATHEMATICAL OPERATION

Concept   Multiplication as a mathematical operation.

Ability   To do this mentally, independently of its physical embodiments.

Discussion of concept

Multiplication becomes a mathematical operation when it can be done mentally with numbers, independently of actions on sets or other physical embodiments. At this stage we concentrate on forming the concept, using the easiest possible numbers as operands. These are first 2, then 5, since the children have already learnt to count in twos and fives. Afterwards they will expand the concept to include multiplication of 4 and of 3.

Note that this corresponds to subitising 2-sets and 5-sets, etc. It does not start us down the path of repeated addition. Note also that in this topic the children are already multiplying these numbers by numbers up to ten.

Activity 1   **'I predict – here' using rods**

An activity for up to 6 children. Its purpose is to introduce multiplication used predictively, as a mental operation followed by testing. It is a development of 'I predict – here' (NuSp 1.1/1).

Materials
- Set cards 1 to 10, as further described below.
- Number track 1 to 50 (2 cm suggested).
- 50 cubes (2 cm suggested).

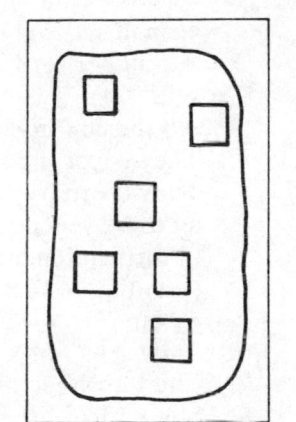

Set cards
On each is drawn a set loop, and within the loop are drawn squares the size of a cube, in number from 1 to 10. These squares should be randomly placed.

Set card.

What they do
1. The set cards are shuffled and put in a pile face down. (Use only cards 2 to 6 to begin with.)
2. Together the children make 10 2-rods which are pooled for communal use. Each rod must be of a single colour.
3. The top activity card is turned face up, and a 2-rod is stood on each square.
4. One of the children then predicts where these will come to when put end to end on the number track. This may be done by counting in twos. He makes his prediction, e.g. with a piece of Blu-Tack. Adjacent rods should be of different colours.
5. His prediction is tested physically.
6. The track is cleared, the long rod broken up into 2-rods, and steps 3, 4, 5 are repeated with another child making the prediction.
7. When the children can do this well, the activity is repeated using 5-rods. The predictions are now made by counting in 5's.
8. After that, the activity is repeated using 3-rods and 4-rods. For these, the predictions may be made by pointing to each rod in turn and counting (for 3-rods): '1, 2, 3; 4, 5, 6; 7, 8, 9' etc.

Activity 2 Sets under our hands

An activity for up to 6 children. Its purpose is to give further practice in the operation of multiplication.

Materials
- Five small objects for each child.*
- Number cards 2 to 6.
- 6 small set ovals.*
- Large set loop.*
- Pencil and paper for each child.
* As for Num 5.1/1.

What they do
1. The first child makes a set, using some or all of her objects. As before, a small set oval is used.
2. A number card is put out to remind them what is the number of this set.
3. All the children then make matching sets, using set ovals.
4. They cover the sets with their hands.
5. They try to predict how many objects there will be when they combine all these sets into a big set. This can be done by pointing to each hand in turn and mentally counting on. E.g. if there are 4 in each set: (pointing to first hand) '1, 2, 3, 4'; (pointing to second hand) '5, 6, 7, 8'; etc.
6. They speak or write their predictions individually.
7. The sets are combined and the predictions tested.
8. Steps 1 to 7 are repeated, with a different child beginning.
9 As in Num 5.1/1, the number of sets made should be varied, by involving only some of the children. All however, should make and test their predictions.

Discussion of activities

In topic 1, the physical activities were used for schema building. The activities came first, and the thoughts arose from the activities. In the present topic it is the other way about: thinking first, and then the actions to test the correctness of the thinking. First mode 1 building, then mode 1 testing. By this process we help children first to form concepts, and then to develop them into independent objects of thought.

Activity 1 gives visual support for the mental activity of counting on, by which the children are predicting. They can see the number of cubes in each rod, as well as the number of rods. In activity 2, this visual support is partly withdrawn. They can see how many hands there are, but they have to imagine how many objects there are under each hand. In this way we take them gently along the path towards purely mental operations.

OBSERVE AND LISTEN   **REFLECT**   **DISCUSS**

Num 5.3   NOTATION FOR MULTIPLICATION: NUMBER SENTENCES

Concept   The use of number sentences for representing the operation of multiplication and its result.

Abilities   (i)   To write number sentences recording multiplication as embodied in physical materials.
(ii)   To use number sentences for making predictions.

Discussion of concept

Several notations for multiplication are currently in use. All the following can be read aloud in ways which fit the meaning of multiplication which we are using.

$$5 \xrightarrow{\times 3} 15$$

means 'Make a set of 5.
Make it 3 times.
Combined result, a set of 15.'

This may be shortened to

$$5 \times 3 = 15$$

and read as '5, 3 times, equals (or makes) 15.'

This is easier to say than '5 multiplied by 3 equals 15.' (I do not recommend 'timesed by', as one sometimes hears. It is not grammar, and no easier for the children.) The above notation has the advantage that the order 'First action, Second action' is preserved.

Other notations for the same operation use parentheses, with an equals sign or an arrow.

$$3(5) = 15 \quad \text{or} \quad 3(5) \rightarrow 15$$

'3 sets of 5 equal (or make) 15', or '3 fives are 15'.

This reverses the order of the operations, but corresponds well to the diagram below which shows the combined result.

3(5)
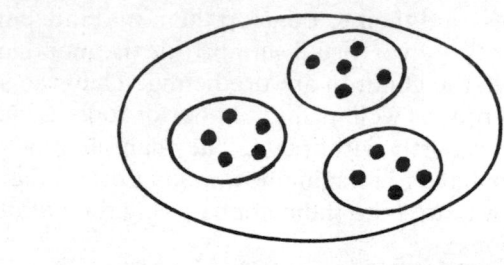

I suggest that you use whichever notation you and the children are happiest with, until topic 5.5. Here I introduce a notation for binary multiplication which combines both, and when properly understood makes everything much simpler.

Until then, the activities can be used with either notation. You might think it useful for the children to understand both notations, since they will certainly meet both in their future work.

Activity 1   Number sentences for multiplication

An activity for up to 6 children. Its purpose is to introduce number sentences for recording multiplication as embodied in physical materials.

Materials
- Actions board.*
- First action cards 2 to 5.*
- Second action cards 2 to 6.*
- Five small objects for each child.**
- 6 small set ovals.**
- 1 set loop.**
- Pencil and paper for each child.

* See figure 10. This shows the actions board for ( ) notation with two cards in position (see step 2). An alternative board for × notation is provided in Vol. 1a.

** As for Num 5.1/1 and Num 5.2/2.

What they do
1. The action cards are shuffled and put in 2 piles face down on the Actions board.
2. The first child turns over the first action card. He does what it says, using some or all of his objects and a small oval set card.
3. The next child turns over the top second action card, and puts it beside the first. The board will now look like one or other of the illustrations opposite.
4. The children make as many of these sets as it says on the second card.
5. They combine the sets by putting them in the large set loop, and count the result.

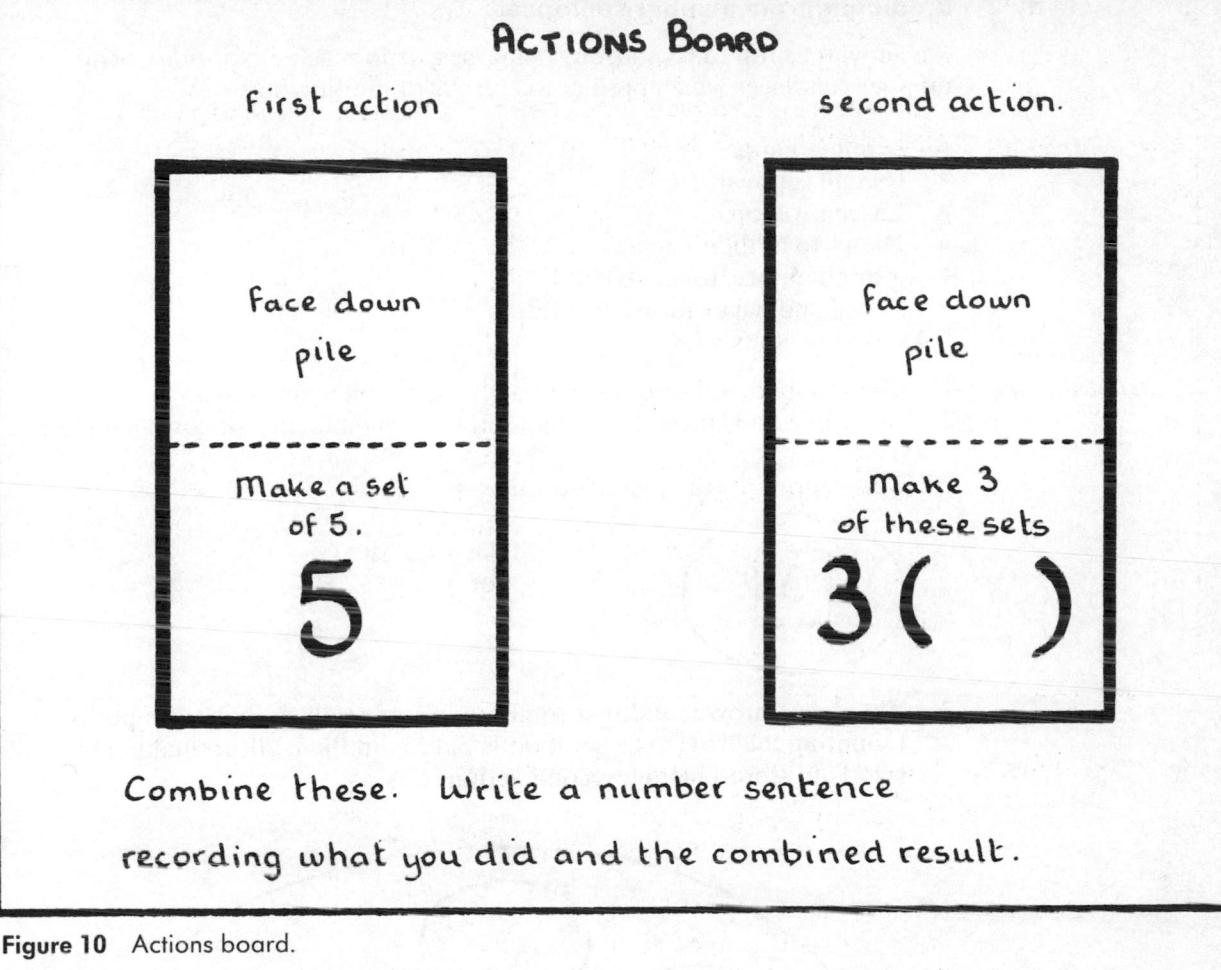

Figure 10   Actions board.

6. They write number sentences in whichever notation you show them. The meaning of these should be carefully explained. In the example shown, either
    this:

    $$3(5) = 15$$

    'Three sets of five make a set of fifteen', or
    'Three fives make (or equal) fifteen'.

    or this:

    $$5 \times 3 = 15$$

    'A set of five, made three times, makes a set of fifteen', or
    'Five, three times, make (or equals) fifteen'.
7. They should learn how to read their number sentence aloud, as in these examples. It is good to be able to say these in several ways. In the process of step 6 they are comparing their results. Any discrepancies offer opportunity for discussion.
8. The objects are taken back, and steps 1 to 6 are repeated, beginning with a different child.

173

Activity 2   Predicting from number sentences

An activity for up to 6 children. Its purpose is to teach children to write number sentences which predict the results of multiplying.

Materials
- Number cards 2 to 5.
- 6 small set ovals.*
- Large set loop.*
- Die (1 to 6, then 1 to 9).
- 5 small objects for each child.
- Pencil and paper for each child.

* As used in Num 5.1/1.

What they do
1. The number cards are shuffled and put in a pile face down.
2. The top card is turned over and put face up on one of the oval small-set cards.
   This represents the first action. E.g.,

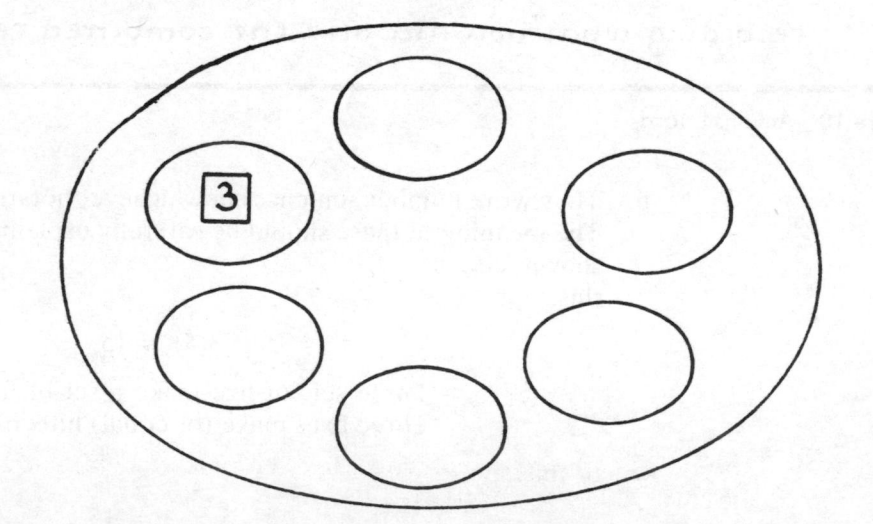

Make a set
of 3

3. The die is thrown, and that total number of small-set ovals are put out (counting the first). The set loop is put round them all, to make a big set. This represents the second action. E.g.,

4. Each child writes the beginning of a number sentence for the above. In this case,

   either 6(3)
   or   3 × 6

5. They then complete their number sentences to predict the combined result when they actually make the sets represented. To do this, they

may use the method for predicting learnt in topic 2. In this case the completed sentences would be

either 6(3) = 18
or 3 × 6 = 18

6. Finally they test their predictions by putting 3 objects on each small-set card, and counting the combined set.
7. The objects are taken back, and steps 2 to 6 are repeated.

Discussion of activities

The children have already learnt to use multiplication predictively, in topic 2. The new factor here is the use of notation.

In this topic and the one before they progress from 'Do and say', to 'Do and record', and then to 'Predict and test'. In activity 1 they use number sentences to record past events; in activity 2 they use number sentences to predict future events. This parallels the progression in topic 2, in which thought begins to become independent of action. Here, we begin to link thinking with notation.

Initially, writing number sentences is an extra task rather than a help, so it needs to be learnt in a situation where the rest is familiar. For more difficult calculations, written notation is no longer an extra chore but a valuable support. It means that we do not have to 'keep everything in our head' at the same time. Pencil and paper give us an external, easily accessible, extra memory store.

Another step has been taken here. Until now, the number symbols have stood for sets of single objects. Now, some of them stand for sets of sets. So we are now handling more information at a time – one might say, in set-sized packages. This is another of the sources of the power of mathematics.

OBSERVE AND LISTEN **REFLECT** **DISCUSS**

Num 5.4 NUMBER STORIES: ABSTRACTING NUMBER SENTENCES

Concept Numbers and numerical operations as models for actual happenings, or for verbal descriptions of these.

Abilities (i) To produce numerical models in physical materials corresponding to given number stories, to manipulate these appropriately, and to interpret the result in the context of the number story: first verbally, then recording in the form of a number sentence.

(ii) To use number sentences predictively to solve verbally **given** problems.

Discussion of concepts	The concept of abstracting number sentences is that already discussed in Num 3.4 (page 110), and it will be worth reading this again. In Num 4.4 it was expanded to include subtraction, and here we expand it further to include multiplication.
	In some applications of multiplication, we need to place less emphasis on the first action and the second action, and more on their results: namely a small set (of single objects) and a large set (a set of these sets). The use of small set ovals and a large set loop from the beginning provides continuity here.

Activity 1   Number stories

An activity for 2 to 6 children. Its purpose is to connect simple verbal problems with physical events, linked with the idea that we can use objects to represent other objects.

Materials
- Number stories on cards, of the kind shown in step 5. Some of these should be personalised, as in Num 3.4/1, but now there should also be some which do not relate to the children, more like the kind they will meet in textbooks. Also, about half of these should have the number corresponding to the small set coming first, and about half the other way about.
- Name cards for use with the personalised number stories.
- Number cards 2 to 6.
- 30 small objects to manipulate: e.g. bottle tops, shells, counters.
- 6 small set ovals.*
- A large set loop.*
- Slips of blank paper.

* As for Num 5.1/1.

What they do   (apportioned according to how many children there are)
1. A number story is chosen. The name, cards and number cards are shuffled and put face down.
2. If it is a personalised number story; the top name card is turned over and put in the number story. Otherwise, explain 'Some of these stories are about you, and some are about imaginary people'.
3. The top number card is turned over and put in the first blank space on the story card.
4. The next number card is turned over and put in the second blank space.
5. The number story now looks like this:

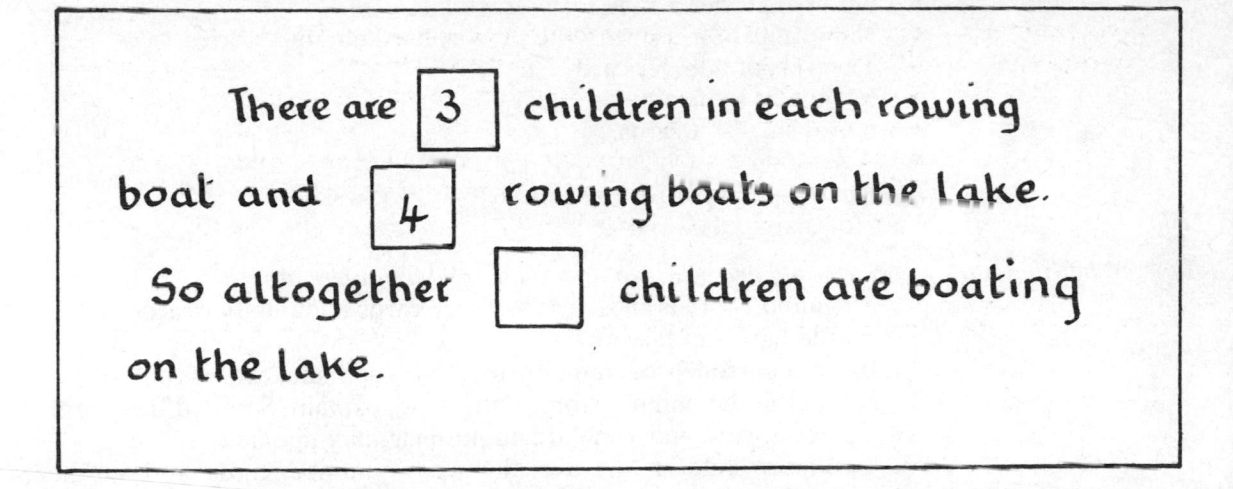

There are [3] children in each rowing boat and [4] rowing boats on the lake. So altogether [ ] children are boating on the lake.

6. Using their small objects (e.g. shells) to represent children, the oval cards for boats, and the set loop for the lake, the children together make a physical representation of the number story. If it is a personalised number story, this should be done by the named child.
7. The total number of shells is counted, and the result written on a slip of paper. This is put in the space on the card to complete the story.
8. While this is being done, one of the children then says aloud what they are doing. E.g. 'We haven't any boats, so we'll pretend these cards are boats, and put shells on them for children. We need 3 children in each boat, and 4 boats inside this loop which we're using for the lake. Counting the shells, we have 12 children boating on the lake.'
9. The materials are restored to their starting positions, and steps 1 to 8 are repeated.

Activity 2   Abstracting number sentences

An extension to activity 1 which may be included fairly soon. Its purpose is to teach children to abstract a number sentence from a verbal description.

Materials
- As for activity 1, and also:
- Pencil and paper for each child.

What they do   As for activity 1, up to step 8.
9. Each child then writes a number sentence, as in step 6 of Num 5.3/1. They read their number sentences aloud.
10. The materials are restored to their starting positions, and steps 1 to 8 are repeated.

Activity 3   Number stories, and predicting from number sentences

An activity for 2 to 6 children. It combines activities 1 and 2, but in this case completing the number sentence is used to make a prediction as in Num 3.5/2.

Materials
- Number stories asking for predictions.
- Name cards for use with the personalised number stories.*
- Two sets of number cards 2 to 6.*
- 30 objects to manipulate.*
- 6 oval small-set cards.*
- A set loop.*
- Pencil and paper for each child.*

* As for activity 1.

What they do   *(apportioned according to how many children there are)*

1. A number story is chosen. The name cards and number cards are shuffled and put face down.
2. If it is a personalised number story, the top name card is turned over and put in the number story. Otherwise, explain 'Some of these stories are about you, and some are about imaginary people'.
3. Two more children turn over the top two number cards, and put these in the first two spaces on the story card.
4. The number story now looks something like this:

Giles   is collecting fir cones in a wood.

He gets   5   cones into each pocket.

and he has   6   pockets.

When he gets home and empties his pockets,

how many fir cones will he have?

5. The named child (if there is one) then puts out an appropriate number of small-set cards, and a number card from the second pack, to represent the situation. (This corresponds to step 6 of activity 1.) For the present example, this is what he should put.

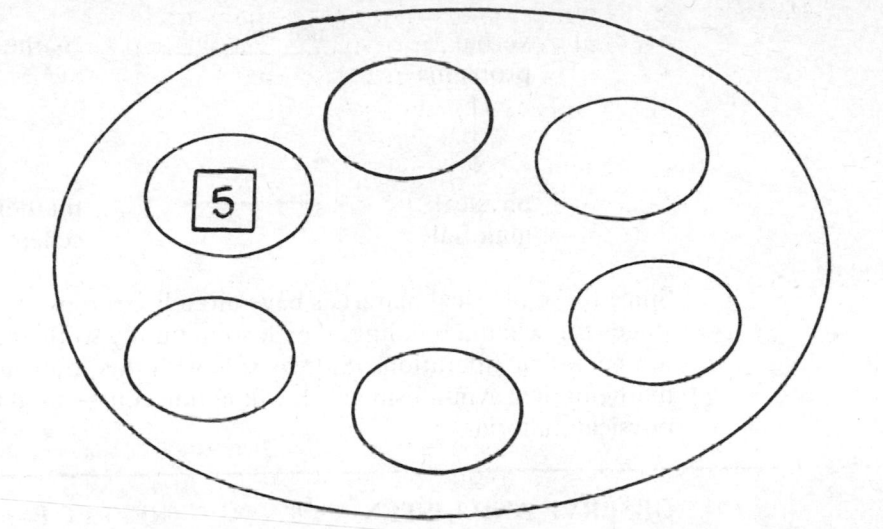

6. He explains, using his own words and pointing: 'These 6 ovals represent my 6 pockets, and this 5 is the number of fir cones I have in each.' (This verbalisation is an important part of the activity.)

7. All the children then write and complete number sentences, as in activity 2. For the present example, these would be

either 6(5) = 30
      'six fives make 30'
or   5 × 6 = 30
      'five, six times, equal 30'

They read these aloud.

8. Another child then tests their predictions by putting the appropriate number of objects in each small-set oval. The number sentences are corrected if necessary.

9. They then write their answers to the question as complete sentences. E.g. (in this case) 'Giles will have 30 fir cones'.

10. The materials are returned to their starting positions, and steps 1 to 9 are repeated using a different number story and numbers.

Discussion of activities	The activities in this topic parallel those in Num 3.4 (addition) and Num 5.4 (subtraction), and in view of their importance it will be worth re-reading the discussion of these.

Solving verbally stated problems is one of the things which children find most difficult, as usually taught. This is because they try to go directly from the words to the mathematical symbols. In the early stages, it is of great importance that the connection is made via the use of physical materials, since these correspond well both to the imaginary events in the verbally-stated problem, and to the mathematical schemas required to solve the problem. The route shown below may look longer, but the connections are much easier to make at the present stage of learning.

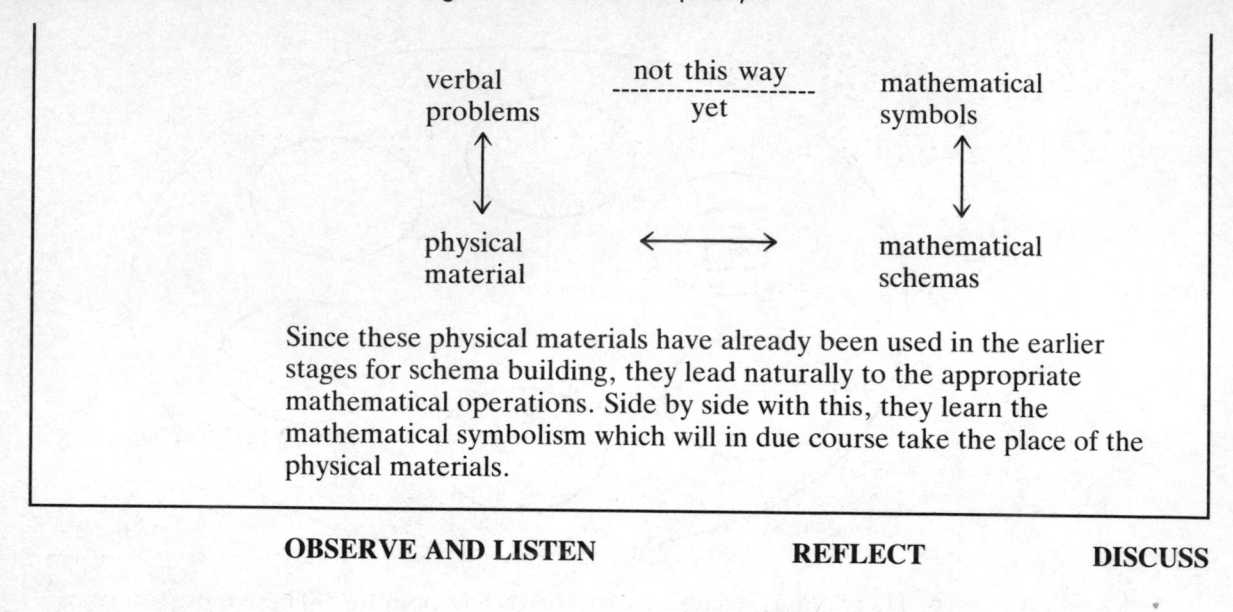

Since these physical materials have already been used in the earlier stages for schema building, they lead naturally to the appropriate mathematical operations. Side by side with this, they learn the mathematical symbolism which will in due course take the place of the physical materials.

OBSERVE AND LISTEN   **REFLECT**   **DISCUSS**

[Num 6] DIVISION

Sharing equally, grouping, factorising.

Num 6.1 GROUPING

Concepts   (i) Grouping.
(ii) Remainder.

Abilities   (i) Given a set of given number, to re-arrange this into equal groups of a required number.
(ii) To state how many groups, and the remainder.

Discussion of concepts	Like subtraction, the mathematical operation of division is derived from several different kinds of physical actions on sets of objects. Though the actions themselves are quite different, they have something in common mathematically; and when the children have realised what this is, they have the higher order concept of division. The two chief kinds of action are grouping and sharing. We also include organising into rectangles, which is closely related to factorising, and shows particularly clearly the relation between multiplication and division. We need to emphasise that 'grouping' is short for 'arranging in groups of equal number'.

Activity 1 Start, Action, Result: grouping

An activity for up to 6 children. Its purpose is to introduce the grouping aspect of division.

Materials
- SAR board (grouping), see figure 11.
- Start cards 10-25.
- Action cards 2-5.
- 25 (or more) small objects.
- Pencil and paper for each child.

What they do
1. The start cards and the action cards are shuffled and put face down in the upper part of their spaces on the activity board.
2. The top card of each pile is turned over.
3. One child then puts out a set of the given number.
4. Another child then re-arranges this set into equal groups of the number stated on the action card.
5. Another child counts how many groups there are, how many objects are left over, and puts this into words.
E.g. 'There are 5 groups, and 2 objects remaining'.

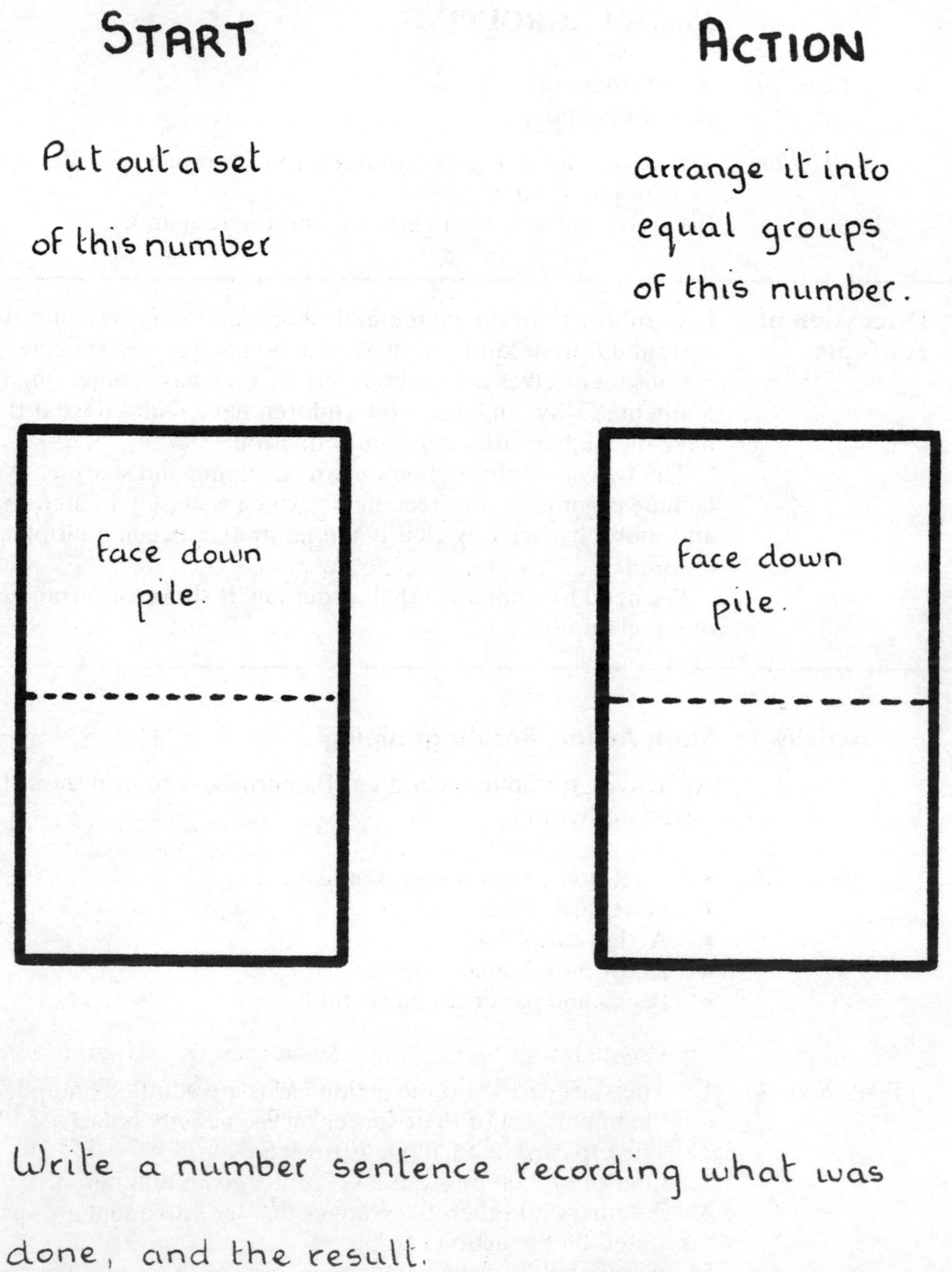

START

Put out a set

of this number

Face down
pile.

ACTION

Arrange it into
equal groups
of this number.

Face down
pile.

Write a number sentence recording what was

done, and the result.

Figure 11 Start, Action, Result: Grouping

6. All the children then write a number sentence recording what was done, and the result. Example:

$$17 \xrightarrow{\text{make groups of 3}} 5 \text{ groups rem } 2$$

This is read as

'Start with 17 and arrange into groups of 3, result 5 groups remainder 2'. If there is no remainder, they should say either '. . . remainder zero' or '. . . exactly'.

7. Steps 2 to 6 are repeated.

Activity 2   Predictive number sentences (grouping)

A game for up to 6 children. Its purpose is to consolidate the concept of grouping by using it in a predictive game.

Materials
- Game board, see figure 12.
- Start cards 10-25.
- Action cards 2-5.*
- 25 (or more) small objects.
- Pencil and paper for each child.

* The same as for activity 1.

Rules of the game

1. The start cards and action cards are shuffled and put face down in the upper part of their spaces on the game board. For most children, you will need to read through the instructions on the board with them.
2. The top card of each pile is turned over.
3. A set of the given number is put out.
4. All the children write their predictions. These are in the form of number sentences, as in activity 1.
5. They check their predictions in two ways: by comparison with each others', and physically, by putting groups of the required size into the boxes.
6. To preserve the connection between the number sentences and their physical meanings, the sentences should be expanded when read aloud, as in the example on the game board for activity 1.
7. Each correct prediction scores 1 point.
8. The board is cleared, and steps 2 to 6 are repeated.

Activity 3   Word problems (grouping)

An activity for up to 6 children. Its purpose is to use the skills acquired in activities 1 and 2 for the solution of problems in the form of number stories, and for checking their solutions. We are now using the term 'word problem' for a number story with a request for a prediction.

Materials
- Problems cards (as illustrated in step 2, page 185).
- Start cards 10-25.*
- Action cards 2-5.*
- 25 (or more) small objects.
- Pencil and paper for each child.

* As for activities 1 and 2.

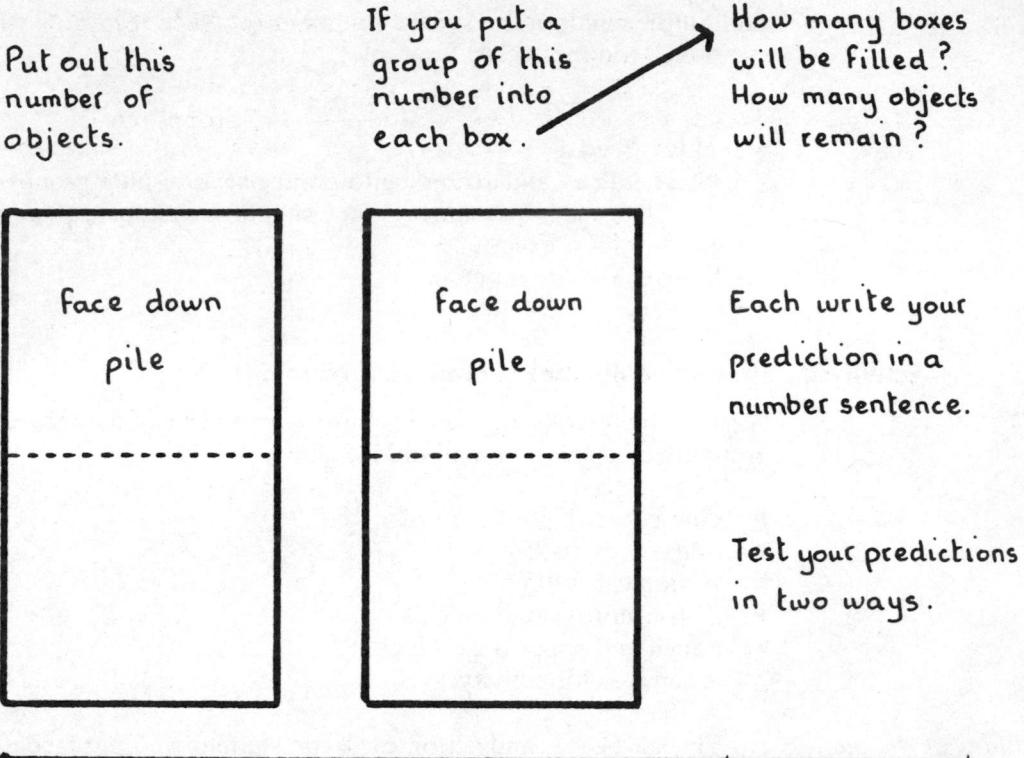

Put out this number of objects.

If you put a group of this number into each box.

How many boxes will be filled? How many objects will remain?

Each write your prediction in a number sentence.

Test your predictions in two ways.

1	2	3	4
5	6	7	8
9	10	11	12

Figure 12 Board for predictive number sentences (grouping).

What they do
1. The problem cards are shuffled and put face down. Likewise for the start and action cards.
2. The top card on the problem pile is turned over. The top cards in the start and action piles are turned over and put in the first and second spaces on the problem card. The result should look something like this.

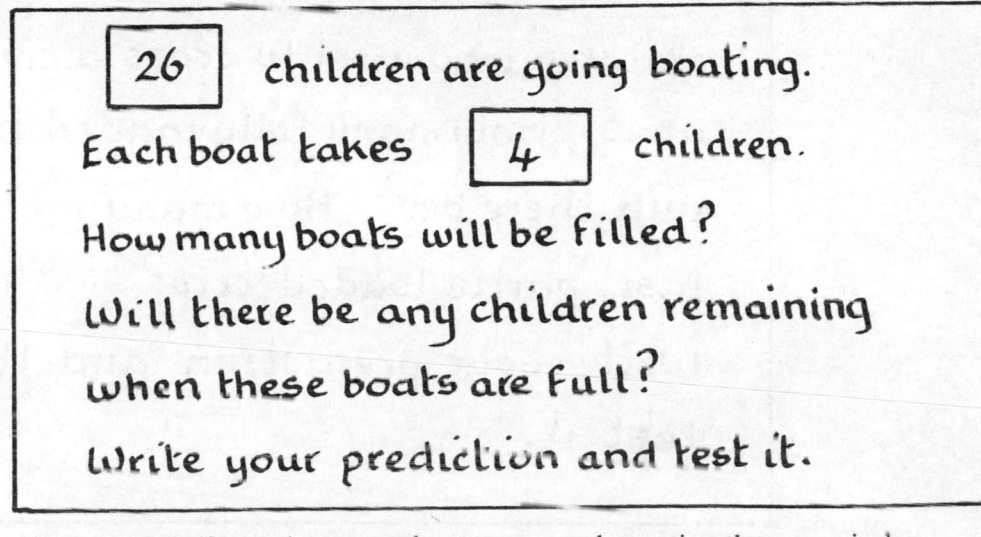

26 children are going boating.

Each boat takes 4 children.

How many boats will be filled?

Will there be any children remaining

when these boats are full?

Write your prediction and test it.

3. Each child first writes a number sentence, abstracting the numerical part of the problem (see Num 3.4/2) and completing the sentence. E.g. (in this example):

$$26 \xrightarrow{\text{make groups of 4}} 6 \text{ groups rem 2}$$

4. They then relate this result back into the number story, and write this also. In this example,

6 boats will be filled

There will be 2 children remaining

5. They test their predictions in two ways:
   (i) by comparison with each others' results;
   (ii) physically, using the small objects to represent (in this case) children.
6. If all get the same result, they may agree that physical testing is not necessary. Otherwise, it should be used.
7. Each correct prediction scores 1 point.
8. Steps 1 to 7 are repeated with a different problem and different numbers.
   Note About one-third of the problems should have the start and action numbers in reverse order, so that children do not develop a mechanical routine. E.g.,

A raft is big enough to support [A] children. If there are [S] children who want to cross a river on it, how many fully loaded trips will there be? How many on the last, partly loaded trip? Write your prediction and then test it.

Discussion of activities

Activity 1 has a familiar look. It is the Start, Action, Result sequence with physical materials for building a new concept. The concept is grouping, one of the contributors to the higher order concept of division.

Activity 2 tests their grasp of the concept, and consolidates it, by using it in a predictive game. At this stage we leave it to the children to devise their own methods. Some may use counting on in twos, threes, fours, fives, with or without the help of finger counting. Others may discover for themselves the relation between this and multiplication. For larger numbers it is necessary to use known multiplication facts, and in topics 5 and 6 this will be taught. For the present, I think it is good to allow room for children to exercise their own ingenuity.

Activity 3 applies the new skill to solving problems given as number stories. This uses and further consolidates two abilities already developed for the operations of addition, subtraction, multiplication: namely abstraction of a number sentence from a number story, and using objects to symbolise other objects.

In activity 2, we ask children to test their results by both mode 2 (comparison) and mode 1 (physical prediction). This is how results are tested in engineering, navigation, electronics, and other areas of applied mathematics. In activity 3, we allow that if everyone agrees on a result, it may be accepted as correct. This is how the pure mathematicians do it.

OBSERVE AND LISTEN   **REFLECT**   **DISCUSS**

Num 6.2   SHARING EQUALLY

Concepts   (i)   Equal shares.
(ii)   Remainders.

Abilities   (i)   Starting with a set of given number, to separate this into a required number of equal shares.
(ii)   To state the number in each share, and the remainder

| Discussion of concepts | Sharing is the next contributor to the mathematical operation of division. Physically it is quite different, as may be seen from the diagrams at the beginning of the next topic (Num 6.3).
Here we have yet another example of how the same mathematical model can represent quite different physical situations. This is what makes them so useful, because multi-purpose; but it is also what can so easily cause confusion if we do not take care in the building up of these multi-purpose, higher-order, concepts. |
|---|---|

Activity 1   Sharing equally

An activity for up to 6 children. Its purpose is to introduce the sharing aspect of division. Note that in the present context, sharing always means *equal* sharing.

Materials
- SAR board (sharing) see figure 13.
- Start cards 10-25.*
- Action cards 2-5.*
- 25 (or more) small objects.
- Pencil and paper for each child.

* As for Num 6.1/1 and 2.

What they do
1. The start cards and the action cards are shuffled and put face down in the upper parts of their spaces on the activity board.
2. The first child turns over the top start card, and puts out a set of this number.
3. The second child turns over the top action card, and distributes this set equally between as many children as appears on the action card. If there are 5 or 6 children, there will always be enough children to do this. If (e.g.) there are only 3 children, and the action card indicates that the set to be shared by 5 children, then 2 children must ask for (and receive) 'A share for my friend, who isn't here.'
4. All the children then write a number sentence recording what was done, and the result. Example:

23   shared between 5 → 4 each rem 3

This is read as
'Start with 23, share between 5, result 4 in each share, remainder 3'. If

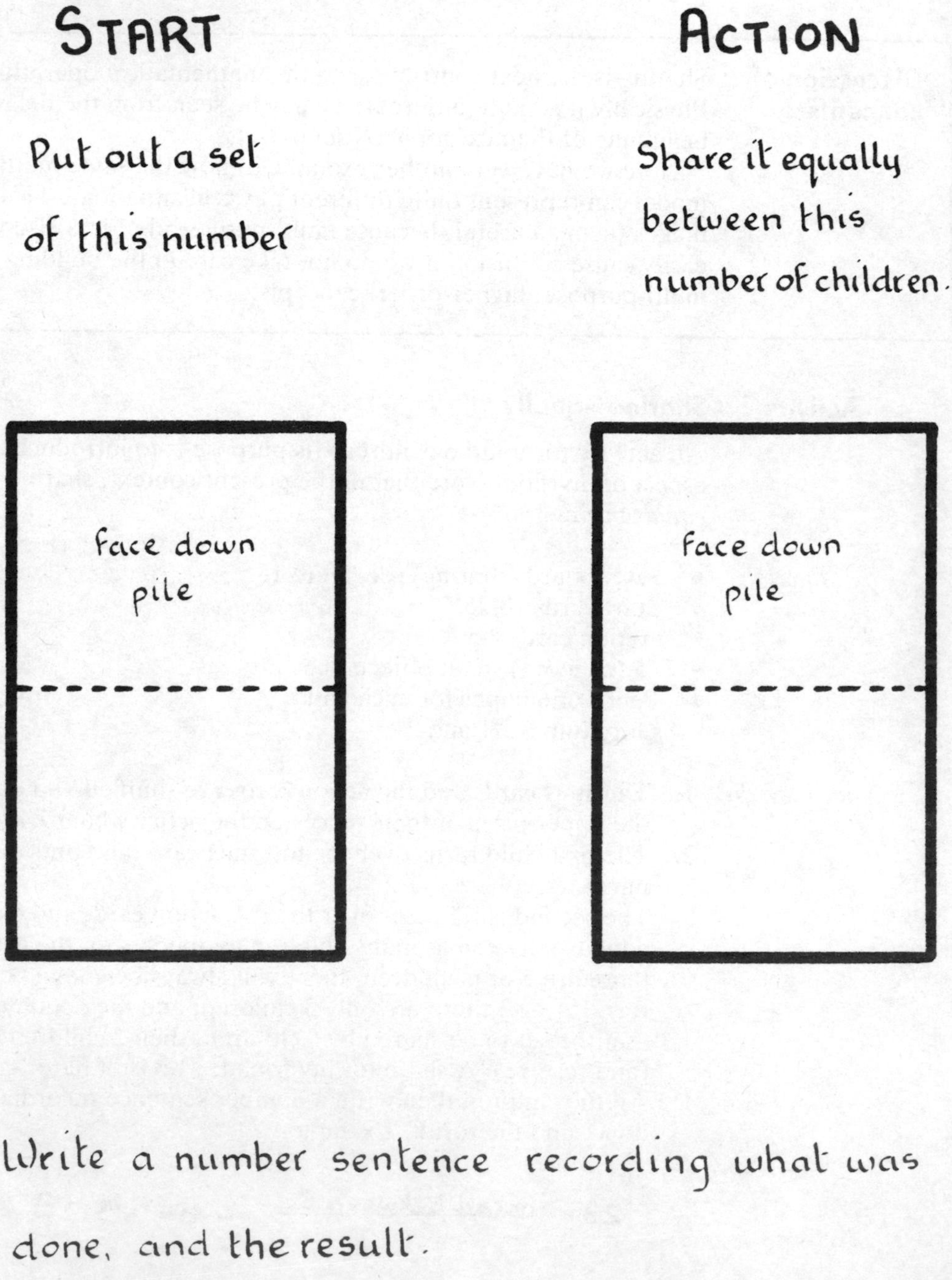

START

Put out a set of this number

face down
pile

ACTION

Share it equally between this number of children.

face down
pile

Write a number sentence recording what was done, and the result.

Figure 13   Start, Action, Result: Sharing

there is no remainder, they should say either '. . . remainder zero' or
'. . . exactly'.

5. They compare their results.
6. Steps 2, 3, 4 are then repeated.

Activity 2   **'My share is . . .'**

A game for up to 6 children. Its purpose is to consolidate the concept of
sharing by using it in a predictive game.

Materials
- Game board, see figure 14.
- Start cards 10-25.*
- Action cards 2-5.*
- 25 (or more) small objects.
- Pencil and paper for each child, and for scoring.

* As for activity 1.

Rules of the game
1. The start cards and the action cards are shuffled and put face down in
   the upper parts of their spaces on the game board.
2. The top card of each pile is turned over.
3. A set of the specified number is put out.
4. Players then take turns, as follows.
5. The player whose turn it is looks at the action card, and decides what
   her (equal) share will be (using pencil and paper if she likes). She then
   says 'My share is. . .', and takes this number of objects.
6. She may need some help, initially. Suppose that 19 objects are to be
   shared between 5. 'If you gave everyone 1 each, how many would that
   use? If you gave everyone 2 each, how many would that use?' (And so
   on).
7. The correct number of other players take the same number of shares as
   the player in step 5. This will show whether she has decided correctly
   or not.
8. One point is scored for a correct prediction.
9. It is now another player's turn, and steps 2 to 7 are repeated.
10. When players are proficient, they may agree to play without pencil and
    paper, except for scoring.

Activity 3   **'My share is . . . and I also know the remainder which is. . .'**

This is a more advanced version of activity 2. The rules are the same,
except that in step 5 the player also predicts the remainder. If correct, she
scores a second point. E.g., if the start number was 23 to be shared by 4,
she might say, 'My share is 5, and I also know the remainder which is 3.'
Since this is correct, she would score a second point.

Activity 4   **Word problems (sharing)**

An activity for up to 6 children. It parallels word problems (grouping)
(Num 6.1/3), and its purpose is similar: to use the skills acquired in
activities 1 and 2 for the solution of number problems

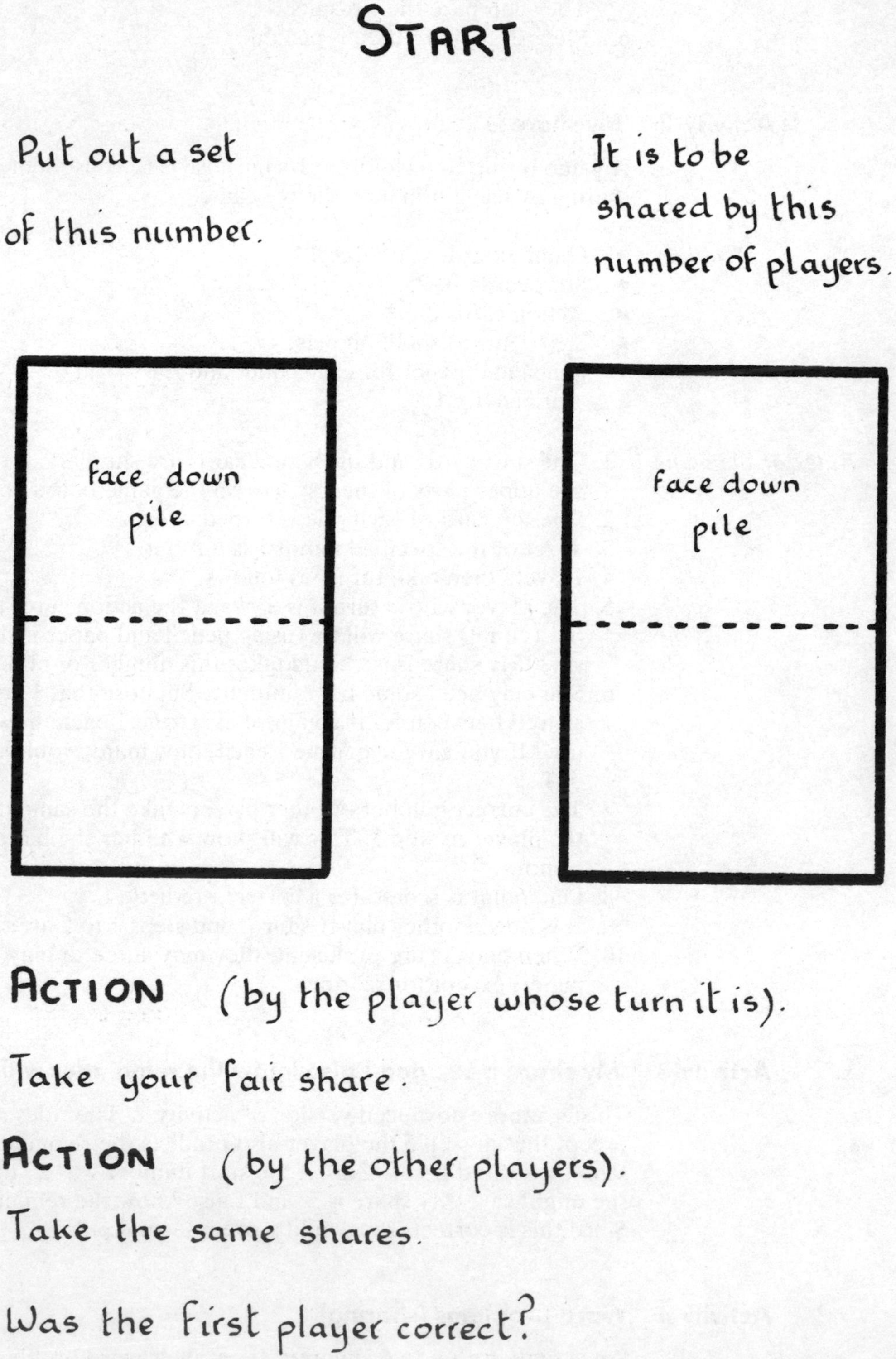

Start

Put out a set
of this number.

It is to be
shared by this
number of players.

```
┌─────────────────┐        ┌─────────────────┐
│                 │        │                 │
│   face  down    │        │   face down     │
│     pile        │        │     pile        │
│- - - - - - - - -│        │- - - - - - - - -│
│                 │        │                 │
│                 │        │                 │
└─────────────────┘        └─────────────────┘
```

ACTION   (by the player whose turn it is).

Take your fair share.

ACTION   (by the other players).

Take the same shares.

Was the first player correct?

Figure 14   Board for 'My share is . . .'

Materials
- Problem cards, as illustrated in step 2 below.
- Start cards 10-25.*
- Action cards 2-5.*
- 25 or more small objects.
- Pencil and paper for each child.

* As for Num 6.1/3.

What they do
1. The problem cards are shuffled and put face down. Likewise for the start and action cards.
2. The top card in the problem pile is turned over. The top cards in the start and action piles are turned over, and put in the start and action spaces on the problem card. The result should look something like this

A packet containing ⬚17⬚ sweets is
to be shared by ⬚5⬚ children.
How many sweets will they have each?
Write your prediction
and then test it.

3. Each child first writes a number sentence, abstracting the numerical part of the problem and completing the sentence. E.g. (in this example):

$$17 \xrightarrow{\text{shared by 5}} 3 \text{ each rem } 2$$

4. They then relate this back to the problem, and write this also. In this example,

They will have 3 sweets each.
(2 left over)

5. They test their predictions in two ways:
   (i) by comparison with each others' results;
   (ii) physically, using the small objects to represent (in this case) sweets.
6. If all get the same result, they may agree that physical testing is not necessary. Otherwise it should be used.
7. Each correct prediction scores 1 point.
8. Steps 1 to 7 are repeated with a different problem and different numbers.
   Note About one-third of the problems should have the start and action

191

numbers in reverse order, so that children do not develop a mechanical routine. E.g.,

A gardeners are asked to plant trees altogether. If they each plant the same number, how many each will that be? How many more trees will there still be to plant? Write your prediction and then test it. S

| Discussion of activities | These activities closely parallel those in topic 1. However, we have found that many children find sharing more difficult than grouping, so plenty of practice is necessary, especially at activities 2 and 3. |

OBSERVE AND LISTEN   **REFLECT**   **DISCUSS**

Num 6.3 DIVISION AS A MATHEMATICAL OPERATION

Concept   The connection between grouping and sharing.

Ability   To explain this connection. (This is most easily done with the help of physical materials.)

| Discussion of concept | Physically, grouping and sharing look quite different.

Start with 15.

Make groups of 3.

Resulting number of groups is 5. |

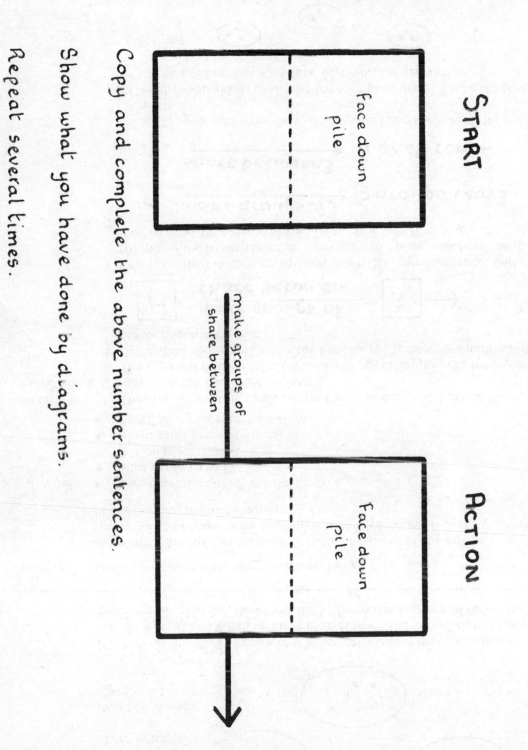

Figure 15 Different questions, same answer. Why?

START

Action

face down pile

face down pile

make groups of
share between

Copy and complete the above number sentences.

Show what you have done by diagrams.

Repeat several times.

What do you notice?   Can you explain why?

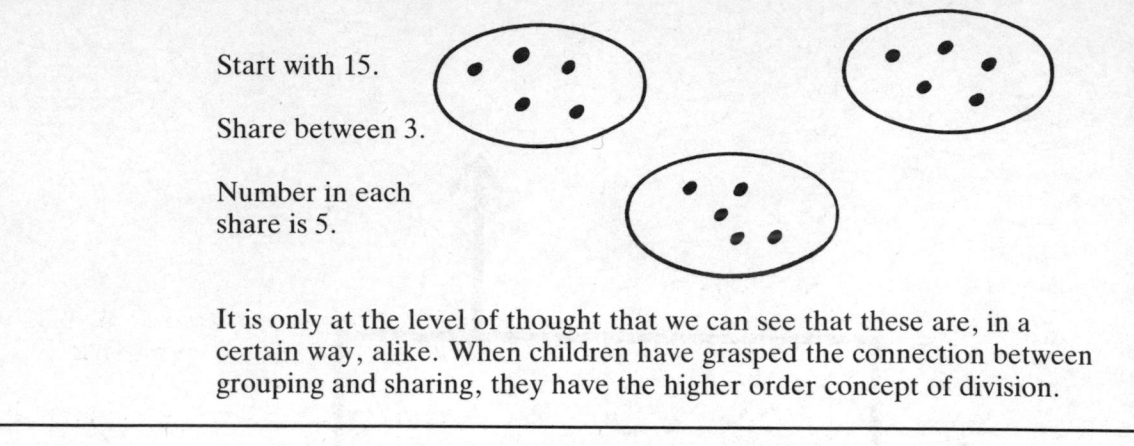

Start with 15.

Share between 3.

Number in each
share is 5.

It is only at the level of thought that we can see that these are, in a certain way, alike. When children have grasped the connection between grouping and sharing, they have the higher order concept of division.

Activity 1   Different questions, same answer. Why?

A problem for children to work at in small groups. (I suggest twos or threes.) The purpose is for them to discover for themselves the connection between grouping and sharing.

Materials
- Two-question board, see figure 15.
- Start cards 10 to 25.
- Action cards 2 to 5.
- 50 (or more) small objects.
- Pencil and paper for each child.

Introducing the problem
1. The start and action cards are shuffled and put face down in the upper spaces on the two question board.
2. The top card of each pile is turned and put face up in the lower space.
3. By reading above and below the line, there are now two unfinished number sentences. E.g.,

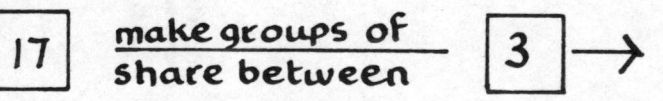

4. One (or more) in each group copy down the upper sentence, and one (or more) the lower sentence. They then complete whichever sentence they have written, using physical objects if they like. E.g.,

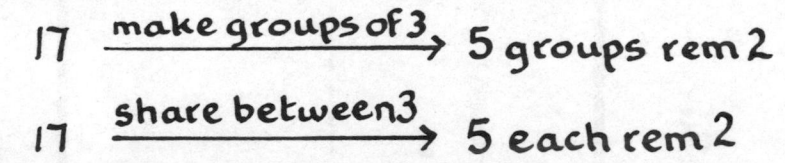

N.B. They should write these neatly, and keep them for later use in Activity 2.
5. They draw diagrams to show what they have done. These diagrams could be used in step 4, instead of physical objects. E.g.,

Grouping

Sharing

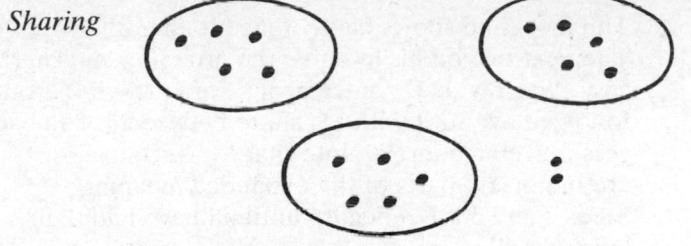

6. They compare the two results.
7. Steps 2, 3, 4 are repeated. Step 5 need not be repeated every time: its purpose is to emphasise that these are two different questions.
8. Ask, 'Will the two results always be the same? If so, why?'
9. Leave them to discuss this, and to arrive at a clear explanation. (One suggestion will be found in the discussion of activities.)
10. Return and hear their explanation, discussing it if necessary.

Activity 2   **Combining the number sentences**

An activity for a small group. Its purpose is to teach the notation for the mathematical operation of subtraction.

Materials   ● The number sentences which they have written in activity 1.
● Pencil and paper for each child.

What they do   1.   Have them compare the first number sentence of each kind. E.g.

$$17 \xrightarrow{\text{make groups of 3}} 5 \text{ groups rem } 2$$

$$17 \xrightarrow{\text{share between 3}} 5 \text{ each rem } 2$$

2.   Tell them that these two meanings may be combined in one number sentence. In this case, it would be

$$17 \div 3 = 5 \text{ rem } 2$$

This is read as
'17, divide by 3, result 5 remainder 2.'
or as
'17 divided by 3 equals 5 remainder 2.'
3.   They then repeat steps 1 and 2 for the other number sentences.

Activity 3   **Unpacking the parcel (division)**

A continuation of activity 2, for a small group. Its purpose is to remind children of the two possible meanings of a number sentence for division.

Materials   ● Pencil and paper for each child.

What they do   1.   They all write a division number sentence on their own paper. The first number should not be greater than 20.

$$11 \div 4 = 2 \text{ rem } 3$$

2. The first child shows his sentence to the others.
3. The next two on his left give the grouping and sharing meanings. In this case, 'Start with 11, make groups of 4, result 2 groups remainder 3' followed by 'Start with 11, share between 4, 2 in each share (or, each gets 2), remainder 3'. Note that '. . . groups', or '. . . in each share', are important parts of the expanded meaning.
4. Steps 2 and 3 are repeated until all have had their sentences 'unpacked'.

Activity 4   Mr Taylor's Game

This game for 2 players was invented by Mr Stephen Taylor, of Dorridge Junior School, and I am grateful to him for permission to include it here. Its purpose is to bring together addition, subtraction, multiplication, division, in a simple game.

Materials
- Number cards: 1 set 0 to 25, 3 sets 0 to 9.
- Game board (see figure 16).
- Counters of a different colour for each player.

What they do
1. The object is to get 3 counters together in a line. They must be in the same row, column, or diagonal.
2. The number cards are shuffled and put face down.
3. The first player turns over two cards. He may choose to add, subtract, multiply, or divide the numbers shown. Division must, however, be exact.
4. He puts one of his counters on the corresponding square.
5. The other player does likewise.
6. Play continues until one player has 3 in a row.
7. Another round may now be played. The loser begins.

Discussion of activities

Activity 1 poses a problem, for children to solve by the activity of their own intelligence. When they have seen the connection between grouping and sharing, they have the higher order mathematical concept of division.

The easiest path to seeing the correspondence is, I think, a physical one. If we have 15 objects to share between 3 persons, a natural way to do this is to begin by giving one object to each person. This takes 3 objects, a single 'round', which we may *think of* as a group of 3. The next round may be thought of as another group of 3, and so on. Each round gives one object to each share, so the number of rounds is the number in each share.

This verbal description by itself is harder to follow than a physical demonstration accompanied by explanation. This I see as yet another demonstration of the advantage of combining modes 1 and 2.

Activity 2 provides a notation for these two aspects of division. Note that the first number is the operand, that on which the operation is done. The operation is the division sign together with the second number, e.g. $\div 3$.

5	20	19	25	1
21	7	14	6	16
3	23	11	18	24
9	17	8	13	2
12	4	10	22	15

Figure 16 Mr Taylor's Game.

© Stephen Taylor. 1981

Activity 3 is another example of 'Unpacking the parcel'. There is much less in this one than in the subtraction parcel, but is still a useful reminder of the two physical meanings combined in a single mathematical notation.

After all this, they deserve a game. Mr Taylor's game fits in nicely at this stage.

OBSERVE AND LISTEN   **REFLECT**   **DISCUSS**

[Space 1] SHAPE

Shapes in the environment and in mathematics

Space 1.1   SHAPES FROM OBJECTS

Concept   Outlines taken from objects, in various positions and aspects.

Ability   To match an object to one or more of its outlines.

Discussion of concept

Though most of the objects in our environment are three–dimensional, our view of them at any given moment is two-dimensional. What we usually see is an outline, with other detail within this outline from which we derive an awareness of solidity This we can do without knowing how we do it. Our perceptual processes take care of it for us, usually without conscious thought.

When we describe a geometrical solid, such as a cube or a pyramid, we do so by saying how many faces it has and what are their shapes, how many edges, how many verticals. This is a more conscious activity, involving seeing, thinking, and naming. In this topic, we begin to make conscious the relationships between objects and the outlines of their faces.

Note that in activity 2, we use the terms 'square' and 'oblong'. These are two kinds of rectangle, in the same way as boys and girls are two kinds of children.

Activity 1   Matching objects to outlines

A game for a small group. Its purpose is to teach children to abstract the outline of an object.

Materials
- A tray of objects, each of which can be put flat and drawn round.
- An outlines card for each child. Each card has on it five outlines (more if you like) obtained by putting one of the objects flat on the card, and drawing round it.

Note on materials   Suitable objects might be a twopenny coin, a rubber, a paper clip, bottle tops of various sizes and shapes, little stones which have at least one face flat or nearly so. If some of the objects can be drawn round in more ways than one, so much the better.

Altogether, there must be at least one object for every space on every card. E.g., if there are 6 cards each with 5 outlines, the tray will have on it at least 30 objects. This will become clearer after you have read the description of the game. The objects need not all be different.

Rules of play   1.   The tray of objects is put in the middle. Each child has an outlines card.

2. The purpose of each player is to fill her card with objects matching the outlines.
3. Each in turn takes an object from the tray and puts it on her card to match an outline.
4. If it does not match, she has to return it to the tray and it is the next player's turn. (This rule may be relaxed at the learning stage.)
5. The winner is the one who first fills her card. However, the others should continue until all have filled their cards.

Activity 2   **'I spy . . .' (shapes)**

A game for 2-4 players, possibly 5 or 6. Its purpose is to consolidate and generalise the concept of an outline.

Materials   • Cut-out cardboard shapes:
a square, a circle, and two oblongs. One oblong should be about 6 cm by 4 cm and the other one about 10 cm by 3 cm.
   • A sheet of paper.

Rules of the game   1. One of the players chooses a shape which she can match with something visible in the environment. This might be, say, a door and an oblong. She puts this shape on top of the paper, the others being out of sight underneath.
2. She then says, 'I spy, with my little eye, something shaped like this – an oblong.'
3. The others try to guess what this is. (You may decide that they take turns, or let players speak when they are able to make a guess.)
4. The first player to guess right is the next to do the 'I spy . . .'.
5. If nobody can guess right, they may give up and the spier tells what the object is.

Discussion of activities

Both of these activities involve quite a lot of abstracting. An outline on card looks very different from a solid object, and a card cut-out looks very different from a door or window. The differences are greater than the resemblances.

Activity 1 allows physical comparison of objects and outlines – mode 1 testing. Activity 2, 'I spy . . .', involves making hypotheses about what the 'spier' is thinking of. These are then tested verbally. So activity 2 is somewhat more abstract than activity 1. Note that two kinds of oblong are provided, one long and thin and the other broader relative to its length, so that the children can choose an oblong reasonably like the object they are thinking of. By naming both of these as oblongs, we convey that these are two different examples of the same geometrical figure.

OBSERVE AND LISTEN   **REFLECT**   **DISCUSS**

Space 1.2   LINES, STRAIGHT AND CURVED

Concept   Straight lines and curved lines.

Abilities   (i)   To recognise examples of each.
(ii)   To produce examples of each.

Discussion of concept

These concepts are straightforward. However, it is worth noting that here again there is a distinction between the everyday usage of the word 'line' and the mathematical usage. In everyday usage, we talk (e.g.) about a thick line and a thin line. To a mathematician, a line has no thickness and no width. Just as the numeral 5 (which is a mark on paper) is a symbol for the number 5 (which is a concept, a mental object), so also the (everyday) lines we draw on paper are ways of representing mathematical lines.

   At this stage we will of course not be explaining this distinction to children, but it is as well to know it ourselves.

Activity 1   **Drawing pictures with straight and curved lines**

An activity for up to 6 children.

Materials   • A picture for each child.
   • Coloured felt-tip pens.
   • A spinner, with spaces marked 'straight line' or 'curved line', each with an example of a straight or curved line.
Note Specimen pictures are provided in Vol. 1a. Each is made up of straight and curved lines. It should be clear where each line starts and finishes. The lines should be somewhat faint, such as are produced by a spirit duplicator.

What they do   1.   Each child in turn spins the spinner.
   2.   He is then allowed to colour one line in his picture, straight or curved according to where the spinner points.
   3.   If (e.g.) there are only straight lines left uncoloured, and the spinner points to 'curved line', he cannot use his turn.
   4.   As they complete their pictures, players withdraw from steps 1 and 2.
   5.   Since this activity is for emphasising straight and curved lines, which are used as outlines, it is probably better not to encourage them to colour in their pictures. If they particularly want to, they could be allowed to do so.

Activity 2   **'I have a straight / curved line, like . . .'**

A game for up to 6 children. Its purpose is to relate the concepts straight and curved to objects in the environment.

Materials   • A pack of cards, each of them having a single line, either straight or curved: about 10 of each.

Rules of the game
1. The cards are shuffled, and the pack is put on the table face down.
2. The first player picks up the top card, looks at it, and says (e.g.) 'I have a curved line, like the edge of that flower pot'.
3. The others respond by saying 'Agree', or perhaps 'Disagree'.
4. If the latter, there is discussion until agreement is reached.
   N.B. Curved lines need not be exactly similar to the shapes in the environment.
5. The next player in turn picks up a card, and steps 2, 3, 4 are repeated until all the cards have been used.

Activity 3   'Please may I have . . . ?' (Straight and curved lines)

A game for 4 or 5 children.

Materials   ●   A pack of cards like those illustrated in step 2 below.

Rules of the game
1. The cards are shuffled, and all are dealt to the players.
2. The object is to form pairs of cards which are alike in their kinds of line,

such as these

or these

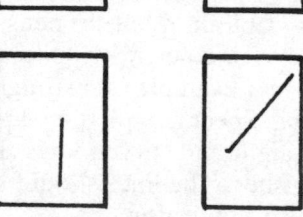

3. Players begin by putting down any pairs which they have.
4. Then, starting with the player to the left of the dealer, children ask in turn for cards which they need to make pairs with cards they already have.
5. They may ask whoever they like. E.g., 'Please, Denise, may I have one straight (line) and one curved (line)?' (The words in brackets may be omitted if you find it necessary to shorten the sentence.)
6. If the player asked has the card, he gives it. Otherwise he replies 'Sorry'.
7. The first player to put down all his cards is the winner, but the others continue play until all have put down all their cards.

Discussion of activities

The first activity requires children to distinguish between straight and curved lines in their pictures. These lines they then copy in the simplest possible way, by tracing over them. Here we have mode 1 concept building by two kinds of experience, seeing and doing. Activity 2 involves putting these concepts to use by seeking out examples in the environment. Differences such as length of line, degree of curvature if curved, have to be ignored, centring only on the property straight or curved. Activity 3 is particularly for linking these concepts with their mathematical vocabulary.

OBSERVE AND LISTEN   **REFLECT**   **DISCUSS**

Space 1.3 LINE FIGURES, OPEN AND CLOSED

Concepts   (i)   Open and closed figures.
           (ii) Boundaries.
          (iii) Inside and outside.
Abilities   (i)   To distinguish between open and closed figures.
           (ii) To associate these with the property of a boundary, as described below.

Discussion of concepts	Here, for a change, the everyday and the mathematical meanings of the words are not very different. If the door is open, we can enter and leave the room. While it is closed, we cannot.
	In mathematics, a figure is *closed* if it makes a boundary between two regions, an inside and an outside, such that we cannot get from one to the other without crossing the boundary. Otherwise the figure is *open*. An open figure does not have an inside and an outside.

Closed figure   *Open figure*

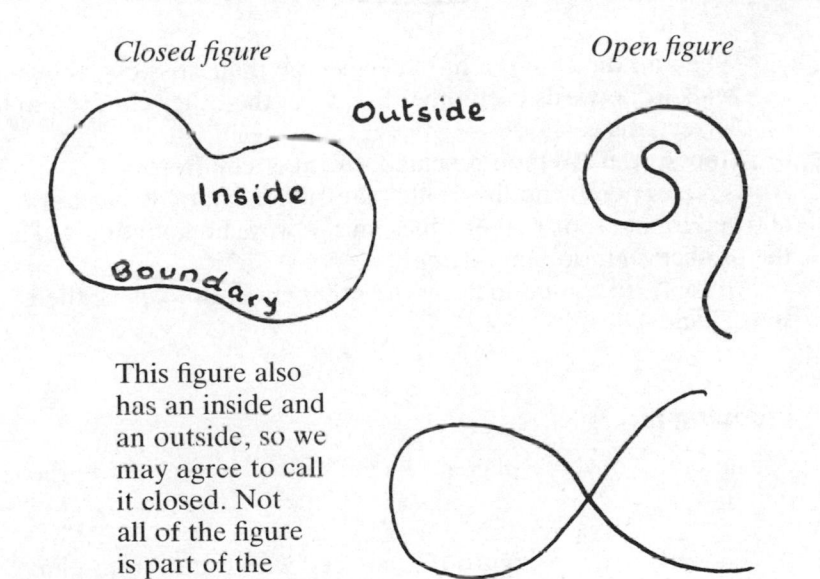

This figure also has an inside and an outside, so we may agree to call it closed. Not all of the figure is part of the boundary.

203

Activity 1 'Can they meet?'

A game for 2 to 6 children. Its purpose is to help children to form the concept of a boundary.

Materials
- Four small animal models. You might choose a pair which are friends, e.g. a sheep and a cow, and a pair which are enemies, e.g. a pig and a wolf.
- A length of cord.

Rules of play
1. Explain that the string represents a fence, which the animals cannot get past.
2. Explain that some animals are friends, and some are enemies.
3. One child now arranges the length of string on the table to represent the fence.
4. She also places two of the animals on the table, and asks 'Can they meet?' (Initially this should be made easy, but as the game progresses children will enjoy making it more difficult to decide: see illustration.)

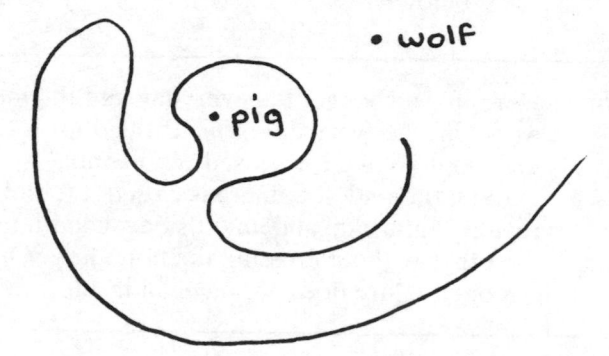

5. When all the children have decided on their answers, the animals are 'walked' towards each other by one of the other children to find the correct answer.
6. Steps 1 to 5 are then repeated, by other children.

Notes 1. There is no fixed rule that friendly animals must always be allowed to meet, or that enemies must always be kept apart. This makes the prediction more interesting!

2. It may be a good idea for the other children to close their eyes during steps 3 and 4.

Activity 2 Escaping pig

A game for 2 or more players. Its purpose is to consolidate the concept of a boundary.

Materials
- Game board (see figure 17), covered with transparent film.
- Pig.
- OHP pen.
- Damp rag to clean board.
- Die marked 'open' on 3 faces, 'closed' on 3 faces.

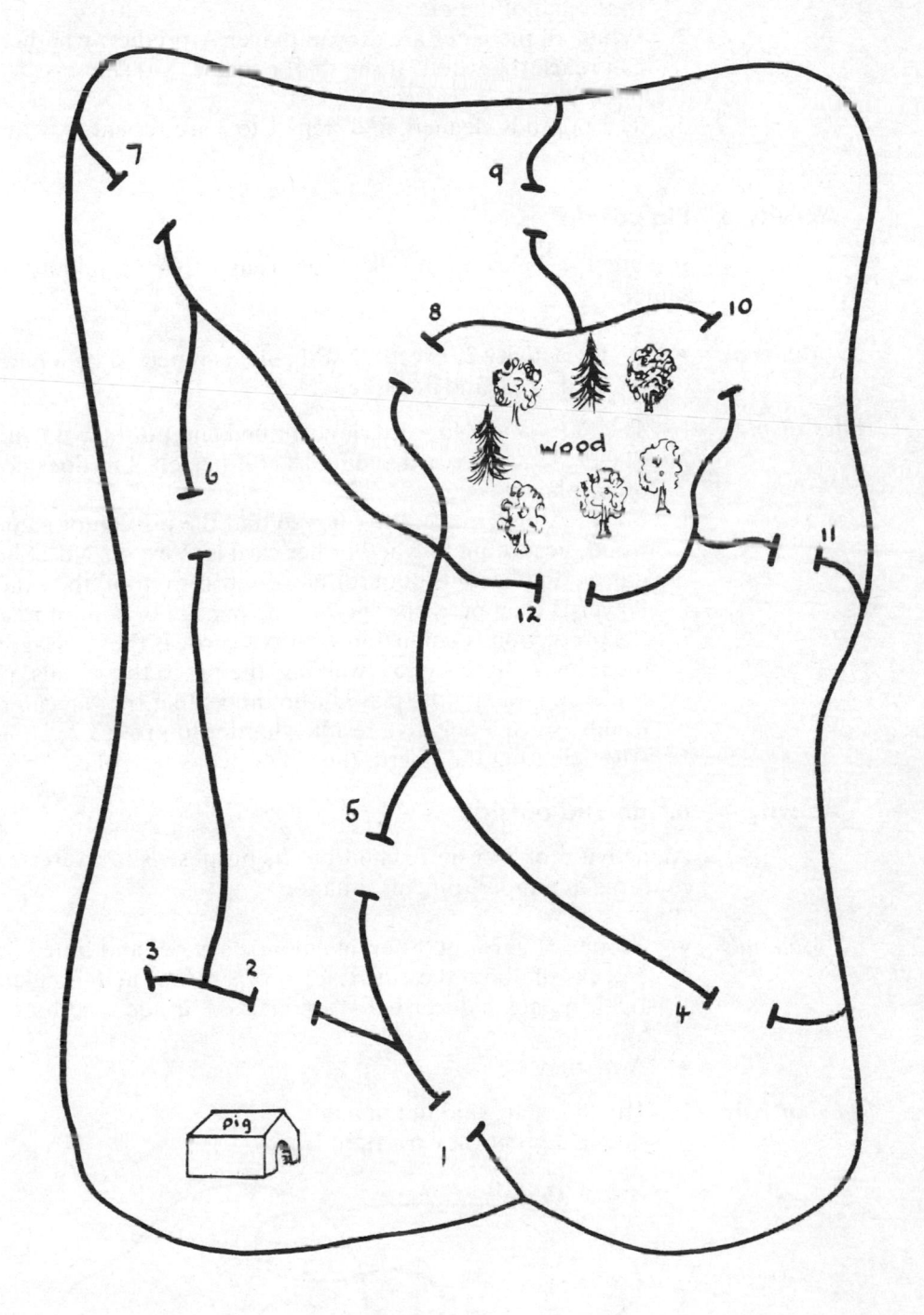

Figure 17 Escaping pig.

Rules of play
1. Player A puts her pig outside the sty.
2. The other player(s) throw the die for each gate in turn. With the overhead projector pen, they draw in the gate open or closed according to the fall of the die.
3. When all the gates are drawn, player A predicts whether or not the pig can reach the wood. If she thinks that it can, she tests by 'walking' the pig there.
4. The board is cleaned, and steps 1 to 3 are repeated with another child as player A.

Activity 3 Pig puzzle

A game for 2 players. It follows on from activity 2, and its purpose is the same.

Materials
- As for activity 2, except that the die is replaced by a pack of 6 cards, 3 marked 'Yes' and 3 marked 'No'.

Rules of play
1. The 'Yes' and 'No' cards are shuffled and put face down.
2. Player A takes a card and looks at it herself, but does not show it to the other player.
3. Player A now marks the gates so that the pig can or cannot reach the wood, according to whether her card is 'Yes' or 'No'. She may make this a complicated route (or non-route), to 'fool' the other player.
4. Player B then predicts whether the pig can or cannot reach the woods.
5. B's prediction is compared with A's card. If these disagree, one of them tests physically by 'walking' the pig to the woods. (The testing could be done by the player who thinks that the pig can reach the woods, since a negative result is harder to prove.)
6. After clearing the board, the children change roles.

Activity 4 Inside and outside

An activity for 2 or more children. Its purpose is to exercise the new concepts in a more difficult situation.

Materials
- 2 loops of cord, in different colours: say red and blue.
- 2 packs of about 8 cards. Each is of a colour matching one of the cords. In each pack half the cards are marked 'inside' and half are marked 'outside'.
- A marker.

Rules of play
1. The loops are laid out in any shapes so that they overlap. E.g.:

206

2. The cards are shuffled and put face down on the table.
3. Player A takes one card from each pile. She looks at these but does not show them. Suppose that the red card reads outside and the blue card reads inside. The marker is put on the table accordingly.
4. Player B must now describe the position of the marker. In this example she would say, 'Inside the blue loop and outside the red loop.'
5. B's description is compared with A's cards.
6. They then check by holding a finger on the table where the marker is, and pulling gently on the loops. First one, then the other (not both together). If the marker is outside, the loop will come away; if inside, the finger will hold it.
7. Steps 1 to 6 are repeated with other children as A and B.

Note This game may be played with a single loop and one pack of cards. This provides a simple introduction to the version described.

Discussion of activities

Activities 1, 2, and 3 all use physical objects for learning and applying the concepts of inside/outside, and boundary. These are properties which a closed figure has, and an open figure does not have. They lead to physical predictions which can be tested. Activity 4 is more sophisticated, and not only in the way which is easily apparent, that of using two overlapping figures. It also uses another property of a closed loop, that it may have its shape changed (as long as we do not cut it) without affecting its inside/outside property.

OBSERVE AND LISTEN   REFLECT   DISCUSS

Space 1.4   PARALLEL LINES, PERPENDICULAR LINES

Concepts (i)   'Is parallel to'
(ii) 'Is perpendicular to'
as relationships between two lines.

Abilities (i)   To recognise examples of parallel or perpendicular lines.
(ii) To construct examples of parallel or perpendicular lines.

Discussion of concepts

Just as we have relationships between two numbers (e.g. 'is greater than', 'is equal to'), so also we have relationships between two lines such as those in the present topic. If line a is parallel to line b, then line b is parallel to line a, so we may also say that these lines are parallel (meaning, parallel to each other). This is true also of the relationship 'is perpendicular to'. This reversibility does not hold for all relationships. E.g. it is true for 'is equal to', but not for 'is greater than'. Here, however, our main concern is with the particular relationships named in this topic, not with the ways in which relationships themselves may be classified.

Activity 1 'My rods are parallel / perpendicular'

An activity for up to 6 children. Its purpose is to help children learn these two relationships.

Materials
- A pack of 20* cards. On 10 of these is written 'parallel' with an example, and on the other 10 is written 'perpendicular' with an example.
- For each child, 2 rods of different lengths. A square section is useful to prevent rolling.

* Any even number of cards will do, provided that there are enough to give a good variety of examples. In the examples, it is important that the pairs of lines should be of different lengths, and oblique relative to the edges of the paper. (See illustrations in Discussion of activities.) Parallel and perpendicular are relationships between lines, independently of how these lines are positioned on the paper.

What they do
Stage (a), with cards
1. The cards are shuffled, and put face down.
2. Each child in turn takes a card and puts it in front of him face up.
3. The children then put their rods on top of the lines in the illustration.
4. In turn, they show their cards to the others and say, 'My rods are parallel', or 'My rods are perpendicular', as the case may be.
5. Each child then takes another card, which he puts face up on top of the card he has already. Steps 3 and 4 are then repeated.

Stage (b), without cards
1. Each child in turn puts his rods either parallel or perpendicular, and says 'My rods are parallel/perpendicular' (as the case may be).
2. The others say 'Agree' or 'Disagree'.
3. A child may deliberately give a false description if he chooses. The others should then all disagree.

Activity 2 'All put your rods parallel / perpendicular to the big rod'

An activity for up to 6 children. Its purpose is to consolidate the concepts parallel and perpendicular.

Materials
- Ruler or big rod.
- Small rod for each child. (It is good if the small rods are of assorted length.)

What they do
1. The teacher puts down the big rod and says 'All put your rods parallel to the big rod.'
2. The children do so.
3. Steps 1 and 2 are repeated several times. Encourage variety in the placing of the children's rods.
4. Then, after step 2, the teacher removes the big rod and asks the children what they notice about their own rods. It should be brought out in discussion that the children's rods are all parallel *to each other*.
5. Steps 1, 2, 3, 4 are repeated with the instruction '. . . perpendicular to the big rod.'

Activity 3   Colouring pictures

An activity for 2 to 6 children.

Materials
- A picture for each child, made up of lines which are all in parallel or perpendicular pairs. The pictures should be in feint lines, e.g. from a spirit duplicator. (See illustration below.)
- A pack of parallel / perpendicular cards, as used in activities 1, 2, 3.

What they do
1. The pack is shuffled and put face down.
2. The first child turns over the top card.
3. He is then allowed to colour two lines in his picture, which must be either parallel or perpendicular according to the card.
4. The other children in turn do steps 2 and 3.
5. Putting pencils on top of the lines helps to show up which lines are parallel or perpendicular.
6. Continue until all the pictures have been coloured.

Discussion of activities

Activity 1 is for building the concepts parallel, perpendicular from a variety of examples. Again I emphasise the importance of choosing examples which do not link these concepts either with length of line, or position on paper. If this mistake is not avoided, children will be able to recognise examples like these:

but not like these:

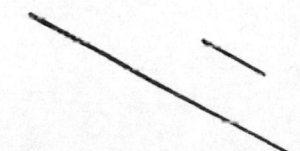

Activity 1 is also for linking the concepts with the appropriate vocabulary. 'Perpendicular' is quite a hard word, so you may decide to practise children in saying it. Initially they are not expected to read these words from the cards. They learn them orally, linked with the visual examples of parallel and perpendicular lines. In this way they will gradually learn to recognise the written words. Stage (b) of this activity uses the newly formed concepts to generate examples, with peer-group checking. Activity 3 is similar, but develops a situation in which more than two rods are involved. Of these, a given pair may be either parallel or perpendicular.

Activity 4 is the payoff. We now have a picture with many lines. Correct recognition of relationships between these lines allows children to colour their lines. You will recognise the development of the earlier activity Space 1.3/1 to make use of these more advanced mathematical ideas. Why more advanced? Because being straight or curved is a property of a single line; being parallel or perpendicular is a property of a pair of lines – a relational concept.

OBSERVE AND LISTEN   **REFLECT**   **DISCUSS**

[NuSp 1] THE NUMBER TRACK and THE NUMBER LINE

Powerful support to our thinking about numbers.

NuSp 1.1 CORRESPONDENCE BETWEEN SIZE OF NUMBER AND POSITION ON TRACK

Concept   Correspondence between these two orders:
size of number,
position on track.

Ability   To relate the number of a set to length on a number track.

<table>
<tr>
<td>Discussion of concept</td>
<td>

The number track is a spatial representation of number. It leads on to the number line, and these together are of importance throughout mathematics, from the reception or kindergarten class in the infant school to mathematics at university level. They provide a valuable support for our thinking about numbers in the form of a pictorial representation.

Some teachers use the term 'number strip' for a number track represented on paper, as in the diagram above. Conceptually, however, it is the same as the physical number track made (usually) of plastic, so I shall use the term 'number track' for both.
</td>
</tr>
</table>

Activity 1   **'I predict – here' on the number track**

A game for children to play in pairs. Its purpose is to establish the relation between size of number and position on the track.

Materials
- Number track up to ten, on card.
- Plastic number track.
- 10 small objects such as bottle tops, conkers, small shells.
- 10 cubes for number track.
- Set cards as illustrated overleaf (1 to 10).

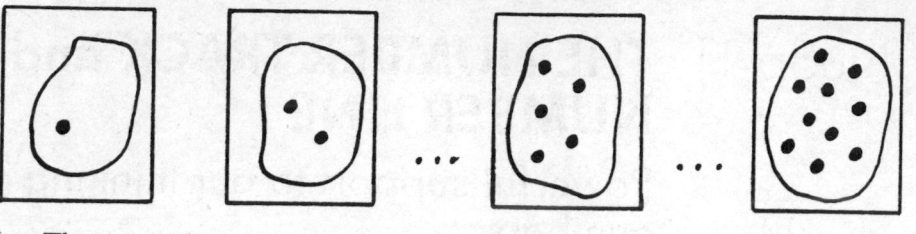

Note The set cards are not numbered, to avoid short-circuiting the conceptual activity by simply matching the numerals on card and track. The only numerals are on the track, and these are written outside the squares.

What they do **Form (a)**

1. The set cards are shuffled and put face down.
2. Child A turns over the top card and puts it face up on the table.
3. Together the children put one of the small objects on each dot in the set loop, to make a physical set matching the set of dots on the card.
4. Child A then predicts how far these objects will come on the number track when one of them is put in each space.
5. He says 'I predict – here' and marks his prediction in some way. (If the number track is covered in plastic film, a blob of Blu-Tack has the advantage that it will stay put.)
6. Child A then tests his prediction physically, as illustrated below.

Card:

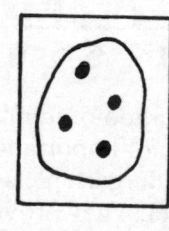

Prediction:

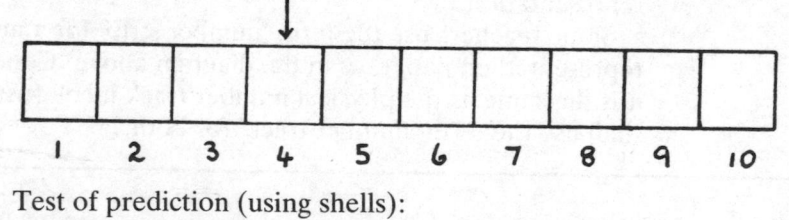

Test of prediction (using shells):

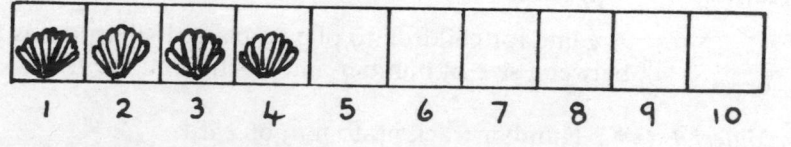

Form (b) This is played exactly as in form (a), except that multilink or unifix cubes are used and a plastic number track. Please use both forms. We do not want the concept linked only with cubes.

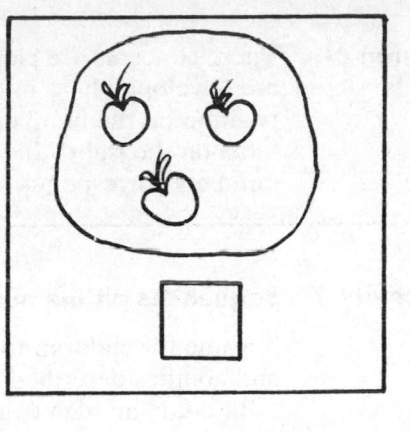

*Variation**
This uses pictures
instead of dots,
with a box under
the set loop.

1. The child counts the pictures and writes their number in the box.
2. He puts one cube on each picture.
3. These are then transferred to the number track. The last square
   reached should have the same numeral as has been written in the box.

* Suggested by Mrs Marion Jones, of Lady Katherine Leveson's School,
Solihull.

Discussion of activity	The number track and the number line have much in common. In the number line, however, numbers are associated with points on a line, not spaces on a track. The number line begins at zero, the number track begins at one. The number line schema, moreover, is developed further in a variety of ways. It is extrapolated backwards to represent negative numbers; points are interpolated to represent fractional numbers, and later on irrational numbers. The number track is much less abstract, and lends itself more readily to activities with physical embodiments of the concepts we want children to acquire. So we shall stay with the number track throughout the earlier part of this network.
	Even here, however, abstraction has begun. When in Activity 1(a) we let the size of the space used up on the track be independent of the size of the object, we are already moving towards the idea of a unit object. The introduction of unit cubes takes this idea a step further.

OBSERVE AND LISTEN   **REFLECT**   **DISCUSS**

NuSp 1.2   CORRESPONDENCE BETWEEN ORDER OF NUMBERS AND POSITION ON TRACK

Concepts   (i)   Successor, predecessor (from Num 1.3).
(ii)   Spatial order on a number track.
(iii)   The correspondence between these two orders.

Ability   To match these two orders correctly, in either direction.

Discussion of concepts

These concepts are closely related to those of the topic just before, but are developed here in greater detail. In the topic before, number and position on the number track were related. 'One larger' corresponds to 'next on the right'. In this topic, the verbal sequence of counting numbers corresponds to the spatial sequence of squares.

Activity 1 **Sequences on the number track***

A game for children to play in pairs. Its purpose is to teach the concepts and abilities described above.
* Based on an idea from Mrs Yvonne Selah, advisory teacher with the Inner London Education Authority.

Materials
- A number track 1 to 10 (later, 1 to 20).
- 7 cubes of a different colour for each player.
- Number cards 1 to 10 (later, 1 to 20).

What they do
1. The pack of number cards is shuffled and put face down. The top card is then turned face up, starting a separate pile.
2. Each player in turn may
   (i) either use the card showing, or turn over another card;
   (i) put down one of his cubes in the corresponding position on the number track, or not. Both players use the same track, and only one cube is allowed in each space.
3. The aim is to get as many cubes next to each other as possible.
4. The game finishes when one player gets 5 in a row, or when both players have put down all their cubes.
5. If before this the pack has been finished it is shuffled and used again as in step 1.
6. Scoring is as follows. 1 by itself scores zero; 2, 3, 4, 5 cubes in a row score respectively 2, 3, 4, 5.

Discussion of activity

These games combine both the first and the second kind of use of mathematics described in the Introduction. Co-operation in playing the game depends on a shared mathematical schema; but choosing the best alternative involves prediction, not in this case at a level of certainty, but based on a variety of possibilities.

Though the concepts of predecessor and successor are strongly involved in these activities, and are not difficult ideas, these terms may well be thought unsuitable for children of this age. Though we ourselves need names for these concepts, they are not particularly required by the children.

What are being matched in these activities are not objects, but orders of two kinds. A relation (matching) is involved between two different order relationships, size of number and spatial order. Once again we see how even at so elementary a level as this, mathematics is a really abstract subject. Yet young children master it without difficulty if it is presented right. If we can help them to use their intelligence to the full, they show themselves much cleverer than they are usually given credit for.

OBSERVE AND LISTEN   **REFLECT**   **DISCUSS**

NuSp 1.3   ADDING ON THE NUMBER TRACK

Concept   Correspondence between addition and actions on the number track.

Abilities   (i)   To link mathematical ideas relating to addition with number track activities.

         (ii)   To use the number track as a mental support for adding.

Discussion of concept

Addition as a mental operation, corresponding to the physical action of putting more, is discussed at length in Num 3. On the number track, putting more objects has the result of taking up more length on the track. Since the track is numbered, we have a built-in technique for showing the number of the result without counting. Alternatively, the result can be predicted by counting on spaces, and tested physically.

This synthesis of numerical and spatial ideas continues to increase in usefulness as we apply it to a variety of mathematical operations. Addition is the first of these.

Activity 1   **Putting more on the number track (verbal)**

An activity for two to four children. Its purpose is to introduce the use of the number track for adding. This should be used as activity 2 in Num 3.1.

Materials
- An SAR board, see figure 18.
- A number track.
- Cubes to fit the track, in two colours.
- Start cards 1-5 (later 0-5).
  which say (e.g.) 'Start with a set of 3'.*
- Action cards 1-5 (later 0-5).
  which say (e.g.) 'Put 2 more', 'Increase it by 5', 'Make it 4 larger'.*
- Result cards numbered from 0-10.*
- A reversible card. On side one is written.
  'Find the card to show your result. Say what you did, and the result.'*
  On side two is written
  'Predict the result.'

* These are the same as used for Num 3.1/1.

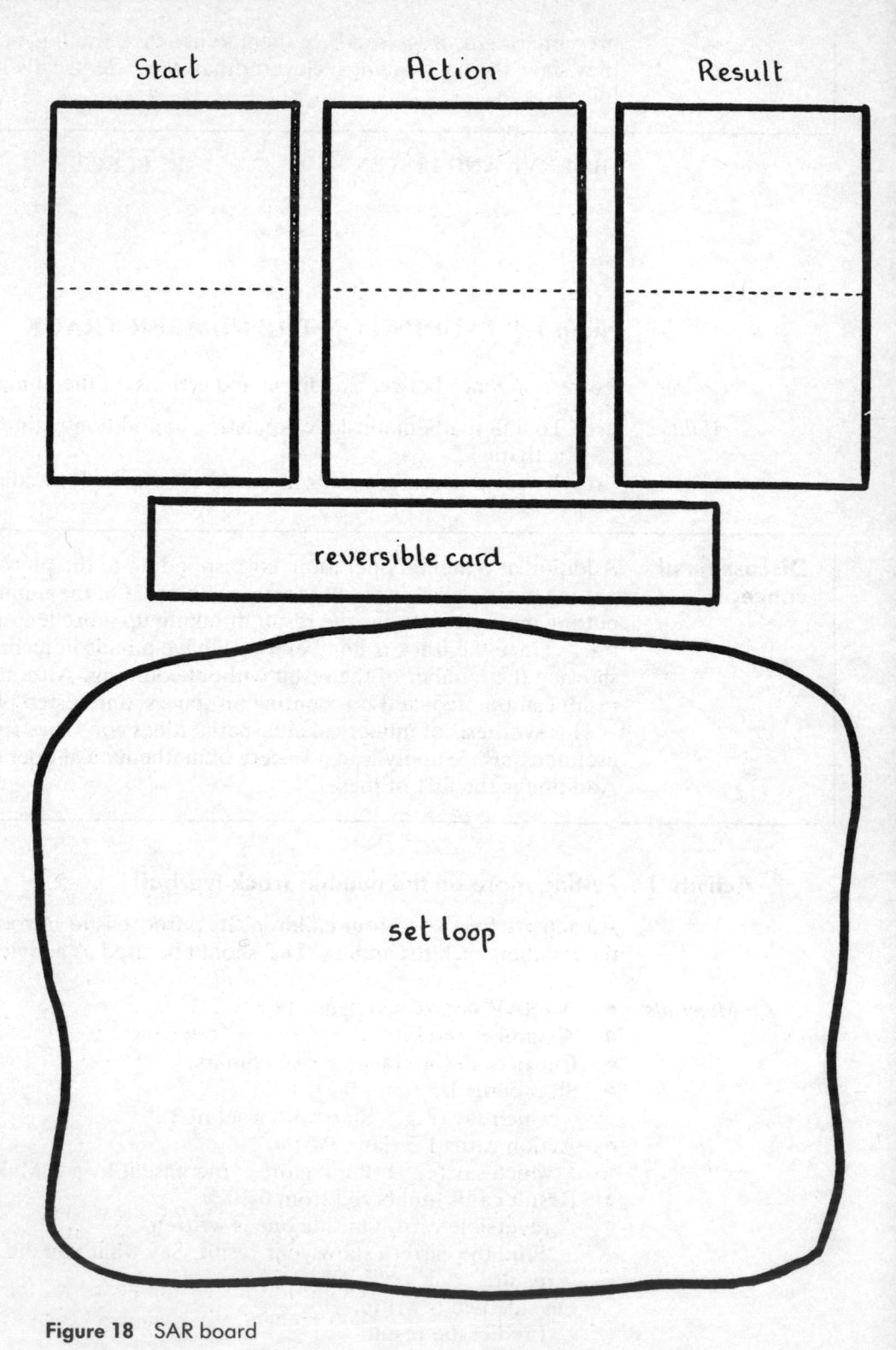

Figure 18 SAR board

What they do 1. The cards are shuffled and put face down in the upper part of their spaces on the SAR board.
2. The reversible card is put below the Result space with side one showing.
3. One child turns over the top start card into the space below, and puts a set of the required number either singly into the number track (in which case the projections will have to be uppermost) or joined into rods.
4. Next he turns over the action card, and puts more cubes into the track as instructed, using a different colour. Note that at this stage we do not talk about adding.
5. Next he finds the appropriate result card to show the number of the resulting set.
6. Finally he must describe to the others what he did, and the result.
7. Steps 3 to 5 are then repeated by the next child.

Activity 2 Where will it come?

An activity for two. This is a predictive form of activity 1, and should be used as Num 3.2, activity 2.

Materials • The same as for activity 1.
• Also, some Blu-Tack.

What they do 1. The cards are shuffled and put face down in the upper part of their spaces on the SAR board. The reversible card now shows side two.
2. The children make up a 1-5 staircase each, in different colours.
3. Player A turns over the top start card, selects a rod of this number and puts it into the number track.
4. Player B turns over the top action card, but does not yet take out a rod. First, he says 'I predict that it'll come to *here*' pointing, and marking his prediction with a blob of Blu-Tack. This will involve some form of counting on, which on the number track corresponds to movement to the right.
5. Then he tests his prediction physically by joining a rod of the given number to the first on the number track.
6. Steps 3, 4, 5 are repeated until all the cards are turned.
7. Then the cards are shuffled, and they begin again with their roles interchanged.

Activity 3 Crossing*

A board game for 2 or 3 children. Its purpose is to consolidate the abilities described above in a situation which requires several predictions to be made in order to choose the best action.
* This attractive improvement to the original board for the 'Crossing' game was suggested by Mrs Mary Hamby, of Leegomery County Infant School, Telford.

Materials • Game board, see figure 19.

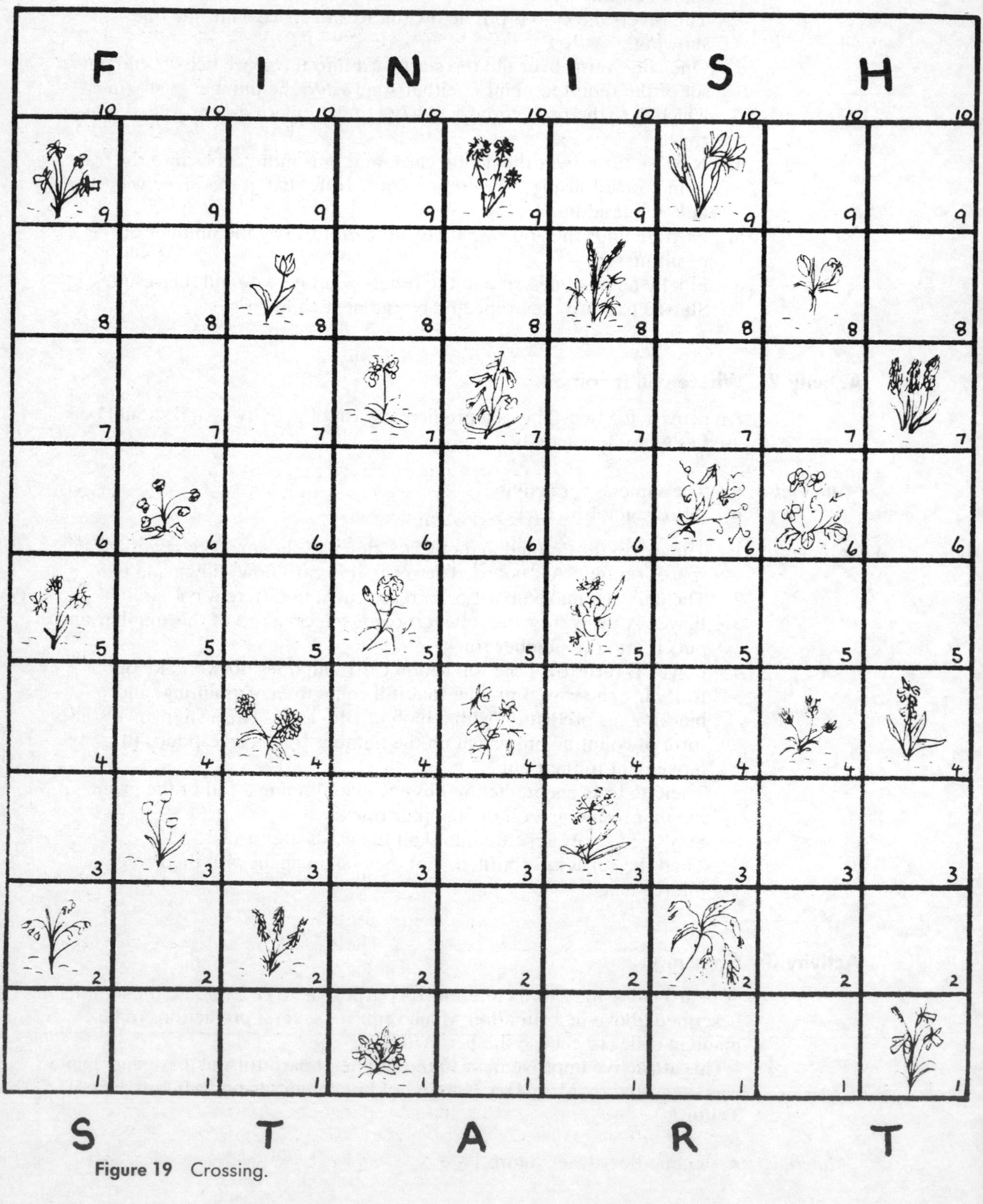

Figure 19 Crossing.

- 3 markers for each player, a different kind or colour for each player.
- Die 1-6 and shaker.

What they do
1. The blank squares on the board represent paving stones. Some of these have been removed to allow flowers to grow. The object is to get across the board from START to FINISH, treading only on the paving stones and not on the flowers.
2. Each player starts with all 3 markers off the board, at the START. The winner is the first to get all his markers to the FINISH (marked 10).
3. Players throw the die in turn. The number thrown shows how many steps they may take. This means that from START, they may put a marker on the board at the square with that number; and from a square on the board, they may move one of their markers forward that number of squares.
4. They may move whichever of their markers they like. When starting, they may choose any vacant track. After that, they must keep moving straight forward along the same track.
5. They may not land on a square marked with a flower. Players may move their markers over them normally, but if they make a move which stops on a square with a flower, that marker must go back to the start.
6. A player may choose not to move. However, if they touch a marker they must move it if they can, or go back to the START if they cannot. This rule may be relaxed when learning.
7. The exact number must be thrown to finish. The first player to get all his markers to FINISH is the winner, but the others may continue playing until all are across.

Variation   Players learning the game may start with just 2 markers.

Activity 4   Where will it come? (Through 10)

This is the same game as activity 2, but with results greater than 10. It should be used as Num 3.6, activity 2.

Materials
- As in activity 2 except:
  Both players use staircase 1-9, the first 5 cubes being of a different colour from the remainder. E.g. an 8-rod would be 5 blue, 3 white. A 5-rod would be all blue, and 1- to 4-rods would all be white. These give the same grouping as finger counting.
- Use 'Start' and 'Action' cards 4-9. These will give a mixture of results which do/do not cross the ten boundary.
- Result cards 1-20.

Discussion of activities   We have now moved on from lengths on the number track, corresponding to numbers, to actions (putting more) on the number track, corresponding to mathematical operations. Activity 1 is for schema building by physical experience (mode 1); activities 2, 3, 4 consolidate this schema by using it for making and testing predictions.

The number track encourages the transition from counting all to counting on.

OBSERVE AND LISTEN   **REFLECT**   **DISCUSS**

NuSp 1.4   SUBTRACTING ON THE NUMBER TRACK

Concept   Correspondence between subtraction and actions on the number track.

Abilities   (i)   To link mathematical ideas relating to subtraction with number track activities.

(i)   To use the number track as a mental support for subtracting.

Discussion of concept

Though subtraction might seem to be no more than the inverse of addition, it is in fact a more complex concept, derived from as many as four simpler concepts. These are discussed fully in Num 4.

The simplest of these contributory concepts is 'taking away', opposite of 'putting more'. It is this aspect of subtraction which is used in activities 1, 2, 3. Activity 4, 'Capture', uses the comparison aspect of subtraction.

Activity 1   **Taking away on the number track (verbal)**

An activity for a small group. Its purpose is to introduce the use of the number track for subtracting. This should be used as activity 2 in Num 4.2.

Materials
- An SAR board.*
- A number track.*
- Cubes to fit the track.*
- Start cards 5-10.
    which say (e.g.) 'Start with a set of 5'.
- Action cards 1-5 (later 0-5).
    which say (e.g.) 'Make it 2 less', 'Take 3 away', 'Make it 4 smaller'.
- Result cards numbered from 0-10.*
- A reversible card. On side one is written
    'Find the card to show your result. Say what you did, and the result.'*
    On side two is written
    'predict the result.'

* The same as for NuSp 1.3/1.

What they do   This is done in the same way as 'Putting more' (NuSp 1.3/1) with appropriate changes to step 4.

Reminders   1.   The children should verbalise their results each time.
2.   It is useful to have colour codes for different kinds of card.

Activity 2   **What will be left?**

This is an activity for two. It is a predictive form of activity 1, and should be used as Num 4.2, activity 3.

Materials
- As activity 1 except for:
- Player A has start cards 5-10.
- Player B has action cards 1-5.
- Blu-Tack.

What they do
1. Player A makes a staircase 1-10.
2. The cards are shuffled and put face down in the upper part of their spaces.
3. Player A turns over the 'Start' card, selects the rod of this number and puts it into the number track.
4. Player B turns over the top 'Action' card. She now has to predict what will be left on the track when a rod of that number is taken away. She marks her prediction with a blob of Blu-Tack.
5. She then tests it by physically removing the appropriate number of cubes.
6. The length left in the track is checked against the marker, and the number taken away against the 'Action' card.
7. Steps 2 to 5 are then repeated with roles interchanged.

Activity 3   **Crossing back**

A board game for 2, 3, or 4 children.

What they do   This is played on the same board as 'Crossing' (Activity 3 of the previous topic), and in a similar way. The difference is that they all begin in the finishing space, corresponding to 10; and end where it says 'Start'.

Notes   (i) Since this game is a little harder than its predecessor 'Crossing', it may be wiser not to use the 'Move if touched' rule initially. But it should come in when the children have sufficient experience in order to make the game a predictive one.
(ii) If children find it confusing to begin where 'Finish' is written, you could make another board. But using the same board helps to show the inverse relation between adding and subtracting.

Activity 4   **'Capture'**

This is a game for two. Its purpose is to introduce the comparison aspect of subtraction.

Materials
- 2 number tracks 1-10.
- 1 die 1-6.
- 10 cubes for each player, a different colour for each.

What they do
1. The two number tracks are put beside each other.
2. Each player throws the die, and puts the number of cubes indicated on the track.

The result might look like this:

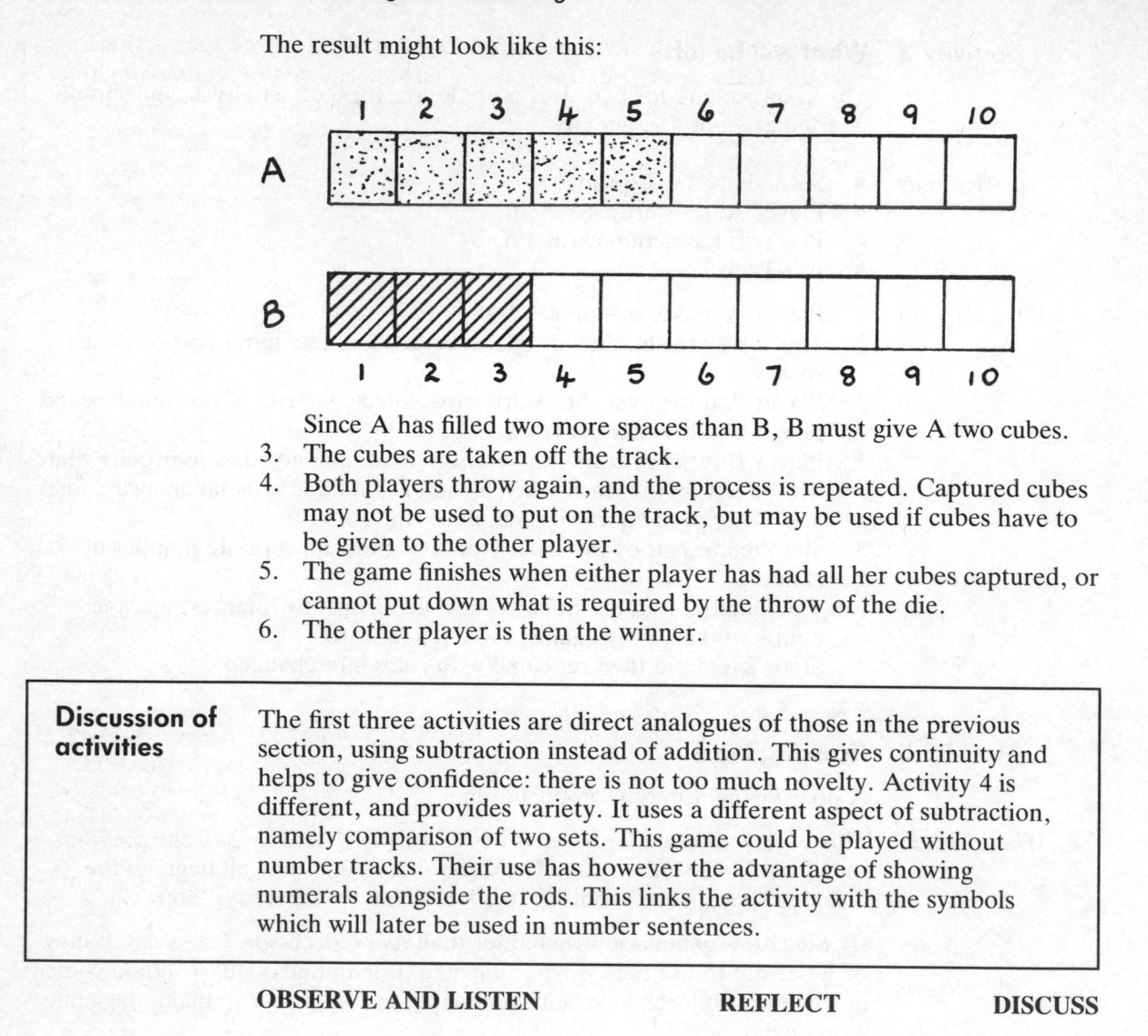

Since A has filled two more spaces than B, B must give A two cubes.

3. The cubes are taken off the track.
4. Both players throw again, and the process is repeated. Captured cubes may not be used to put on the track, but may be used if cubes have to be given to the other player.
5. The game finishes when either player has had all her cubes captured, or cannot put down what is required by the throw of the die.
6. The other player is then the winner.

Discussion of activities	The first three activities are direct analogues of those in the previous section, using subtraction instead of addition. This gives continuity and helps to give confidence: there is not too much novelty. Activity 4 is different, and provides variety. It uses a different aspect of subtraction, namely comparison of two sets. This game could be played without number tracks. Their use has however the advantage of showing numerals alongside the rods. This links the activity with the symbols which will later be used in number sentences.

OBSERVE AND LISTEN   **REFLECT**   **DISCUSS**

NuSp 1.5   RELATION BETWEEN ADDING AND SUBTRACTING

Concept   That addition and subtraction are inverse operations.

Ability   To translate into action the opposite effects of these two operations.

Discussion of concept	If we add 4 and then subtract 4, we are back to the number we started with. These two operations cancel each other out, so each is called the inverse of the other.
	In more advanced mathematics (e.g. group theory) this concept plays an important part. At this stage, children need only to be introduced to

the concept. Also, since equal operations of addition and subtraction, which exactly cancel, get one literally nowhere, activities embodying the concept in this form are not likely to be very interesting. So those which follow emphasise simply the opposite effects of these two operations, which is what is important at this stage.

Activity 1 **Slow bicycle race**

A game for a small group. Its purpose is to introduce the inverse relationship between adding and subtraction.

Materials   For each player:
● A 1-10 number track.
● A cube.
For the group:
● 2 1-6 dice.
● A shaker.

What they do   1. The number tracks are put alongside each other.
2. To decide who starts, they each throw a single die, and the highest starts.
3. They then throw both dice together, taking turns clockwise round the group.
4. Each player moves his cube forward according to the larger number shown on the two dice, backward according to the smaller number. (The start, corresponding to zero, is just before 1 on the track.) If for example a player throws 6 and 2, he must actually move forward 6 and then back 2, and not just go forward 4.
5. If his forward move takes him past the finishing line, i.e. past 10, he is out of the race.
6. The winner is the last player to be left in the race.

Variation   Players combine the forward and backwards moves mentally, and move forward the resulting amount. This will keep them longer on the track. Players must agree beforehand which form of the game they are going to play.

Activity 2 **Ups and downs**

This is a board game of the 'snakes and ladders' kind for up to four players. It relates the mathematical symbols for adding and subtracting to movements on the number track.

Materials   ● Ups and downs board,* see figure 20.
● 1 small marker for each player.
● 1 die 1-6.
● Shaker.
* Interesting situations arise at one or two places. You can devise your own variations.

223

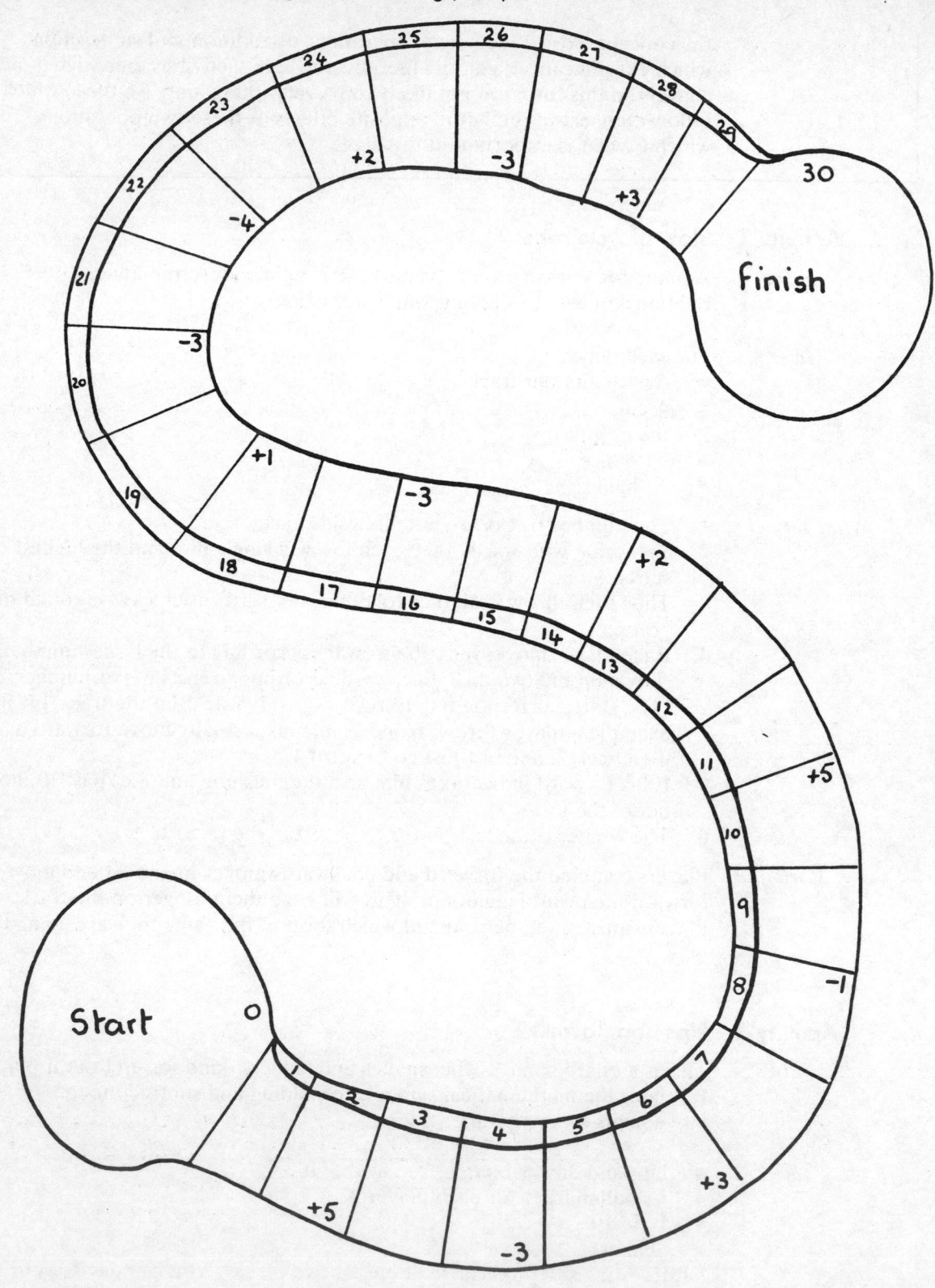

Figure 20 Ups and downs.

What they do
1. Each player throws the die in turn and moves forward according to the number thrown.
2. If they land on an action square they go forward or backward according to whether the operation is addition or subtraction.
3. There is no rule against two players occupying the same place.
4. The exact number must be thrown to finish, and the winner is the player who does so first.

Discussion of activities

Both of these activities are of a schema building kind. Mode 1 schema building is used – from physical embodiments of these two operations, children's awareness of their opposite nature is strengthened. This relationship is a higher order concept derived from ones which they already have, so mode 3 schema building, creativity, is also involved.

OBSERVE AND LISTEN   REFLECT   DISCUSS

NuSp 1.6   LINEAR SLIDE RULE

Concept The linear slide rule as a method of adding and subtracting.

Abilities Simple whole-number addition and subtraction by the linear slide rule.

Discussion of concept

This is, in essence, two number tracks side by side, one of which can be slid relative to the other. The slider needs an extra space at the beginning, marked S/R corresponding to 'Start' for addition, and 'Result' for subtraction. The rule may be of any length you choose to make: 1-20 is a practical size to begin with. Its working is best conveyed by illustrations.

Adding

$5 \xrightarrow{+7} 12$ $5 + 7 = 12$

Subtracting

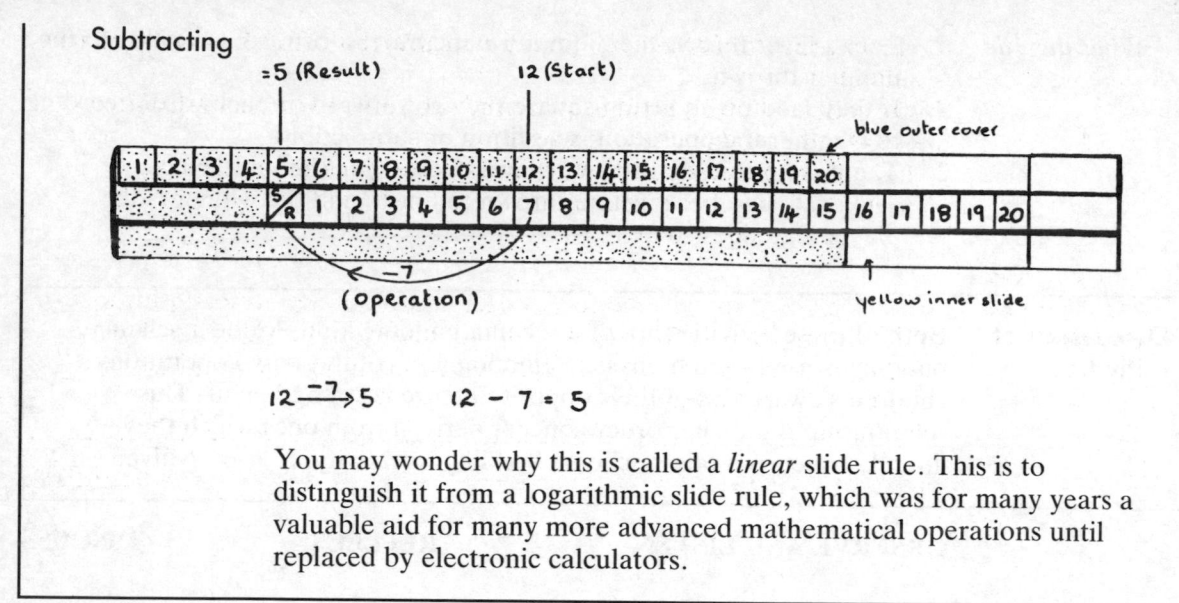

$$12 \xrightarrow{\;-7\;} 5 \qquad 12 - 7 = 5$$

You may wonder why this is called a *linear* slide rule. This is to distinguish it from a logarithmic slide rule, which was for many years a valuable aid for many more advanced mathematical operations until replaced by electronic calculators.

Activity 1   Add and check

An activity for two players. This provides an interesting way of practising addition facts.

Materials
- Linear slide rule 1-20.
- 2 dice 1-9, or spinners.
- Shaker for die.

What they do
1. Child A has the pair of dice.
2. B has the linear slide rule.
3. A throws the dice, and speaks the numbers and their sum.
4. B then checks A's result using the linear slide rule.
5. Examples:
   A: 'Six add two, result eight.' Or 'Six add two equals eight'.
   B: 'Correct.'
   A throws again. 'Five add seven, result thirteen.'
   B: 'No, twelve.'
6. They continue until A has got (say) ten correct, and then change about.

Activity 2   Adding past 20

A problem suitable for some of the brightest children.

Materials   As in activity 1.

What they do
1. Ask, 'If your linear slide rule only goes up to 20, can you find a way of using it to add when the result comes to more than 20? Say, 17 + 8, or 13 + 15?'
2. One way – there are others – is to use 20 as the start mark, and add 20 to the result. E.g. 17 + 8. Set 20 (instead of letter S) on the lower rule against 17. Opposite 8 on the lower rule, read 5 in the usual way, and

add 20: result 25. (When you do it physically, this is much easier than it sounds.)

3. If the problem in this form is too hard, you could show them the above method, and ask them why it works.

4. When this method has been mastered, it may be used to repeat Activity 1 with more difficult numbers.

Discussion of activities

The linear slide rule is, in effect, a useful physical tool for counting on and counting back. It provides further connections between concepts which children already have; and its use in the foregoing activities serves to strengthen these concepts.

OBSERVE AND LISTEN   **REFLECT**   **DISCUSS**

NuSp 1.7   UNIT INTERVALS: THE NUMBER LINE

Concepts   (i)   Unit intervals on a line.
          (ii)   The number line.

Ability   To use the number line in the same ways as the number track, in preparation for other uses of the number line.

Discussion of concepts

```
0   1   2   3   4   5   6   7   8   9   10   11   12   13   14   15   16
|___|___|___|___|___|___|___|___|___|___|____|____|____|____|____|____|___>
```

The differences between a number track and a number line are appreciable, and not immediately obvious.

The number track is physical, though we may represent it by a diagram. The number line is conceptual – it is a mental object, though we often use diagrams to help us think about it. The number track is finite, whereas the number line is infinite. However far we extend a physical track, it has to end somewhere. But in our thoughts, we can think of a number line as going on and on to infinity.

On the number line, numbers are represented by points, not spaces; and operations are represented by movements over intervals on the line, to the right for addition and to the left for subtraction. The concept of a unit interval thus replaces that of a unit object. Also, the number line starts at 0, not at 1. For the counting numbers, and all positive numbers, we use only the right-hand half of the number line, starting at zero and extending indefinitely to the right. For positive and negative numbers we still use 0 for the origin, but now the number line extends indefinitely to the right (positive numbers) and left (negative numbers).

Activity 1 Drawing the number line

This is a simple activity for introducing the concept.

Materials • Pencil and paper for each child.

What they do 1. Ask the children to draw a line, as long as will conveniently go on the paper.
2. They mark off equal intervals.
3. They number these 0, 1, 2 . . . as in the diagram above.
4. At this stage, the two differences between the number track and the number line which need to be pointed out are: (i) With the number track, numbers are represented by spaces; with the number line, numbers are represented by points on the line. Though it is helpful to use different marks for tens, fives, and units, it is the points on the line which represent the numbers; (ii) The number track starts at 1, the number line starts at 0.

Activity 2 Sequences on the number line

NuSp 1.2/1, 'Sequences on the number track', may usefully be repeated here. Smaller markers will be needed. (See activity 3.)

Activity 3 Where must the frog land?

A game for two players. Its purpose is to introduce the use of the number line for adding.

Materials • As long a number line as you like.
• A marker representing a frog for each player, occupying as small a base as possible.*
• 1 die 1-6, or 1-10 for athletic frogs.
* A short length (about 2 cm) of coloured milk straw, with a small blob of Blu-Tack on the end, makes a good marker for this and many other activities.

What they do 1. The frogs start at zero.
2. Player A throws the die and tells the frog what number it must hop to. This is done mentally, using aids such as finger counting if he likes. (To start with, children may use counting on along the number line, but should replace this by mentally adding as soon as they have learnt the game.)
3. Player B checks, and if he says 'Agree' the frog is allowed to hop.
4. If B does not agree, he says so, and they check.
5. If A has made a mistake, his frog may not hop.
6. Two frogs may be at the same number.
7. They then exchange roles for B's throw of the die.
8. The winner is the frog which first hops past the end of the line. (The exact number is not required.)

Activity 4 **Hopping backwards**

The subtraction form of activity 3, starting at the largest number on the number line and hopping backwards past zero.

Activity 5 **Taking**

Another capture game for two, but quite different from NuSp 1.4/4 'Capture'. Its purpose is to give further practice in relating numbers to positions and movements on the number line.

Materials
- 1 number line 0-20.
- 3 markers for each player.
- 1 die 1-6.

What they do   *Form (a)*
1. The markers begin at zero.
2. The die is thrown alternately, and according to the number thrown a player may jump one of his markers forward that interval on the line.
3. A piece which is jumped *over* is taken, and removed from the board for the rest of the game.
4. An occupied point may not be jumped *onto*.
5. A player does not have to move at all if he doesn't want to. (We introduced this rule when we found that starting throws of low numbers were likely to result in the piece being taken next throw, with no room for manoeuvre.)
6. The winner is the player who gets the largest number of pieces past 20. (It is not necessary to throw the exact number.)

Form (b)
This may also be played as a subtraction game, backwards from 20.

Activity 6 **A race through a maze**

This is a board game for up to 3 players. Its purpose is to bring out the correspondence between the relationships smaller/larger number and left/right on the number line.

Materials
- Board (see figure 21).
- Number line 1-20.
- Number cards 1-20.

For each player:
- 1 coloured pointer for the number line.
- 1 marker to take through the maze.

What they do
1. The pack of number cards is shuffled and put face down.
2. In turn, each player turns over the top card and puts it face up, starting a new pile. He may then use this number to position his pointer on the number line, or decide not to (since an extreme left or right position is not helpful). In that case he repeats this step at his next move.
3. When he does position his pointer, he also puts his marker at the start of the maze.

229

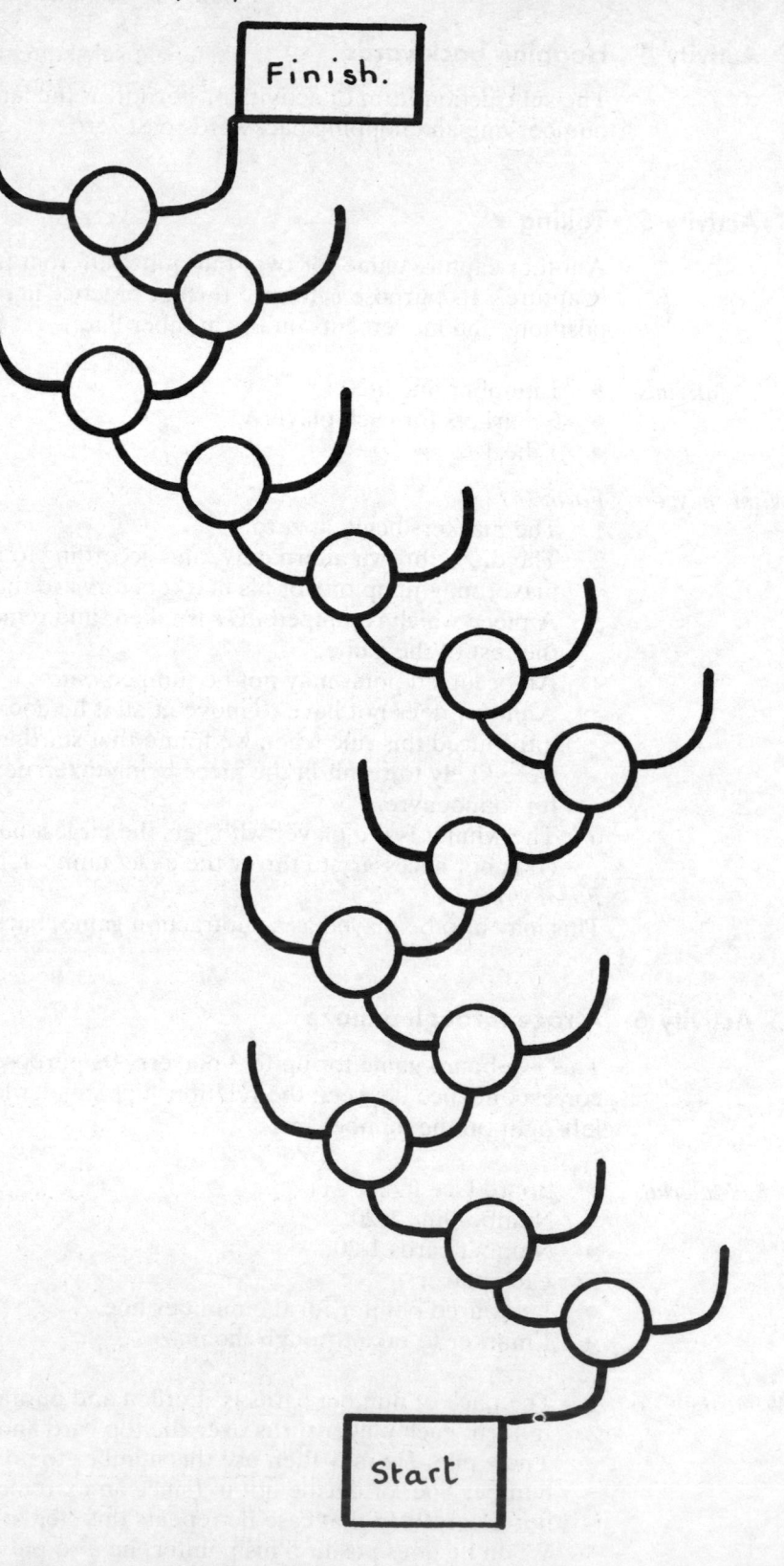

Figure 21 A race through a maze.

4. After taking steps 2 and 3, players at subsequent turns move forward through the maze if they can. The number they turn over determines whether they can or not.
An example will make it clear.

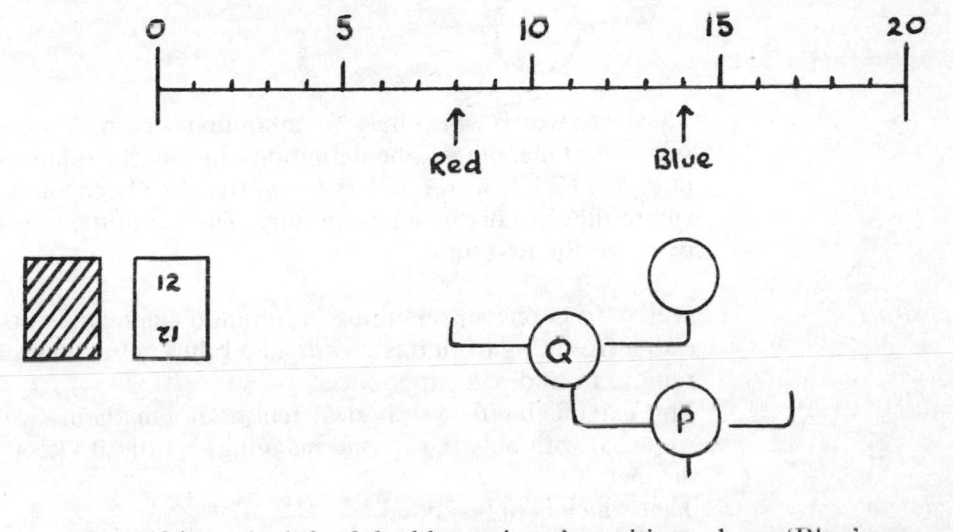

Since 12 is to the left of the blue pointer's position, player 'Blue' can move forward if he is at P on the maze, but not if he is at Q. However, the reverse is the case for player 'Red', since 12 is to the right of his pointer.

5. There is no limit to the number of players at a given position on the maze.

6. When all the cards are turned over the number pack is shuffled and used again.

7. The winner is the first player to reach the finish.

Note   If the children have difficulty in remembering their left and right, you could help with labelled arrows.

Discussion of activities

The first four activities are concerned first with introducing the number line, and then with linking it to concepts which are already familiar. Activity 5, 'Taking', is more difficult, since it involves mentally comparing a number of possible moves before deciding which one to make.

Activity 6 involves correspondence not between objects, but between two different relations. One is the relation of size, between two numbers, and the other is the relation of position, between two points on the number line. Here is another good example of the conceptual complexity of even elementary mathematics. Yet young children manage this without difficulty if we make it possible for them to use their intelligence to the full.

OBSERVE AND LISTEN   **REFLECT**   **DISCUSS**

GLOSSARY

These are words which may be unfamiliar, or which are used with specialised meanings. The definitions and short explanations given here are intended mainly as reminders for words already encountered in the text, where they are discussed more fully. This is not the best place to meet a word for the first time.

abstract   (verb) To perceive something in common among a diversity of experiences. (adj.) Resulting from this process, and thus more general, but also more remote from direct experience.

add   This can mean either a physical action, or a mathematical operation. Here we use it with only the second meaning, in order to keep these two ideas distinct.

addend   That which is to be added.

base   The number used for grouping objects, and then making groups of these groups, and so on. This is a way of organising large collections of objects to make them easier to count, and is also important for place-value notation.

binary   Describes an operation with two operands.

canonical form   When there are several ways of writing the same mathematical idea, one of these is often accepted as the one which is most generally useful. This is called the canonical form. A well known example is a fraction in its lowest terms.

characteristic property   Property which is the basis for classification, and for membership of a given set.

commutative   This describes a physical action or a mathematical operation for which the result is still the same if we do it the other way about. E.g. addition is commutative, since $7 + 3$ gives the same result as $3 + 7$; but subtraction is not.

concept   An idea which represents what a variety of different experiences have in common. It is the result of abstracting.

congruent   Two figures are congruent if one of them, put on top of the other, would coincide with it exactly. The term still applies if one figure would first have to be turned over.

contributor   One of the experiences from which a concept is abstracted.

counting numbers   The number of objects in a set. The cardinal numbers, 1, 2, 3 . . . (continuing indefinitely). Zero is usually included among these, but not negative or fractional numbers.

digit   A single figure. E.g. 0, 1, 2, 3 . . . 9.

equivalent   Of the same value.

extrapolate   To expand a schema by perceiving a pattern and extending it to new applications.

higher order concept   A concept which is itself abstracted from other concepts. E.g. the concept of an even number is abstracted from numbers like 2, 4, 6 . . . so *even number* is a higher order concept than 2, or 4, or 6 . . .

232

interiority	The detail within a concept.
interpolate	To increase what is within a schema by perceiving a pattern and extending it inwards.
low-noise example	An example of a concept which has a minimum of irrelevant qualities.
lower order concept	The opposite of *higher order concept*, q.v.
match	To be alike in some way.
mathematical operation	See *operation*.
mode 1	Schema building by physical experience, and testing by seeing whether predictions are confirmed.
mode 2	Schema building by receiving communication, and testing by discussion.
mode 3	Schema construction by mental creativity, and testing whether the new ideas thus obtained are consistent with what is already known.
model	A simplified representation of something. A model may be physical or mental, but here we are concerned mainly with mathematical models, which are an important kind of mental model.
natural numbers	The same as the counting numbers.
notation	A way of writing something.
numeral	A symbol for a number. Not to be confused with the number itself.
operand	Whatever is acted on, physically or mentally.
operation	Used here to mean a mental action, in contrast to a physical action.
pair	A set of two. Often used for a set made by taking one object from each of two existing sets: e.g. a knife and a fork.
place-value notation	A way of writing numbers in which the meaning of each digit depends both on the digit itself, and also on which place it is in, reading from right to left.
predict	To say what we think will happen, by inference from a suitable mental model. Not the same as guessing. Prediction is based on knowledge, guessing on ignorance.
schema	A conceptual structure. A connected group of ideas.
set	A collection of objects (these may be mental objects) which belong together in some way.
subitise	To perceive the number of objects in a set without counting.
sum	The result of an addition. Often used, incorrectly, to mean any kind of calculation.
symmetry	A relation of a figure with itself. If a line can be found which divides a figure into two congruent halves, the figure has symmetry about this line. This is the only kind of symmetry considered in this book. Rotational symmetry is another kind.
transitive	A property of a relationship. E.g. if Alan is taller than Brenda, and Brenda is taller than Charles, then we know also that Alan is taller than Charles. So the relationship 'is taller than' is transitive.
unary	Describes an operation with a single operand.

ALPHABETICAL LIST OF ACTIVITIES

Abstracting number sentences, 111, 139, 177

Add and check, 226

Adding past 10 on the number track, 119

Adding past 20, 226

Adfacts at speed, 121

Adfacts practice, 121

'All put your rods parallel/perpendicular to the big rod', 208

Attribute cards, 43

Backwards number rhymes, 90

'Break into halves, and what will we get?', 79

'Can I fool you?', 46

'Can I fool you?' (Canonical form), 64

'Can they all find partners?', 76

'Can they meet?', 204

Capture, 143, 221

Change by counting on, 150

Change by exchange, 150

Colouring pictures, 209

Combining order of number, length, and position, 48

Combining the number sentences, 195

Commutativity means less to remember, 128

Comparing larger sets, 59

Conceptual matching, 42

Conservation of number, 59

Counting 2-rods and 5-rods, 93

Counting in tens, 94

Counting money, 2p and 5p coins, 93

Counting sets in twos and fives, 93

Counting two ways on a number square, 95

Counting with hand clapping, 92

Crossing back, 134, 221

Crossing, 106, 217

Different questions, same answer. Why?, 194

Diver and wincher, 143

Dominoes, 42

'Double this, and what will we get?', 78

Doubles and halves rummy, 80

Drawing pictures with straight and curved lines, 201

Drawing the number line, 228

empty set, The, 51

Escaping pig, 204

Exchanging small coins for larger, 64

Explorers, 123

Finger counting from 5 to zero, 73

Finger counting to 5, 70

Finger counting to 10, 72

Finger counting to 20: 'Ten in my head', 74

Giant strides on a number track, 165

Gift shop, 161

handkerchief game, The, 148

Hopping backwards, 229

'How many more must you put?' 114

'I have a straight/curved line, like . . .', 201

'I predict – here' on the number track, 211

'I predict – here' using rods, 169

'I spy . . .' (shapes), 200

Inside and outside, 206

Introducing commutativity, 126

Introducing non-commutativity, 127

Introduction to Multilink or Unifix, 44

Joining dots in order, to make pictures, 87

Laying the table, 143
Lucky dip, 46

Make a set. Make others which
    match, 164
Making picture sets, 44
Making sets in groups and units, 58
Making successive sets, 68
Matching objects to outlines, 199
Matching pictures, 41
Mentally pairing, 53
Missing stairs, 49
Missing stairs, 1 to 10, 72
Mr. Taylor's game, 196
Multiplying on a number track, 165
'My rods are parallel/perpendicular',
    208
'My share is . . .', 189
'My share is . . . and I also know the
    remainder which is . . .', 189

Number comparison sentences, 145
Number rhymes, 84
Number rhymes to ten, 85
Number rhymes to twenty, 89
Number sentences for multiplication,
    172
Number sentences for subtraction,
    135
Number stories, 176
Number stories, and predicting from
    number sentences, 177
Number targets, 97
Number targets beyond 100, 99
Number targets in the teens, 101
Numbers backwards, 91

'Odd or even?', 77
On to cubes, 62
Ordering several rods by their
    lengths, 47

Perceptual matching of objects, 41
Personalised number stories, 110, 138
Personalised number stories –
    predictive, 112
Personalised number stories –
    predictive, 140
Personalised number stories: what
    happened?, 116
Physical pairing, 52
picture matching game, A, 42

Picture matching game using dot sets
    and picture sets, 67
Pig puzzle, 206
Planting potatoes, 71
'Please may I have?', 87
'Please may I have . . .?'
    (complements), 148
'Please may I have . . .?' (straight and
    curved lines), 202
Predicting from number sentences,
    137
Predicting from number sentences,
    174
Predicting the result, 133
Predicting the result (addition), 104
Predictive number sentences
    (grouping), 183
Predictive number sentences past 10,
    123
Putting and taking, 82
Putting more on the number track
    (verbal), 104
Putting more on the number track
    (verbal), 215
Putting one more, 68

race through a maze, A, 229
Returning over the stepping stones,
    134

Saying and pointing, 87
Secret adder, 115
Seeing, speaking, writing 11–19, 100
Sequences on the number line, 228
Sequences on the number track, 214
Sequencing numerals 1 to 10, 88
Sets under our hands, 170
Sets which match, 54
Sets with their numbers, 87
Sharing equally, 187
Slippery slope, 120
Slow bicycle race, 223
Sorting dot sets and picture sets, 66
Start, Action, Result (do and say),
    102
Start, Action, Result (do and say),
    131
Start, Action, Result over ten, 117
Start, Action, Result: grouping, 181
Stepping stones, 105
Subtracting from teens: 'Check!', 160
Subtracting from teens: choose your

method, 158
Subtraction sentences for
  comparisons, 146

Taking, 229
Taking away on the number track (do
  and say), 132
Taking away on the number track
  (verbal), 220
Tens and units tray, 95
Throwing for a target, 81
Till receipts, 151
Till receipts up to 20p, 160

Units, rods, and squares, 61
Unpacking the parcel, 156
Unpacking the parcel (division), 195
Ups and downs, 223
Using commutativity for counting on,
  128
Using set diagrams for comparison,
  153
Using set diagrams for finding

complements, 154
Using set diagrams for giving change,
  155
Using set diagrams for taking away,
  153

What will be left?, 133, 221
Where must the frog land?, 228
'Where will it come?', 105, 217
Where will it come? (Through 10),
  219
'Which card is missing?', 69
'Which card is missing?' (Including
  zero), 73
'Which set am I making?', 44
'Which *two* sets am I making?', 45
Word problems (grouping), 183
Word problems (sharing), 189
Write your prediction, 108
Writing number sentences for
  addition, 108

'Yes or no?', 76